D1632422

E0001687082001

STACK.

THE LONG FURROW

White Bryony. Charles Darwin observed that this was the single plant in the world, whose tendril reverses the direction of its spiral. It is a common plant in Bulmer and Gestingthorpe.

Cover Photograph:
I am indebted to Jack Palmer for allowing me to use the photograph on the front cover, which he took on a Stambourne farm in the late nineteen thirties. The picture normally hangs in the small bar of the Castle Hedingham "Bell".

The Long Furrow

BY

Ashley Cooper

BULMER HISTORICAL SOCIETY

*All rights reserved. No part of this publication may be reproduced, stored in a
retrieval system, or transmitted, in any form, or by any means, electronic,
mechanical, photocopying, recording or otherwise, without the prior
permission of the author.*

First published 1982

© *Ashley Cooper*

E 630.9
30998

ESSEX LIBRARIES
LOCAL STUDIES DEPT.
COLCHESTER

*Printed in Great Britain by
Halcyon Print, Ipswich*

Foreword

Ashley Cooper farms in Gestingthorpe and Bulmer. He has supported W.E.A. lectures in the villages on local studies and has been active in the local history group for Bulmer and district. His father is well known for his discovery of the big Roman farm site on his land.

Now Ashley has been persuaded to write "The Long Furrow" which tells the story of the land in our part of Essex from the earliest times through to the 18th Century improvements and the later depressions. He looks at present day farming practice and speculates interestingly about the future.

It is a farmer's view, is the better for being confined to a small area and for being a personal document, and it contains a wealth of living memory from the older men and women who have worked on our fields. Ashley would be the first to agree that their contribution is vital to this book. I could hear some of them speaking as I read their words.

It is just the sort of book that a local history society should be encouraging and the Bulmer group is proud of Ashley's work.

Basil Slaughter
Chairman
Bulmer & District Local History Group

In memory of Bob Daniells, Cecil Smith and Harry Winch
who passed away whilst their story was being written,
and especially for Jack Cornell,
still very much alive,
whose humour and enthusiasm inspired a
five sided "hand-out" to become a
history of 120,000 words.

Acknowledgments

The telephone rang in the middle of lunch; it was Doreen Desmond, Secretary of Bulmer Historical Society.

"Ashley, you promised to write an article for us, about changes in farming and land use . . . could you have it ready in a fortnight?" she asked enthusiastically. Two weeks later, she rang up again . . . and again . . . and again.

Twelve months and many hours of interviews and research later, the investigation into the agricultural past of north east Essex has finally ended. I must express my sincere gratitude for the tremendous co-operation of all those whom I visited and who gave me their time, memories and assistance with great humour and frankness.

In particular the following:

Frank & Gladys Billimore, Tom Bird, Peter Burke, Jane Carson, Charlie & Mabel Chatters, George "Jute" & Rose Chatters, the late George Chatters, Hazell Chinnery, Gertie Coe, Joe Dallimore, the late Bob Daniells, Richard Dawson, Evelyn & Ken Day, Susan & Doreen Desmond, Alan Dixey, John Dixey, Tom Edgeley, Horace Elsie, Sandra Ferguson, Dick Finch, George "Rover" Finch, Gladys Finch, Edith Freeman, John Gardiner, Thelma Gardiner, Jim Hastie, Freda & Douglas Hasler, Emily Hearn, Tommy Hogsbjerg, David Howard, Freddie Hunt, Jack Hunt, Tim & Yvonne Jeggo, Philip Lawson, Ken Leech, Ernest Lott, Paul Mann, the late Jack Mann, Charlie "Pod" Martin, Alfred "Happy" Meekings, Hubert Meeking, Peter, Belinda, Tony & David Minter, Frank Nice, Kenneth Nott, Jack Palmer, Lawrence "Bunny" Hyde Parker, Cyril Pearson, the late Roland & Oliver Pearson, Benjamin Perkins, Cyril Philp, Bob Pinhey, Nick Pluck, Bob Raymond, Evelyn Reeve, Dennis "Chick" Rippingale, Reg & Elizabeth Rippingale, Danny Rowe, Maudie Rowe, Peter Rowe, Philip & Mary Rowe, Tom & Elsie Rowe, Tony, Vic & Alice Self, Hilda & Cecil Smith, Gordon Steed, Ruth Steed, Bert Surridge, Stanley Surridge, Ian Swift, Francis Teverson, Alastair Tuffill, Mike Tracy, Eric Warburton, Bill Waters, Harry Winch, Bill Yeldham.

In addition I must also thank David Yarham and John Llewellin of the Agricultural Development and Advisory Service, Geoff Copsey and P. A. L. Bamberger of Halstead Historical Society, Colin Ranson of the Nature Conservancy Council and Ron Allen of the Soil Survey of England and Wales, for their help in specialist chapters.

Finally, I must pay tribute to the fund of agricultural knowledge which my mother and father have laid at my disposal, and acknowledge the special debt that I owe to Basil Slaughter for all that he has done to encourage an interest in local history in the area.

Publication acknowledgments:

I would like to thank Dr. Oliver Rackham for allowing me to quote from his "Trees and Woodlands in the British Landscape" (published by J. M. Dent, 1976) and the editors of Cambridge University Press for permission to include extracts from "The Agrarian History of England and Wales" Vol. IV and Vol. VIII. The photograph of "Mr. and Mrs. Robert Andrews" is provided by the courtesy of the Directors of the National Gallery.

A note on names:

I have referred to Mr. G. Chatters of Belchamp Walter as the late George Chatters; whilst his namesake of Belchamp St. Pauls is more widely known by the sobriquet of "Jute".

Sadly, since the first draft of this work was written, two of our oldest contributors, Harry Winch and Cecil Smith have passed away.

Contents

Photographs facing pages 32, 48, 128, 208, 224.

Measurements in the Long Furrow

1 acre = 4,840 square yards
1 football pitch = 2 acres (approximately)

20 cwts = 1 ton (imperial)
1 cwt = 112 lbs
112 lbs (1 cwt) = 51 kgs (approximately)
1 cwt = 8 stone
2 cwt (16 stone) = 1 sack (coomb) barley
1½ cwt (12 stone) = 1 sack (coomb) oats
2¼ cwt (18 stone) = 1 sack (coomb) wheat
1 sack = 4 bushels
2 sacks = 1 quarter

PART ONE

The Historical Furrow: From Ancient Woodland to 1893

CHAPTER ONE

Origins

Like most young men, I was in a hurry; like most farmers, I was worried about the weather. The forecast on the morning of September the tenth was for rain. Standing beneath the grey-black skyscape that hung low across the undulating hills from Bulmer to Belchamp Walter and beyond, I kicked the yellow brown clay soil of Goldingham Wood field: it was notoriously "heavy" land, inclined to become relentlessly sticky, inert and unworkable after the first rain. It seemed right to sow it as soon as possible.

Years before, of course, it had been a real wood. On the earliest map of 1755 it extended to thirty three acres. By 1808 reclamation and "stubbing out" had reduced its size to thirteen acres. That remnant had survived until 1947. Wheelwright Hazell Chinnery, born in 1892 recalled that hornbeam was the principal timber, whilst Ruth Steed who played there as a child, remembered the early purple orchids of spring: Philip Rowe had cut hazel "springels" from the stubs and shepherd "Pod" Martin had pastured his flock on adjoining fields. In those days the gaunt old barn that stands close by, was stabling for two horse teams and along the windswept road had passed the rival threshing machines and traction engines of the Rowes and Cornells. Later, when the woodland was cleared, Bob Daniels had pulled sugar beet by hand, Ken Day had ploughed on contract work, Frank Billimore spread fertiliser and Horace Elsie had combined.

Now on the morning of the tenth of September, it was left to Paul Mann, whose grandfather had been head horseman a century before, to finish discing from the seat of his 180 horse powered tractor, and Dennis Rippingale to harrow it, prior to sowing and leave a seedbed "like the channellings in a new piece of corduroy" where he passed.

Why? I wondered irritably, as I began to load up the seed drill, did some blasted historical society want me to research local agriculture for them! As if there wasn't enough contemporary farming to be getting on with! Anyway, where the devil would I start? The horse era? Agricultural revolution? Norman conquest? Or the Romans and Celts? It all seemed absolutely crazy and absurd. One ought to be living for the future, not the past, and like a fool I had been talked into this crazy time consuming project.

"Years ago, when we did it all with horses, they didn't reckon on drilling afore the tenth of October . . . it gave the weeds chance to germinate first," an old horseman had observed the evening before, "of course, now you've got weedkillers and chemicals, you can push on a bit sooner." This then is the theme of this work. We will follow the progressions and developments of agriculture and rural life from the earliest soil-forming geological phase to the latest yields and trials work of the 1982 harvest. We shall examine the effect of the ice ages and the subsequent recolonisation by plant life in the millenniums that followed. We will observe Celtic, Roman and medieval agriculture before detailing the activities and lore of the "horse age", with the recollections of those whose labours were to garner and sow with scythe and with horse. Within this context we will record the memories of the shepherd, stockman, horsekeeper, blacksmith, stackbuilder, thatcher and threshing contractor. Finally, we shall explain the technological innovations of the last fifty years and investigate their effect upon farmer, farmworker, wildlife and landscape.

But before we do this, let us briefly describe the geographical location of the villages of which this history is written. In doing so, we will introduce you to another Bulmer farmer. He had his portrait painted in the eighteenth century and the subsequent picture is recognised throughout the world of art for its perfection of detail, balance of composition and brilliance of execution.

Approximately sixty miles south of the Bulmer-Gestingthorpe road, in the heart of central London, hangs a portrait of one of Bulmer's previous estate owners. Walking past the fountains of Nelson's Column and up the stone steps of the National Gallery, one turns right on entering through the doors and passing the Van Goghs, Monets, Renoirs and other French Impressionists, one arrives in a long gallery, dedicated to British artists of the eighteenth and nineteenth centuries: there beside Constable's 'Haywain' and Turner's 'Fighting Temeraire' is Thomas Gainsborough's 'Mr and Mrs Robert Andrews'. Born in 1726, Andrews is portrayed with gun in hand, dog at heel and elgant wife beside him. She is sitting in an elaborate rococo iron chair, and in the background are the neatly arranged fields, sheep meadows and plantations of the Auberies–their Bulmer estate. Today the village has a population of 562 and is situated two miles from Gainsborough's birthplace of Sudbury. The latter stretches back from the verdant meadows of the River Stour on the border of the countryside immortalised by the landscapes of John Constable.

Sudbury itself is in Suffolk, but on the Essex side of the river, Bulmer adjoins Henny, Wickham St. Pauls, Belchamp Walter and Gestingthorpe. Gestingthorpe lies equidistant between Halstead and Sudbury, has a population of 363 and is approximately mid way between Chelmsford and Bury St. Edmunds on a north-south line; and Colchester and Cambridge on an east-west axis. The village has its own renowned hero–Captain L. E. G. Oates "the very gallant gentleman" who walked out into the blizzard in the hope that his colleagues might reach safety during Scott's ill fated return from the South Pole in 1913, and whose family lived at Gestingthorpe Hall.

This then is the cartographical location of the farms and activities recorded in this history. But what of the land itself? What of the rolling hills that fall away behind "Mr and Mrs Robert Andrews"? What of the chalky outcrops, the sandy seams and the sticky clay patches of Goldingham Wood field that we still encounter when ploughing, cultivating and seeding? What process contrived to provide the parish with soils varying from lightest sand to the heaviest pug that have been the curse of horsemen and farmers ever since?

The answers to these questions were provided during the summer of 1978 and early 1979 when tractor drivers and farmworkers may well have observed a slender figure emerging from the mists and hedgerows between Sudbury and Halstead with notebook open and soil auger in hand. His name was Ron Allen, and the Soil Survey of England and Wales is shortly to publish his report on the soils of the Halstead District in North East Essex.

Initially he mentions the chalk which underlies the whole area and outcrops at Bulmer and Henny. He suggests that this chalk consists of microscopic marine algae laid down 70-100 million years ago. Later in the Palaeocene and Eocene eras, 36-65 million years ago, a shallow sea covered the region and during this time the Thanet sands, Reading Beds and London clays were deposited. These strata are still visible and identifiable, especially in the locality around Gestingthorpe and Bulmer, where the London clay was particularly important for the brickmaking industries that flourished in both villages. Fossils found in the London clays suggest that conditions at the time were tropical, and possible similar to those in Malaya or Southern India today.

But the climate was not always to be so pleasant. The investigation continues with a telephone call to the offices of the Soil Survey at Wrecclesham in Surrey.

"By about two million years ago the alternating glacial and temperate conditions of the ice ages had begun.* During one glacial period, a sheet of ice possibly between twenty to two hundred feet thick extended as far south as Brentwood and on its retreat deposited the chalky boulder clay which is so good for wheat growing, and erratic boulders which are still visible in the area. Subsequent glacial and temperate phases each modified soil conditions, and with the retreat of the most recent ice cap around 10,000 years ago the landscape and terrain began to take on something of the appearance that it has today, although the process of natural erosion aided by rivers and streams was to continue."

So what of the rapid changes in soil types, that leave the villages of our survey like a geological kaleidoscope with soil classifications from boulder clays to lightest sands?

"In an old glaciated landscape", says Ron Allen, "where geological deposits have been added to, and altered by highly contrasted climatic conditions, then the range of soil types is going to be varied and their distribution complex. In this, Bulmer and Gestingthorpe are no exception and a selection of soils will be found on most farms and sometimes in a single field."

Even with the vast resources of mechanisation now at hand, these rapidly altering soils–a direct consequence of millions of years of geological activity, continue to provide headaches for those of us who follow where the old horsemen once trod, muttering as they passed that a field was "boys land", "full of mells", "dead ol stuff" or "puggy as hell".

Another interesting geological phenomena of the area are the pits which sometimes appear in fields where the thin surface membrane of soil suddenly collapses into a hollow below. One persistently repeated local story, tells of head horseman Arthur Rippingale harrowing on Overidges field, Gestingthorpe in 1921, when the soil beneath one of his horses subsided. Son Reg, now eighty three years old, and resident of Wickham St. Pauls recalls the incident:

"Overidges field had got all "twitchy" (grassy) so we ploughed it up and used three horses on the plough, so that we could get hold of it a bit deeper. When we finished, we took a mould up so the last furrow was a good bit deeper than normal.

* Bones found at Brundon near Sudbury date to 174,000 B.C. and indicate that man had settled in the area during an inter glacial phase. Similarly from the F-eemain interglacial phase of 100,000 years ago the fossilised animal bones of Steppe Bison, Straight Tusked Elephant, Hippopotamus, Giant Deer, Lion (or) Tiger have been found a few miles from Colchester in Pleistocene deposits in East Mersea.

Well, when we come to pull it about, we took the drag harrows with four horses; I went to drive them and my father came to work the handles (lift up the harrows if one got full of grass). When we got into the narrowest bit of the field one of the horses suddenly stopped. It had got its hind hoof through the bottom of the furrow and it couldn't get it out. When we saw what was happening, we went to the front and undid all the leaders and lines, but whilst we were undoing them the horse was gradually sinking into this hole . . . come to the finish it almost disappeared altogether . . . so we went and got some spades and cut a trench in front of the direction it was standing and it got out that way. But this old horse never really got over it, and my father who had worked on the farm all his life was hully upset as well."

But with recollections of the horse era we are moving forward to rapidly: let us return momentarily to the bleak desolate landscape that hauntingly emerged from the receding ice some ten millenniums ago. Denuded, barren and lifeless it must have resembled something more closely akin to the empty brown silence of a stark wasteland. But even then, as the streams of melted ice ran rivulets through the depressions and hillocks to the Belchamp Brook and River Stour, the first transient warmth of summer sun would have caught the slight breeze that blew across this eerie phenomenon. And in those winds would have come seeds and pollen and with them, the slow regeneration of plant life in north east Essex.

Speaking at a meeting of Bulmer, Wickham and Gestingthorpe W.E.A., Colin Ranson from the Nature Conservancy Council described the process of reforestation in the area.

"By 8200 B.C. the climate had improved and birch began to colonize the otherwise treeless area: around 7500 B.C. pine began to replace the birch and this was followed by hazel, elm, oak, elder and finally somewhere about 5500 B.C. we have the arrival of lime."

In a fascinating work "Trees and Woodland in the British Landscape"* Dr Oliver Rackham states that by 3000 B.C. "almost the whole of Britain was covered with virgin forest". Clearance of this wildwood by mankind becomes increasingly noticeable from this time onwards.

Metal ornaments were developed during the bronze age (1700-400 B.C.) although the stronger stone tools continued to be used until the Celts arrived around 400 B.C., bringing with them the art of making iron tools and implements. Even then, it must have required a colossal expenditure of human energies, to clear, laboriously and manually, the smallest area for cultivation. Oliver Rackham believes that, "to convert millions of acres of

* "Trees and Woodland in the British Landscape", published by J. M. Dent & Sons Ltd.

prehistoric forest into farmland is unquestionably the greatest achievement of our ancestors who had a much smaller population than ours and no power tools".

Two and a half thousand years later, Colin Ranson believes that the most important conservation priority in the area today, is to preserve these last lingering remnants of "ancient woodland" that have survived from those prehistoric times to the present day. They are, he explains, "reservoirs of wild life that cannot be recreated". Within this context he believes that Waldegrove, Butlers and Parsonage Wood in the village of Bulmer, "are almost certainly ancient woodland and extremely important". So too, were Goldingham and Wiggery Wood, and he gives a few guidelines to the identification of ancient woodland–or an ancient hedgerow that may be the last boundary of a previously wooded area.

"There will be a tremendous variety of both trees and shrubs," he says, "At least 20 species are commonly found in the most ancient of woods of five acres or more. These ancient woods," he continues, "may well be on parish boundaries and bordered by a deep ditch; it is possible that small-leafed lime, oxlip and wood anemone may be growing and bluebells and dogs mercury will normally be found."

The hedge around Goldingham Wood field, described at the beginning of this chapter, certainly falls within this category, containing numerous species of both plant and insect life.

These then are the last woodlands against whose knarled and knotted trunks our predecessors hacked with flint and iron or burnt with fire. Of that era itself, from 3000 B.C. to the birth of Christ we have only a skeletal knowledge: Flint arrow heads and a bronze age urn* have been discovered in Bulmer: through the uncertain dusk of this phase all we can safely assume is that at some point in the first millenium B.C. bronze age settlers may have scratched small irregular plots of soil with hand hoes on the gentlest soils of the area. These plots might be abandoned after a few years to allow natural recuperation. Later, around 400 B.C., a light ox-drawn plough was introduced by iron age invaders. They established elementary Celtic farmsteads, maintained clearly defined fields and are known to have grown barley, common bread wheat and Emmer (wheat). Oxen and pigs were eaten. Harvested grain was stored in pits dug in the soil and was often roasted to assist preservation.

Around 50 B.C., a wave of refugees from Caesar's campaigns in Gaul invaded Southern Britain. Known as the Belgae they developed a sophisticated political infrastructure and minted their own coins. The emblem of some was an ear of barley. Colchester became an important tribal capital.

---

* Discovered by farmer and proprietor of the Bulmer Brick and Tile Company, Peter Minter when he was sheltering from a snowstorm whils applying fertiliser "on the frost" to sugar beet land in the February of 1958.

it is from this point that we have clear evidence of an agricultural home-stead situated on the boundary between our two villages. It was carefully selected and was surrounded by the kindest and richest of soils.

These newcomers to our 'vicinity' stored their grain in pottery jars and it is argued that they introduced a heavier plough with wheels, mouldboard and coulter.* Irrespective of whether or not such a plough was used in Iron Age Gestingthorpe we have established that the furrow which was drawn—by whatever means—is one which has stretched on unbroken across the falling dynasties of history from the Roman Empire to the present day, where the same soil is still tilled, harrowed and sown with the recurring forebodings of weather and season. It is a furrow we shall follow for another two thousand years.

But as we approach the age of Imperial Roman grandeur, we suddenly have an illuminated picture of farming in our villages. To see it, we have first to return to an afternoon in the late summer of 1947.

---

* Point of contention between academics. Some feel it may only have been introduced in certain localities. Others that it did not arrive until the Saxon era.

CHAPTER TWO

Roman Gestingthorpe

"The lion and the deer"

As farmer and bulldozing contractor Harold Cooper walked across the stalks of kale stubble, he knew that he had a problem. Standing on the Gestingthorpe-Bulmer boundary 400 yards from Goldingham Wood field, in the late summer of 1947, he wondered what to do about Cort field. The kale stalks were tough, twisted and stiff. No ordinary plough would bury them without "driving up" which would leave an unsatisfactorily trashy soil behind. Shrugging, he decided to hire a single furrow deep digger plough. Later, it was hooked on to a John Deere Model D tractor which was driven by erstwhile horseman, Jack Mann of Belchamp Walter.

It was when he went to inspect the progress of this new extra deep plough, that he was struck by the large quantities of red tile and brick that it had turned up to the surface. He made a point of taking a few samples to Colchester museum, where the curator identified them as Roman. Subsequently, he suggested some guidelines for excavation and recommended that a trial hole be dug.

For 30 years, Harold Cooper was to patiently excavate the site on bank holidays and Sunday afternoons. He used a brush and a two-inch trowel. Throughout this time, he was encouraged by leading archaeological authorities such as Major John Brinson, late President of Essex Archaeological Society; Max Hull, Curator of Colchester Museum and Professor Shepherd Frere of All Souls College, Oxford.

Finds were carefully examined, preserved and displayed, and Harold Cooper is now able to outline the history of Cort Field, Gestingthorpe as it developed 2000 years ago.

"There is evidence" he says, "of a small Begic hut settlement from about 50 B.C. But with the Roman Conquest of 43 A.D., the developing village becomes increasingly Romanised, possibly colonized by retired soldiers from Camulodunum—Colchester."

The latter is about 20 miles from Gestingthorpe and when Camulodunum was sacked by Boadicea in 61 A.D., the reverberations of her rebellion will have presented the Romano-British villagers who toiled on our Long Furrow with a cruel dilemma. Either they could remain loyal to the Caesars and risk annihilation by the Iceni, or they could participate

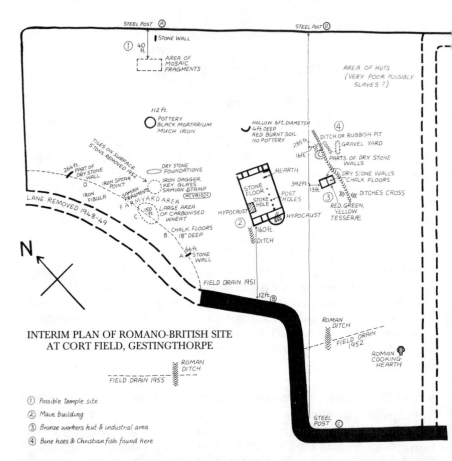

INTERIM PLAN OF ROMANO-BRITISH SITE
AT CORT FIELD, GESTINGTHORPE

① Possible temple site
② Main building
③ Bronze workers hut & industrial area
④ Bone hoes & Christian fish found here

in the insurgency and face retribution in the event of a Roman triumph. Either way, it is evident from the charred remains of the era that a conflagration took place and that the settlement was partially destroyed.

It was soon to recover; by the close of the Second Century, it extended to nearly 10 acres and the site plan locates the principal building, bronze worker's shop, slave huts, farmyard area, temple and hearth site.

Finds from these Centuries include a bronze steelyard (a hand-held weighing mechanism), a glass-bronze milliefiori, necklaces, ladies' hair pins, surgical equipment, keys, brooches, iron styli and a signet ring. The iron styli are particularly interesting, having been discovered beneath the slave hut area of the site which suggests that the latter were literate. The smooth, polished, red coloured samian-ware pottery was in wide use and this indicates a degree of refinement at the settlement. Similarly, the millie-fiori must have made a dazzling jewellery ornamentation for one of the family.

But the most tantalizing of the jewellery finds must surely be the signet ring, with its representation of a lion killing a red deer. Possibly it belonged to the head of the family who lived in the principal building and we wonder

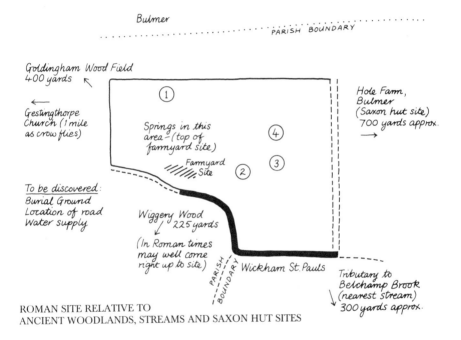

ROMAN SITE RELATIVE TO
ANCIENT WOODLANDS, STREAMS AND SAXON HUT SITES

if it was passed down from father to son across many generations beside the harvests and seasons of our Long Furrow.

Of the 500 coins recovered, the greatest majority are from the house of Constantine in the early Fourth Century. This was also a time of high inflation with a debasing currency and the preponderance of coins should not imply a commercial boom. Conditions however, were generally prosperous and a few years later, in 360 A.D., the fields of our Roman settlement will have fallen beneath the imperial edict of the Emperor Julian, decreeing the export of wheat from Britain to barbarian ravaged Germany. That the villa owner and farmsteaders of Bulmer and Gestingthorpe produced wheat for German consumption in the Fourth Century is a phenomenon that was not to be repeated until entry into the Common Market, 1600 years later.

In 410 A.D., the Emperor Honorius withdrew the last Roman legions from Britain's shores. Coins found after this date consist of the increasingly illegible radiates of a declining civilisation. But there was no immediate collapse. Rather, it is probable that the village continued until at least 450 A.D. and finds of Romano-Saxon pottery and brooches confirm that our Furrow was being drawn well into the Fifth Century.

But what was the village like? the reader may ask.

There is some evidence that the settlement may have served as a 'staging post' or 'mansio' in the highly efficient network of the Empire's communications. But in essence, Romano-British Gestingthorpe centred as a large market village for the smaller outlying homesteads of the area. The community was a hive of activity and from the finds in the museum, it is easy to imagine the clang of hammers, thud of chisels and jangle of harness as a carpenter, wheelwright, blacksmith, cobbler and bronze worker pursued their professions in buildings with flint foundations, wooden walls and thatched or tiled rooves. One pictures slaves carrying bundles of firewood to the hypercausted main house, women toiling over quern stones, tradesmen weighing meat and oxen being taken to the surrounding fields.

Agriculturally, it was the ox that was used for ploughing and draft work, whilst hoeing and weeding would be done by hand. Amongst the finds from the site is the base of a deer antler which had been used as a hoe. A hole is cut into the centre to accommodate the handle. The crops were hand-picked or cut by sickle, although grass was mown by scythe. The Romans improved the existing Celtic sickle which was straight, by "balancing" it with the introduction of the still familiar curve. The scythe was also a Roman innovation and the facility to mow grass and make hay was an important development which allowed the overwintering of livestock. Animal bones from Gestingthorpe have yet to be professionally examined, but the majority of cattle on the other Romano-British sites were 3-4 years old when slaughtered. Taken together, the improvements in the sickle, the development of the scythe, the introduction of new crops and the overwintering of livestock, amount to a tremendous phase of agricultural improvement—indeed, a revolution of agricultural practice in the centuries of Roman occupation.

Some of the iron tools which did the work have also been discovered and include an almost complete set of carpenter's tools, two axe heads, a bill-hook and a plough share. In a work entitled: "The Long Furrow", it is appropriate that we should examine the first tangible evidence of that

Furrow in some detail. To a Twentieth Century farmer, the Roman plough share from Gestingthorpe resembles something more closely akin to a contemporary wide cultivation point. Harold Cooper endorses this view . . .

"It was used to scratch through the ground rather than invert it: to make a friable seed bed, several passes would be required and most Roman authorities, such as Columella, Pliny or Varro, suggest that land should be ploughed–or more accurately, cultivated, at least twice and if possible, three or more times. The soil might then have been harrowed and there are several descriptions in classical literature of wooden frames and wicker brushes which could be fitted with iron or wooden teeth."

Yet as a practical farmer with over half a century of experience, Harold Cooper also believes that alternative methods of establishing seedbeds could have been employed by Celtic, Roman and Saxon homesteaders. He explains:

"The use of the sickle for harvesting cereals suggests that the straw was left standing and only the ears of the plant removed. The straw could then be grazed, cut for livestock use, or alternatively burned.* Now the effect of burning is to produce a temporarily ideal and friable seed bed– without the need for cultivation into which our Romano-British predecessor could have dibbed or broadcast their seed prior to harrowing. Such a practice would be especially suitable on reclaimed woodland where the roots of felled trees and bushes might damage a wooden plough".

He concludes by suggesting that:

"Although the pressure for land would eventually demand a settled field structure, the advantage of the slash and burn approach on woodland are such that I believe it is a system that may well have continued as a small proportion of total acreage well into the Second Century".

Of the crops themselves, we have evidence that the peasants who tilled our fields in the epoch of Roman grandeur were growing wheat, barley and rye. Carbonised grain (preserved as a consequence of being burnt during the Roman era) and recovered in excavation 1800 years later has been examined by archaeological scientist, Jane Renfrew.

From a few charred samples, she is able to discern not only the type of cereal that was grown but also the particular variety. These include "a free

---

* Harvesting of rice continues in this manner in parts of South East Asia today; so too does the grazing and burning of rice straw. Writing in the first century B.C., Virgil commented in the Georgics, "often again it profits to burn the barren fields, firing light stubble with crackling flame".

threshing bread wheat, a rye and a six row barley". She believes that the barley "may have been used as much for bread making as for brewing . . . it gives fairly solid, but very tasty bread". Concluding her report, she writes that the inhabitants of Romano-British Gestingthorpe had "very efficient means of removing chaff and unwanted weed seeds in their winnowing practices".*

The latter would have been organised in the traditional way, with animals walking over the ears of corn and then using the wind to blow away the chaff. It is possible, although as yet we have no proof, that elementary flails were also in use.

Once threshed, the corn was believed to have been stored in large urns. But initial excavation of the farmyard area and of dwelling premises on the site has produced little evidence of these large amphora, suggesting that either the crop was stored in bulk, left unthreshed until required, or that fabric was used. Equal uncertainty exists in our knowledge of grain drying systems in our Long Furrow at Roman Gestingthorpe. There is widescale evidence of barns designed to dry grain within the Roman world: interestingly, they operate on the hypercaust or hot air principle which is still a fundamental feature of the contemporary drying plants installed recently on local farms.

As yet, there is no evidence of this at Gestingthorpe and Harold Cooper believes that the damp grain harvested from the Romano-British fields in Gestingthorpe, Bulmer, Wickham St. Pauls and the Belchamps would have been exposed in a thin layer to the open sunshine in a manner which continues in Third World countries today.

But what other crops were grown by our Gestingthorpe and Bulmer farmers in the centuries of Claudius, Marcus Aurelius and Constantine? We have Jane Renfrew's evidence of wheat, barley and rye; but what else might we imagine in the fields, gardens and orchards of our Romano-British farmstead? As yet, no other seeds have been identified at Gestingthorpe. On other sites, however, parsnips, peas, cabbages, onions and leeks were grown as vegetables. Most were introduced to Britain by the Romans and may have been grown in the Long Furrow at Gestingthorpe. The acreage of oats also increased, being particularly suitable for feeding cavalry horses. In the orchards of Roman Britain, the cherry, apple, plum and raspberry were grown, whilst sloes, blackberries and bullace from nearby woodlands were part of the diet. On favourable south facing slopes, vines, figs and mulberries were introduced. As yet, we have no firm evidence of any of these plants or crops but Harold Cooper lives in hope, exclaiming:

"What is so important and exciting for the archaeological agriculturalist is the discovery of one carbonized seed, or a piece of rusty

* Jane Renfrew, "Gestingthorpe, the Cereal Finds". To be published.

iron that would prove the existence of vines, turnips or oats at our settlement. Each in its own way would provide another clue or piece in the huge jigsaw of re-creation on which we are embarked. There is still a fantastic amount to discover about grain storage, crops, rotation, cultivation techniques and livestock housing".

The layout of the cattle byres and stockyard at Gestingthorpe is equally uncertain. But animal bones recovered include those of sheep, pigs, cattle, red deer and the domestic dog: the domestic fowl was another Roman introduction and the pheasant–source of so much contemporary fascination–arrived at the same time. Arboriculturally, the Romans brought the walnut, the sweet chestnut and cherry. Moreover, adjoining parts of Wiggery and Goldingham woods were almost certainly coppiced and would have continued to be managed in this way until their removal in the Eighteenth and Nineteenth Centuries.

This then is our picture of Roman Gestingthorpe in its heyday. It is of a village with rotated fields and neat boundaries; of blackthorn stock-folds and carefully built hay stacks standing beside the palpable warmth of the cattle byre; it is a picture of barns and threshing floors or well pruned orchards and tidy vegetable plots, of blacksmiths and carpenters and the sounds of industry, commerce and labour emanating from the workshops, huts and farmyard of the settlement. From all of the available information, it is evident that a complex, multi-laminated agricultural discipline had developed, providing a variation in diet and sophistication in farming practice that was not to be repeated until the Sixteenth Century.

It was a village that had used refined surgical and weighing equipment: its inhabitants had fine jewellery. They were literate, had paid their taxes and worshipped their gods. Of these, a clay Venus, a bone Cupid and Christian fish* are evidence. But ultimately and inexorably it was to be undermined by the deteriorating military and political conditions of the late Fourth and Fifth Century. At some point, the settlement was abandoned and left to oblivion. In which decade this transpired, we do not know: a Saxon hut site from the Sixth and Seventh Century has been unearthed on neighbouring Hole Farm, suggesting a lingering, tenuous and desperate continuity of our Long Furrow in these years of political cataclysm and barbarian invasion.

As the historical dusk of the Sixth Century thickens into the darkness of the Seventh, our last impression of Roman Gestingthorpe must be of the fields neglected and overgrown; of the fruit trees wild and unpruned. The buildings are derelict and abandoned; the thatch and tiles have collapsed. Weeds and moss are seen straggling over the crumbling walls. Finally, the course of nature completed the indifference and savagery of man and the agricultural settlement became buried and lost in its own debris for 1400 years.

* Early Christian symbol.

CHAPTER THREE

The Manorial Epoch

"The furrow and the fold"

As the twilight embers of Roman Gestingthorpe and the Saxon hut sites fade into darkness, our story must again return to conjecture and hypothesis.

Was our Furrow still drawn? Was the well-tilled soil still turned? Who were the people whose hands grasped the shafts and who squinted into the sun as they hobbled across the clods where the tractors and combines now pass?

There is little factual or firm information to illuminate the two hundred years from the Sixth to the Eighth Centuries: rather, there is a growing belief amongst archaeologists that the "Dark Ages" were not as bleak as they have been previously portrayed. Despite the prevailing political instability, there is some evidence for a continuity of some wood and farmland management.

Harold Cooper firmly believes that many of the smaller Romano-British settlements that had been satellite homesteads around Gestingthorpe were not completely neglected. Citing Overhall, Gestingthorpe; Little Yeldham Hall; Fowes Manor, Belchamp Otten; Wickham Hall and Goldingham Hall, Bulmer, he suggests that these Romano-British farmsteads continued to be farmed, eventually becoming the nucleus of later Manorial centres.

"The Saxon invaders", he explains, "were not the nomadic barbarians who swept across Asia to plunder Rome: rather, they were country men on the move: like all country men they would quickly appreciate the kinder soils and the lingering orchards of the previous clearings". Explaining the apparent desertion of the site at Cort Field, Gestingthorpe, Harold Cooper continues, "the degree of permanence at Gestingthorpe was such that the notion of old gods and spirits could not be dispelled by the newcomers in the way that a conflagration would destroy a simpler wooden site". Dr Oliver Rackham in 'Trees and Woodlands in the British Landscape' reflects this opinion by suggesting that some woodland coppicing may have continued almost uninterrupted during these years.

By the early Ninth Century, conditions were sufficiently stable to allow trade, currency and travel to return to Eastern England. A mint existed in Sudbury from this time and we have a record of Gestingthorpe from the same Century. It has been suggested that the name Gestingthorpe itself is a mixture of Anglo Saxon (Guest-ing) and Danish (thorpe) and that upon the arrival of the latter, the Saxons were allowed to remain, possibly in servitude to new masters.

Agriculturally, the Saxons, who followed our Furrow, may well have introduced a stronger plough, with mouldboard, coulter and wheel. This would have required several oxen to pull it but facilitated the working of "heavier" land and reduced the need for "cross ploughing". A good deal of controversy centres around this implement. Some writers arguing that it was only used to break up virgin land, whose sods would need to be completely inverted and the plough strong enough to cut through the lingering roots of trees and bushes.

Once a field was ready for sowing, it is thought that our Saxon ancestors grew a larger quantity of barley than wheat and less oats than in Roman times. At harvest time the sickle was still used for reaping corn, the scythe for mowing grass and threshing was performed by a flail* or treading out by animals. Wheat was still ground by traditional methods, although Water-mills were making their appearance and there is evidence of one at Nether-hall, Gestingthorpe, prior to the Norman Conquest.

Prior to their conversion to Christianity, the Saxon farmsteaders paid homage to their own gods, whose names Tiu, Wodin, Thor and Freya are still commemorated in our weekday names. Freya was a fertility goddess who was taken about the countryside in a wagon to receive offerings and bless the crops. Sometimes in the squalling gale of an autumn evening, when one is loading up the seed drill, on the track by the Roman site, the scudding clouds scarify the moon through the gaunt boughs of the hedges and trees, and one hears in the half shadows and semi forms of dusk, the pent-up call of the old spirits; the archaic gods with their animistic field altars and Beowulf legends, whose power has since waned and whose rituals have long been neglected.

With the arrival of William the Conqueror in 1066 and the commissioning of the Doomsday Book 20 years later, a clearer picture emerges of conditions prevailing at the time. In Bulmer, the Manors of Goldingham, Butlers and Smeetham Hall are documented whilst in Gestingthorpe, those of Netherhall and Overhall are identifiable.

---

* It is believed that with a wooden flail one man could thresh 7 bushels of wheat, 8 of rye, 15 of barley and 18 of oats in a day.

The Doomsday reference to Overhall, Gestingthorpe is a good example of the rural inventory of the time.

. . ."The land of Otto the goldsmith. Hundred of Hinckford. Count Algar held Gestingthorpe (before the conquest) for half a hide, now Otto holds it for the like. Always 3 teams in demense and 3 teams in homage. Then 13 bordars now 16. Always 6 serfs. Wood for 60 swine, 25 acres of meadow, 80 sheep, 32 beasts (cattle) 88 swine and 3 horses. And there were 12 socmen in the time of King Edward, now there are 11 remaining in this Manor and they hold half a hide and 30 acres".

By comparison, the manor of Goldingham consisted of 2 plough teams, twelve beasts, one horse, two hundred sheep, sixty six swine and five hives of bees. There were sixteen acres of meadow and eighteen of arable.

Eight hundred and ninety six years later, Goldingham has no beasts, horses, sheep swine or bees. Instead there are two hundred and seventy acres of wheat, eighty of barley and forty of woodland and plantation.

The Doomsday picture that emerges, however, is one typical of Manorial England with its highly stratified feudal society of serf, bordar and socmen, presided over by the Lord of the Manor or his bailiff. The serfs provided compulsory labour for the Lord of the Manor in addition to seasonal offerings of eggs, fowls and firewood. The socmen were essentially free peasants who paid rent to the Lord. Whether of not the peasants of Goldingham Hall, Bulmer or Overhall, Gestingthorpe were working the "3 field system" with its subdivision of one acre strips, we cannot tell: some historians suggest that this feature of Medieval England was not common in East Anglia.

Irrespective of distribution, the fields almost certainly followed a three year rotation of winter cereal (wheat or rye) followed by a spring crop (barley, oats, peas or beans) with a fallow every third year. The level of production has been estimated at 10-12 bushels or 5-6½ cwt/acre. (Compared with 50-80 cwts in 1982). Oxen were used for ploughing and allowed half a sheaf of oats a day. Cows were kept on rough meadows. Sheep were also milked and pigs scavenged amongst the woods. In the winter, exhausted oxen and unproductive cows were killed off and salted down.

The peasants of our villages who plodded wearily along this phase of our Long Furrow indeed had a burdensome and frugal existence. When they were not at work on their Lord's land, weeding their own strips, gathering firewood or feeding their livestock, they would have struggled through the woodlands to the old Roman site on Cort Field and plundered the bricks and flints from the ruined buildings for the walls and foundations of Gestingthorpe Church. Even the introduction of the windmill in the Twelfth Century did little to ease their burden, for they were expected—indeed compelled—to use that of their Manorial Lord at charges they could ill afford. Interestingly, we have evidence of a windmill in neighbouring Wickham St. Pauls in 1222.

Woodland management was clearly understood by our predecessors, who required replenishable firewood, conveniently close to their hearthside. Oliver Rackham confirms that "coppicing was widespread by Doomsday". During Saxon times, many of our local woods—Wiggery, Oakley, Goldingham and Butlers, may still have formed part of a larger semi-forest, supporting animals such as deer and wild boar, wild cats and possibly wolves.

Many changes have occured in the flora and fauna beside our furrow. We have witnessed the introduction of the pheasant, walnut, sweet chestnut and cherry in the Roman era; sycamore arrived in the Middle Ages and the horse chestnut, potato, tomato and turkey in the Sixteenth and Seventeenth Centuries. The black rat reached England in 1348 and the brown rat in 1728. The red legged partridge was brought to the county in 1770, and exactly a hundred years later, the grey squirrel a native of North America was unfortunately released from captivity into the hedgerows and woodlands of Southern England.

Another animal to make its appearance in England after the Norman Conquest was the rabbit. By 1298, it had already become a controversial creature in the warrens beside our Long Furrow as John Buteturte of Overhall, Gestingthorpe laid a complaint at Westminster:

"That while he and his men were under the King's protection, Alan de Goldingham, William and John his brothers . . . entered his free warren at Gestingthorpe, County Essex, hunted therein, carried away hares and rabbits and assaulted John son of Matthew his warrener".

The Goldingham family were to remain in Bulmer, for another 300 years and recently returned to look over their ancestral homeland. The rabbits, however, are still with us. Source of so much deperately needed food to our Eighteenth Century poacher and Nineteenth Century horseman, they are today a frustrating and irritating economic problem. Later, along our Furrow, we will meet Charlie Martin, the last genuine horseman to have "had the rabbitting" in the 1930's. Recently, however, their numbers have increased dramatically and after harvest and in the early spring, I thin them down with a shotgun from an open-topped Land Rover. Kevin Leech and Dennis Rippingale go round in a separate vehicle and in 1976, we shot over a thousand. Moonless nights with a slight breeze we find are the most satisfac-

tory. Sometimes an old farmer tells me to "bulldoze away all your woods, so there's no room for any warrens . . ." but more recently, I have initiated a policy of "wiring them in", and it seems to be successful both commercially and ecologically.

Clearly, the rabbit was common in Essex by the Thirteenth Century. But it was the arrival in 1348 of another animal, the Black Rat, that was to bring to England the ghastly epidemic now known as the "Black Death". This plague is estimated to have killed one in three people and will have had devastating consequences upon the social and economic development of our medieval villages.

In 1381, the area would have reverberated with the repercussions of the "Peasants Revolt" which has several local connections. Not only did Simon of Sudbury crown the young Richard II, but it was another Sudburian—John Wrawe, who co-ordinated the peasants rebellion. The local connection with this phase of British history is maintained and in the second week of June 1381, at the height of the rebellion, the Manor of Liston was sacked, whilst in Gestingthorpe, goods and property were stolen, presumably by the peasants of our furrow. Later however, they were punished and fines were extracted from the village.*

Meanwhile the men of Essex, who had marched on London, had withdrawn to Colchester and subsequently to Sudbury, where a remnant are traditionally supposed to have made a last stand on the Market Hill.

Despite the Peasants Revolt and the gradual decline of feudal authority over the following three centuries, the "Manorial Courts" continued to function as the local arbiter of justice, hearing agricultural, parochial and social complaints in addition to witnessing property transactions. Those from Goldingham extend from 1314 to 1865, whilst a series from Overhall, Gestingthorpe, translated from latin at the expense of the late Miss V. Oates, illuminate rural controversies of the time.

The Gestingthorpe courts were held on the day of the vigil of Saint Philip and Saint James.

We read in 1519, that "Henry Hale is ordered to free a clogged watercourse" whilst the subsequent court held in 1521 declared that:

> "Anna (the wife of Robert Foster) keeps a common inn for vagabonds and others of bad and riotous behaviour and keeps bad and unlawful rule in her house by night . . . it is ordered that she do so no more under penalty of 20 shillings".

In 1526, the townsmen of Gestingthorpe are instructed to make a pair of butts to encourage shooting with the long bow; but in 1527, we read that

---

* From "Essex and the Peasants Revolt", published by Essex Records Office, 1981.

the townsmen of Gestingthorpe "have not made the butts as ordered and therefore incur a penalty of 3s. 4d." Normal human lethargy seems a feature of our Gestingthorpe citizens during this era as at the same (and subsequent courts), the Hale family are again instructed to clean their ditches.

In general, the great majority of the manorial manuscripts are concerned solely with the admission of new tenants and the acknowledgement of inheritance or purchase. However, a number of additional snippets are worth quoting. For despite occurring thirty years before Shakespear's birth, the rustic life that they portray has a definite Falstaffian flavour.

In 1538, it is recorded that:

"Thomas Parker, keeps a certain servant girl called Agnes Wheeler, who is a great nuisance to the neighbours both by her tongue and her hands; by striking and killing their geese and poultry. He is ordered to get rid of her by Whitsuntide".

At the court of 1542, the jury announced that:

"Edmund Fletcher, farmer of the Vicarage is a nuisance to his neighbours by letting his pigs and cattle stray at large on the highways and elsewhere"

and in 1563, of John Sache, who

"assaulted Robert Mascyall and has struck him on the head with a stone and drawn blood against the Queen's peace, therefore he is fined 20d".

Finally, of more direct agricultural significance we read that:

"a ewe lamb has been a stray within the manor for a year and a day (and more) and is not yet claimed. Valued at 16 pence".

Yet in reviewing the agricultural conditions of the Middle Ages, one's thoughts must eventually turn to the importance of sheep and the magnificent "wool" churches of Lavenham and Long Melford. It is with a brief review of the wool industry that we close this chapter.

Writer, teacher and historian, Edith Freeman of Ballingdon, Sudbury, is a keen student of social conditions in Medieval England and she explains:

"During the Thirteenth Century a 364 lb sack of wool might fetch fourteen marks if it came from Herefordshire or Shropshire but only four marks if it was East Anglian, where the fleece was of an inferior quality."

"So sheep didn't become pre-eminent in this area until later?"

"No. But with the development of the spinning wheel from the spindle and whorl, the long staple wool sheep of Eastern England – which seem to have arrived at about this time, became more important."

"Were there any other factors which influenced the size of the sheep population?"

"Yes. The Black Death of 1348, released large acreages of land from tillage which could still be grazed by sheep and shepherded by the temporarily plague depleted manorial labour force–there were quite certainly more sheep in this part of the country in the Fifteenth Century than the Thirteenth."

"And what about the wool trade?"

"This developed simultaneously with the increase in sheep and also reached its zenith in the Fifteenth Century. Locally, an important woollen cloth-making industry was established in towns and villages such as Sudbury, Halstead, Kersey, Glemsford and Lavenham."

Agriculturally, sheep were an ideal component of the Medieval parochial economy. Edith Freeman continues:

"not only did they provide in a wool, a saleable item, but they can also be milked, their manure was valuable, they survived on poorer land than cattle, they can safely graze winter corn in the early spring, and ultimately, they can be eaten".

Thomas Tusser, the Sixteenth Century poet declares in his 500 points of good husbandry:

"The land is well hearted with sheep from the fold
For one or two crops, if so it will hold".

It is fair to assume that sheep and the shepherd developed a great importance in the meadow, pastures and folds beside the Long Furrow of our Manorial farmsteads and Medieval villages. Lambing and especially shearing developed a seasonal importance equal only to harvest.

Within the traditional woodland and hedge, it was found that some plants and shrubs could be particularly well adapted to the needs of the sheep industry.

The Spindles used in elementary hand spinning were made from spindleberry wood, whilst "teasing" and "carding" utilised the teasels that

This rock, unearthed when Paul Mann was ploughing rape land in the summer of 1982, may have originated as far away as Scandinavia. It was brought to Gestingthorpe on the glaciers of the third ice age which also left us the chalky boulder clays so good for contemporary wheat growing.

Reg Rippingale, with ferret. Reg was with his father, Arthur, when the soil subsided on Overidges field in 1921. For the story of the ferret see Chapter 7.

"Mr. and Mrs. Robert Andrews" by Thomas Gainsborough. Andrews owned Bulmer's largest estate–The Auberies–in the eighteenth century. In the distance are the outlines of the Sudbury-Stour Valley, whilst the neat rectangular fields epitomise the disciplines of the Agricultural Revolution of which Andrews and Arthur Young so enthused. Note the sheaves, which are tied up with straw bands. (See Chapter Nine). (Reproduced by the courtesy of the Directors of the National Gallery, London)

Harold Cooper examining some of the "finds" from the Romano-British site on Cort Field, Gestingthorpe. Note the deer antler hoe, the axe head, the carpenter's tools, billhook, bone hairpins and jewellery including the "lion and the deer" signet ring in the display case.

Quern stone for grinding wheat.

Carbonized Wheat. This grain was harvested 1700 years ago.

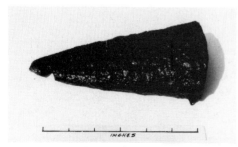

Roman Ploughshare.
(The small triangle was removed for metallurgical analysis)

This bronze fish was an early Christian symbol.

Alastair Tuffill–Photography

still grow in the valley bottoms beside the Belchamp Brook. An understanding of natural dyes would have been especially important and several locally grown plants were used in the process. "Saffron"* Walden for example, gets its name from the availability of the flower dye colouring in the area. Green and yellow were obtained from plants such as onion, privet leaves, nettles, cow parsley and oak bark. Red could be extracted from sorrel and yellow from ladies' bestraw: magenta is produced from dandelions. The bark of alder and the yellow of iris provide black and grey, whilst elderberries, damsons, sloes and privet berries made blues and purples. With the exception of "saffron" all of the remaining plants, including the spindleberry and teasels are still to be found in the hedgerows of Bulmer and Gestingthorpe today.

But if the wild flowers and shrubs may still be located, the sheep themselves have disappeared. As recently as 1900, every large Bulmer and Gestingthorpe farm carried a sizeable flock. One by one, however, they have been sold and dispersed and the last "commercial" lambing on Bulmer's acres occurred in 1962. In a subsequent chapter, we will investigate the shepherd, his sheep, lambing, shearing and "tupping" and we shall examine the associated crafts of hurdlemaking and droving.

But even the decline of the sheep and cloth industries provides a number of interesting and amusing local incidents.

As early as 1571 Parliament attempted to assist the wool and cloth trade and ordered that anyone under the rank of gentleman, should wear an English woollen cap on Sundays and Bank Holidays. These coarse woollen caps do not appear to have been well received by the young men of late Sixteenth Century Sudbury. For in 1576 we read in the Town Books that the authorities:

"pd for 2 pottes of beere at the Crowne for the collecturs of the statute of Cappes . . . 2d".

But this refreshment can not have been a sufficient inducement to encourage the inspectors to turn a blind eye to the vainer elements of Sudbury manhood, for a subsequent entry records an early example of connivance and corruption:

"pd to them (the inspectors), that they should not meddle within the towne . . . 7s 7d".

Later in the reign of Charles II, it was enacted that the dead were "to be buried in a woollen garment". Doubtless this statute like many others provided the opportunity for some cryptic and desert dry humour, by the men of our Furrow:

* "Wool–East Anglia's Golden Fleece" by Nigel Heard.

CHAPTER FOUR

The Seeds of Change

The First Agricultural Revolution

Thomas Tusser farmed near Manningtree around 1571. It is appropriate to include a selection of his verses, for although written over four centuries ago, they illustrate the principles and controversies which the bailiffs and labourers of Gestingthorpe and Bulmer would have argued and discussed in the Sixteenth Century.

However, the fundamental tenets of agriculture have not changed and we will show how the basic contentions of Tusser's time, are as much a point of conversation across the half filled beer tankard in the Gestingthorpe "Pheasant" of 1982, as they were to our predecessors whose goblets of mead were consumed in the "Common Inn of Anna Foster" in 1571.

On seeding he offers the following suggestions:

> Though beans be in sowing but scattered in
> Yet wheat, rye and peason, I love not too thin
> Sow barley and dredge with a plentiful hand
> Lest mead stead of reed overgroweth the land.

If the discussions over seed rates were important in Tusser's time, they cannot have exceeded the degree of enthusiasm with which the proponents of high seed rate wheat (Schleswig Holstein system) ware arguing their case with the low seed rate doctrines of Professor Laloux in the late 1970's. But Tusser is also anxious to protect his crops from the birds who today plague our crops of rape and dried peas.

> "No sooner a sowing but out by and by
> With mother or boy, the alarum can cry
> And let them be armed, with sling or with bow
> To scare away pigeon the rook or the crow".

Later, in our chapter on the Twentieth Century, we will discuss "bird scaring" with one of our older respondents who paid a shilling a day for that very task in the 1920's. And maybe, if the reader is living in rural surroundings, he may sometimes hear the regular explosions of a propane "banger" on a neighbouring field that is threatened with pigeons or rooks.

Tusser continues his 500 Points of Good Husbandry by emphasising the need for good land drainage. But he also recognises that big thistles are an indication of good land. More recently during the depression of the nineteen thirties farmers would argue that unless there were thistles "big enough to tie you horse to", a farm was not worth buying or hiring.

> "Much wetness, hog rooting and land out of heart
> Make thistles a number forthwith to upstart
> If thistles so growing, prove lusty and strong
> It signifieth land be hearty and strong".

In evaluating his crops, he provides a ditty of which a similar version is still quoted in contemporary circles . . .

> "Cold May and windy
> Makes barns fat and findy
> Calm weather in June
> Corn setteth in tune".

Finally, with the fruition of the year's labours, at the approach of harvest, he offers this ultimately unchanging truism:

> "If weather be fair and tidy the grain
> Make speedily carriage, for fear of a rain
> For tempest and showers deceiveth a many
> And lingering lubbers lose many a penny".

400 years later, with all of the resources of mechanisation at hand—500 horsepower of tractors, combines, and electronic grain dryers, the same urgency of harvest is expressed with even more brevity and bluntness in a seven word motto:

> *"When the weather's right . . . go like hell".*

Throughout these centuries, a gradual transition was occurring in British agriculture. The discovery of America in 1492 introduced a new crop—potatoes, which represented a colossal improvement to the diet of the entire nation. In the following century, tomatoes and turkeys were imported from the New World and attempts were made to establish tobacco in Britain.

Hops, which are indigenous, were also cultivated from this time. In 1631, twenty acres of Hop Bines at Earls Colne were estimated to be worth £400.*

Other crops which came to be grown on a field scale at this time include turnips, cabbages, cauliflowers, parsnips and carrots, some being introduced from the low countries. It is thought by some authorities that carrots were being use to fatten livestock and we have evidence that a local farmer included them in his rotation for:

"In January 1638 Robert Beversham of Sudbury† a yeoman had eighteen cows, forty bullocks, thirty eight acres of rye and five acres of carrots".

It was possibly from the use of carrots as cattle feed, that turnips came to be used for the same purpose. Similarly, it was found that with clover, an improved rotation could be applied that "fixed" nitrogen in the soil, and avoided such frequent and unproductive fallowing of land as the three field system demanded.

Another major transformation of the era, occurred with the development of the heavy horse and the manufacture of a more suitable collar which led to its increasing adoption as a draft animal to replace the oxen which had previously ploughed, hauled and carted in the fields of our Manorial Furrow. But the debates between the advocates of the horse, against the proponents of the oxen were intense and Arthur Young repeats the arguments in 1800.

Of even greater interest, however, were the lingering farmers who continued to work with oxen, not only in the Eighteenth and Nineteenth Centuries but into the first years of the Twentieth Century itself. At High Barn Hall, Halstead, the farm office contains a photograph of a two ox team pulling a plough and farmer Bill Waters explains:

"The photograph was taken on my grandfathers farm at Burlingham in Norfolk where he used oxen until 1905".

Did he breed them up himself?

---

* Agrarian History of England and Wales, Vol. IV 1500-1640 edited Joan Thirsk, C.U.P., quoting Robert Reyce, Suffolk in the Seventeenth Century, p. 31. Nordern op. cit. p 206. John Beale, Herefordshire Orchards, p. 47.

† Agrarian History of England and Wales, Vol IV, quoting: Plot, op. cit., p. 155; Folkingham, op. cit., p. 42; Blith, op. cit., pp. 246-8; Worlidge, op. cit., p. 147; Nordern, op. cit. p. 207; P. McGrath, The Marketing of Food, Fodder and Livestock in the London Area in the Seventeenth Century, London M.A. thesis, 1948 p. 197; Hugh Platt, the Jewell House of Art and Nature, p. 13.

"No. He would go to Banbury market and buy a train truck load of four year old Devons. A truck load consisted of about eight bullocks and out of this number three might prove satisfactory for draft work. Unlike horses these bullocks required a 'split' collar, as the ordinary type wouldn't pass over the horns. But these big Devons would do almost as much work as horses, and they had one advantage".

What was that?

"Well, unlike a horse, they were always 'growing into money'. When their working life was over they were fattened up on parsnips or swedes. By this time they weighed about a ton each and likely as not would win first prize at Norwich Fatstock Show".*

Returning to the Seventeenth and Eighteenth Centuries, we are reminded by our schoolboy history books, that it was during this era that a number of leading land-owners began to take a serious interest in the agricultural practices of their estates, and with the distribution of their ideas, a trend developed towards innovation and improvement. The results of years of experience and trials work were published by men such as "Turnip" Townsend who advocated the Norfolk four course rotation; Robert Bakewell became notable as a specialist in selective animal breeding. Viscount Leicester (Coke of Holkam) applied theory to practice and provided long leases with enforced rotations to his tenants and Jethro Tull pioneered the concept of planting seed in rows with a seed drill rather than broadcasting them by hand.

The importance of the latter principle was manifest when the neatly defined rows of emerged corn could be weeded with a horse hoe, a practice which continued until the development of chemical herbicides in the Twentieth Century.

The consequence of these developments was to lead to the final breakdown of the old "open field" system. How extensive this form of tenure had been in North East Essex in the Sixteenth Century is uncertain. From the Overhall Manorial records with the descriptions of farmers and tenancies and the remark of Morant that "much of Essex was enclosed from time immemorial", one has the impression that the great social upheaval created in much of central England by "Enclosure", may have been mitigated in our two parishes.† A lingering acreage of common land was reorganised and enclosed in Bulmer. This amounted to only twenty five acres, and was requisitioned by the parish poor authorities who subsequently let it out as allotments to parishioners.

---

* Britain's last "commercial" ox team continued to be working near Cirencester until 1930.

† There is, however, some evidence of lingering strip fields on the earliest maps of Gestingthorpe by not on those of Bulmer.

It is from these centuries that several of the family names that will recur along our Furrow first make their appearance. We may imagine them, broadcasting their seed by hand, and then experimenting with the first seed drills and horse hoes. We can visualise them ploughing in autumn—flailing in winter—hoeing in spring and harvesting—still with the sickle, in summer. Possibly, their ancestors have been here on the same fields and along the same Furrow since the earliest times—we cannot tell, but some at least have been part of the ethos for over four centuries.

John Coo for example, made a will in Gestingthorpe in 1520, and the Manorial Court of 1526 makes mention of Joan Cornell. Eventually, descendants of John Coo were to run Bulmer's last threshing tackle in the 1960's; one of their rivals was John Cornell.

In 1648, a Manorial court was held at Goldingham Hall, and amongst the witnesses were members of the Hurrell and Barrell families, Thomas Coo and Thomas Downs. Two hundred years later, the Downs family were to start an agricultural foundry in Gestingthorpe and one of the Hurrells had become a farmer. The Coo family has been previously mentioned, whilst that of Barrell—once fairly common—can never be spoken of in Belchamp Walter, without the memory of a kind, wizened, cheerful old man with a plastic neck-guard; whistle in mouth, ferret nets in pocket and beater's stick in hand, amongst the damp autumnal mists of a Belchamp valley pheasant shoot.

In the year 1700, the ringers of Gestingthorpe church bells, included Butcher Rippingale, Jeffrey Carter, Nicholas Stebbing and William Rayner, whilst in 1728, William Finch attended a vestry meeting with the churchwarden and vicar.

Today, the Finch family are well represented in Gestingthorpe, and the village's oldest contributor to our survey, George "Rover" Finch, is now 87 years old. The Rayners meanwhile are remembered for brick making. During the 1930's the late Harry Rippingale ran a local bus service and his nephew, Dennis, may still be seen during harvest at the controls of a combine harvester, cutting three acres an hour where his forefathers passed with sickle and scythe.

A few other snippets extracted from the W.E.A. publication "Bulmer: Then and Now" provide a background for these centuries. In 1658, at the Quarter Sessions, the farmers of Bulmer were instructed to repair the Bulmer to Ballingdon highway; Daniel Defoe mentions in 1725, that droves of turkeys and geese were driven through Bulmer Tye on the journey to London. Fishponds and a Tithe Barn stood close to Bulmer Church, while in 1768, a bitter tithe dispute between farmers Ruffle and John Brewster of Butler's Hall, erupted against the Rector of Wickham. We shall be retuning to the contentious problem of tithes later in out story. It is recorded that in 1774, Smeetham Hall was burnt down, and that the local "pound" for stray animals that wandered into the village was at Kitchens Farm at the top of Batt Hill.

Meanwhile, the pressure for agricultural land was increasing. Bulmer's population of 240 in 1700 had reached 421 in 1800 and peaked at 801 in 1851.

The consequences of these demographic trends upon the remaining areas of ancient woodland was considerable. From the earliest maps and the remarks made by the six men and two boys who "beat the bounds" in the perambulation record of 1794, we can estimate that of Bulmer's 2759 acres in 1785, at least 300 were woodland; in 1808, the figure had fallen to 263. By 1848 only 244 remained. This "grubbing out" with horses, axes and spades, represented a colossal human undertaking. Those woods that remained were "coppiced" at twelve-yearly intervals, writes Arthur Young, who reports that "their value at stubs" was ninety five shillings an acre.

It is time that we looked more closely at the writings of this man—Arthur Young—for the light that he throws on the Bulmer of 1800, illuminates our Long Furrow with the vitality and vibrance of living people, real ideas and inspired propositions. *

---

* If you think that this chapter is a little short, then you're right. After visiting the Royal Show, I was hoping to include a few paragraphs on the animal breeds of Seventeenth Century East Anglia, with particular reference to the "Rare Breeds Survival Trust". Unfortunately—harvest beat me to it!

CHAPTER FIVE

A Visitor to Bulmer

The Curfew tolls the knell of parting day
The lowing herd winds slowly over the lea
The plowman homeward plods his weary way
And leaves the wold to darkness and to me.

Grays Elegy

Travelling under commission for the Board of Agriculture, Arthur Young visited our Long Furrow at Bulmer, during the years of Nelson and Napoleon. It is evident from his observations, that by 1800, farming had become a highly enquiring and progressive profession.

To anyone involved with the land today, his survey makes fascinating reading.

We can imagine Young, journeying on horseback from parish to parish, through the deep and narrow lanes, with their muddied puddles and rutted tracks. As he travelled he will have passed the manors and the farms, the thatched cottages, the woods and hedgerows of our Eighteenth Century villages. As his sharp eye surveyed the terrain, he may have seen the squinting eyes and straining limbs of our agricultural ancestors whose great grandchildren are contributors to this book.

In many ways, Young was the arch apostle of the "great campaign" of improved farming, higher yields, and scrutiny of detail. Later we will follow this doctrine, of which Young was a standard bearer, through the Nineteenth Century to the coming of tractors and combines.

Possibly, what is most astonishing about Arthur Young, is the detailed and accurate observations he made of each village in a journey that encompassed the entire Eastern Counties.

"At Brickwall Farm, Bulmer" (the home of Gerty and the late Lawrence Coe) he writes, "finer land is rarely to be seen . . . in the state of fallow, after rain it is nearly white . . . there is a strong principal of adhesion in these soils; though so sandy to touch, if placed in the wet they become hard clods . . ."

Ken Day whose father farmed on such strip at Hilltop Farm confirms this 'principal of adhesion" and described it as "lashy old land" . . . "gets 'capped' in no time at all".

It is evident that hops were being grown in the Hedinghams and Maplesteads: Mr. Vancover, (a slightly earlier writer) put the value of an acre of Bulmer, hopground at 30 shillings. Two hundred years later wild hops are still to be found in the area, especially beside the Belchamp Brook.

Besides hops, farmers in the area were also growing other unusual crops such as coriander, carraway and teasels.

Rotations were of considerable interest at the time and Robert Andrews of the Auberies, "gave a good specimen, his husbandry excellent; the course: (year) 1. fallow   2. barley   3. clover   4. wheat   5. peas   6. barley   7. clover   8. wheat."

A latter day criticism of this sequence is that there is insufficient "break" between the clover and pea crops, to prevent the "carry over" of fungal stem and root diseases. It is now recognised that leguminous crops should not be grown more frequently that one year in five. Arthur Young observes later, that this problem, "clover sickness" is particularly severe in the Belchamp-Borley area. He is, however, unable to diagnose the cause.

A hundred and eighty years later most of Bulmer's farmers are growing a larger proportion of continuous cereals. Oilseed rape has become the predominant break crop although there is still a diminishing acreage of sugar beet and beans.

Later, Robert Andrews was asked to estimate his yields. Just as he appears on Gainsborough's portrait as a self disciplined, organised, efficient squire, so too he must have impressed Young, when he was able to provide the following table of his yields per acre:

In the Year	Wheat		Barley	
	Coombs	Bushels	Coombs	Bushels
1773	6	1	8	2
1774	5	2	9	0
1775	8	0	7	0
1776	6	0	11	2
1777	7	1	11	0
1778	6	0	8	3
1779	7	2	11	1
1780	10	3	11	2
1781	10	0	10	2
1782	6	0	7	0
1783	7	0	11	0
1784	0	0	9	1

At this point we should attempt to clarify the various categories of weight that have come off the fields of our Long Furrow.

A coomb of wheat weighs eighteen stone, whilst that of barley sixteen stone and oats twelve. Coomb itself (pronounced c-ugh-mb), is a term involving the four bushels full of any produce, that could be weighed into a "sack" whose shape and dimensions were consistent. A coomb is half a quarter (4½ cwt of wheat) the measure by which wheat was sold until the late nineteen sixties.

Consequently, yields from the fields of our Long East Anglian Furrow, have been expressed in either bushels, hundredweights, coombs, sacks or quarters of an acre. After the Second World War, as yields increased, it became feasible to talk in terms of tons an acre and more recently tonnes an hectare. But by far and away the most popular measure until the last few decades was that of coomb or sack an acre. *

From the table of Robert Andrews' harvests we can illustrate how yields have risen across the centuries of human cultivation. Our mediaeval peasant with his flail, sickle and ox drawn plough was harvesting around six hundredweights an acre. By comparison, in the decade from 1773-1783, Andrews is averaging around 16.3 hundredweight an acre of wheat and nineteen of barley. These were certainly good average crops for the late eighteenth century. They were averages moreover that did not substantialy improve again until the second world war. Now, exactly 200 years after Robert Andrews provided Arthur Young with a table of his yields, Nigel Burke who farms the Auberies today, will hope to average between 55-65 cwt of Barley and 50-70 cwt of wheat an acre in the harvest of 1983.

Young continues his enquiry into crop yields, by reprinting Vancovers table of produce which compares the approximate potential of crops grown in neighbouring villages. He expresses his findings in bushels.†

	Barley	Wheat
Alphamstone	32	22
Belchamp Walter	36	24
Bulmer	36	24
Great Yeldham	32	26
Halstead	32	20
Henny	20	20
Pebmarsh	32	18
Pentlow	32	24

* Ironically the grain tank of the latest electronically assisted combine harvester to arrive from Canada is still calibrated in bushels–the unit of weight which was used by our medieval peasants.

† Young also reports that in 1805, Mr. Raymond at Belchamp Hall had above 5 quarters (10 coomb an acre) of wheat and that from Belchamp meadows it was not uncommon to get 2 loads of hay an acre. The Raymond family still occupy the same land.

But like all thinking agriculturalists and countrymen, Young was not only interested in the yield of crops. He enquired into the "How?" and asked "Why?" one field had outperformed another. Examining the factors which produced good or poor results, his report surges with farmer's suggestions, bailiffs' memories, blacksmiths' inventions and landowners' projects. Numerous plates illustrate locally designed ploughs, hoes, seed drills and mole drainers.

"Mr. Hale of Bulmer", he wrote, uses a ridge skim. He had a summer fallow ploughed on two bout ridges, on which thistles and other weeds got up: the cutting blade of the skim carved a ridge at a time and cut to its base, leaving all the weeds to die . . . a stout lad and a pair of horses worked it".

One wonders whether the Mr. Hale of Bulmer was a descendant of those whose ditches were blocked and unmaintained in the Gestingthorpe court rolls of 1520?

Commenting on diseases, Young observes that "the land beside the River Stour is very subject to the mildew and to be root fallen". The latter may possibly be the disease that farmers now identify as eyespot and is controlled by a fungicide applied during the weeks around Easter. Similarly, Robert Andrews described to Young how:

"about the 26th of June, walking by the side of one of my fields of wheat, I observed a great number of ears of smut, which very much surprised me . . . as I had taken every precaution to prevent it."

Later, Andrews established that his bailiff had sown the infected part of the field with unprepared (undressed) seed.

200 years later, another Bulmer farmer examined the smut in his own field of winter barley, and wished that he too had had more patience and waited for the proper seed to arrive the autumn before, instead of rushing on with his own untreated supply. Thankfully, at the end of the day, it didn't seem to reduce yields very much.

Published in 1805, the same year as the battle of Trafalgar, Young's account has a remarkably contemporary ring about it. He calls for long "fixed term" tenancies, he enthuses about land improvement schemes, particularly mole draining, (performed with horses) and he devotes space to the controversy between broadcasting seed by hand or drilling it in rows. He quotes also from the dwindling number of farmers who were still ploughing with oxen and he includes proposals for manuring systems, rotations, implement design and barn architecture amongst he observations. He is a strenuous advocate of drainage and in the following summary he gives us an idea of the costs involved:

> The heavier parts of the parish of Bulmer consist of well mixed loamy soil, upon a brown and a white chalky clay; and a smaller portion of a lighter nature, upon a gravel. South, and extending towards Wickham St. Pauls, a wet, cold, thin soil prevails, lying upon a yellow, or woodland clay: this has been much improved by hollow draining, at a rod apart, and at the expense of 50s. per acre   £2. 10. 0.

The cost of chalking however is greater and he enumerates how the expenditure is incurred:

First cost of eight waggon loads of chalk, containing
90 bushels each, at 9s. per load is:–   £3. 12. 0.

To this add filling, carriage and spreading,
and allowance for beer, 8s. per load:–   £3. 4. 0.

     £6. 16. 0.

One wonders whether the chalk was extracted from the rabbit infested, blackthorn surrounded pit at Goldingham Hall, or those at the bottom of Ballingdon Hill which are now utilised by Total Petroleum. Irrespective of the answer, the philosophy of land improvement through chalking and drainage has continued. In 1982, the cost to the farmer to drain an acre of Bulmer is between £120-£200 an acre.

Let us take our leave of Arthur Young with his general impressions. "The country around Belchamp, Borley, Gestingthorpe and Bulmer" he observes excitedly, "is very much improved in the past twenty years: in hollow draining, in the use of chalk and in converting to tillage all waste scraps of land and in throwing together many little enclosures crowded together with pollards into open, airy fields". If the latter sounds like a euphemism for hedge removal, he continues with the messianic fervour of a Twentieth Century bulldozing contractor as he rejoices that, "the rabbit warrens are converted to corn fields".

But Young was not isolated in his enthusiasm for improving standards of husbandry. On 30th September, 1793, at a meeting in Chelmsford, "The Essex Society for the Encouragement of Agriculture and Industry" was formed. Amongst the original members were Ralph Simpson of Wickham St. Pauls and George Walker of Gestingthorpe, to whose son there is a memorial plaque on the wall of the Gestingthorpe Church.* The monarch George III, who reigned form 1760-1820 was genuinely interested in agri-

---

* Sadly, Young does not appear to have spent much time in Gestingthorpe and his comments on the village are limited to a few general remarks.

culture and dedicated a good deal of time to farming himself. And far away on the estates of Tsarist Russia the nobles and landowners admired, copied and discussed the innovations of English agriculture.

Amongst the epic historical philosophising of "War and Peace", the world's greatest novelist, Leo Tolstoy describes how, Nikolai Rostov "was a plain farmer and did not like innovations, especially the English ones then coming into fashion".

Similarly, in "Anna Karenina", Tolstoy's later masterpiece, we are introduced to Farmer Levin. Among the descriptions of the intentions and objectives that he holds for his estate, we read with interest his envious remarks on the established nature of English agriculture and of his purchase of English cattle and English oat seed.

With Tolstoy and Russia we may appear to have moved a long way from the Bulmer of 1800. Yet in the mid Nineteenth and Twentieth Centuries, international circumstances were to considerably influence the prosperity, cropping and livestock numbers on the farms of our Furrow. Fertilisers arrived from South America, wheat flooded in from the United States and refrigerated beef was imported from Australia.

CHAPTER SIX

The Nineteenth Century

"Discord and Tension"
A farmworkers strike at Belchamp Walter

The impetus of agricultural improvement and market stability recorded by Arthur Young continued until the full impact of imported American wheat was felt on the domestic market in about 1870. For the farmers of our Furrow, the first seven decades appear to have been profitable and rewarding. Innovation and development continued at a pace that was not to be repeated until 1940. Chevalier Barley was first grown in 1820, Red Poll cattle, Suffolk sheep and the large white pig were developed by selective cross breeding. Nitrate of soda was imported from Chile. Rothampstead Experimental Station was founded in 1843 and "Farmer & Stockbreeder" first published. Similar progress was sustained in the engineering industry and agricultural steam engines were marketed commercially from the mid nineteenth century. Later we shall meet steam enthusiast Cyril Philp, and threshing contractor Jack Cornell, who will provide memories of this equipment in use during the 1930s.

One interesting exponent of steam power was I. J. Mechi of Tiptree. His treatises in the 1850s echo the enthusiasm of Arthur Young for increasing yields and include arguments for the fertilising, subsoiling and tile drainage of heavy land. Provocative and stimulating, he conducted experiments into seed rates, rotations, manuring systems and more optimistically, "the application of the free electricity in the atmosphere to the vigorous growth of plants". He rapidly established a wide reputation with his enquiring and controversial arguments for "high input" capital intensive farming. The debate between high and low cost farming techniques in which he was so forceful an advocate still continues, with stormy altercations in untidy farm offices, between father and son, to the present day.

Doubtless the Nineteenth Century farmers of Gestingthorpe and Bulmer discussed Mechi's ideas with enquiring cynicism and suspicious encouragement. Meanwhile the "Suffolk Free Press" carried numerous weekly articles which manifest the preponderant importance of local agriculture. Some indication of the growing impetus for improved standards of husbandry can be seen in copies from 1855 with their advertisements for:-

"Prentice's* Patent Liquid Ammonical Phosphate, £6 ton"

Yet the peak in the cycle of agricultural buoyancy was reached in 1841 with the inauguration of Sudbury Corn Exchange. Today the building has been converted into a public library, but the imperial, lofty and confident style of its architecture has been preserved. It was here, on Thursday afternoons, that for 120 years, the farmers of our Long Furrow met to discuss their yields, crops, problems and theories. Possibly they argued about selective breeding, Mechi or the Corn Laws; more probably they vented their wrath against tithes, rents and the weather. Later, they bargained and haggled with local merchants and showed them their samples of barley and wheat. Thomas Hardy has immortalised the atmosphere of the nineteenth century 'Corn Exchange' with episodes in "Far from the Madding Crowd" and "The Mayor of Casterbridge".

But if circumstances were rewarding and profitable for landowners and farmers, they were much less favourable for the workers who were tilling the fields and tending the livestock. The nineteenth century is more starkly remembered for the Tolpuddle Martyrs, rural unemployment, machinery smashing and rick burning. After several hours of reading, studying and searching through old manuscripts, we are able to provide an outline to events and conditions of the time.

Food riots had occurred in Wickham St. Pauls in 1772[†] and the "poor relief" distributed in Gestingthorpe is symptomatic of the increasing social malaise of the era.[‡]

1739	£61	1803	£517
1776	£229	1813	£1006

In 1816, with the conclusion of the Napoleonic Wars, the widespread frustrations of unemployment and low pay erupted into an outbreak of machinery smashing. The machines that so aroused the indignation of those who saw their livelihoods imperilled, were the elementary threshers whose introduction reduced the need for work generative flailing—traditionally a winter or rough weather job. Vehement opposition to these threshing machines was expressed within our Long Furrow and is evinced by the following report, which was printed in the Essex Herald on June 4th, 1816.

* This company, based at Stowmarket, later became a part of the Fisons organisation.
† The Matmaker and the Magistrate" by Richard Deeks.
‡ "Gestingthorpe 1693-1903" Slaughter and Brown.

Dogs Mercury. This inconspicuous plant with its small green flowers will often be found on the site of ancient woodland.

Teasels. During the middle ages the strong needle points of the plant were used for teasing or carding wool. They still grow in the area and as late as the eighteenth century were cultivated commercially.

Spindle-berry. Recognised by the bright orange berries of autumn.

The Belchamp Walter "Eight Bells". In 1893, it was known as the "Five Bells" and featured in the farmworkers strike of that year.

Alastair Tuffill–Photography

Land Drains. In 1800, Arthur Young reports that the cost of draining an acre of Bulmer's land was £2.10.0. In 1982, drainage schemes are still being installed. In the photograph, Clarence Clark, Eric Garrard, Edward Truin and Anthony Lyster from "Waspe of Cockfield" drainage contractors are laying 6 in. pipes on Goldingham Wood field.

Jim Bunn, shepherd of the Auberies, photographed in the style of the early 20th century.

Cyril Philp explaining the principles of steam ploughing. Five furrows are in the soil and are being pulled by the wire rope (on the ground), which is winched up by a traction engine at the other end of the field. Arriving at the far end, the five furrows currently in the air will be put into work and pulled back towards the engine in the background. The driver's wheel and seat are clearly visible. The two Fowler engines, which had been working at Kirby Hall in October 1982, were nominally rated at 18 horsepower and named Lion and Tiger (numbers 15262 and 15263). Whilst ploughing, the engines might use 6-700 gallons of water a day each. In heavy mole draining this requirement would considerably increase.

Alastair Tuffill–Photography

"A riot commenced at Halstead on Tuesday evening last.* by a mob liberating four prisoners who were being lodged in Halstead 'House of Correction' for destroying some (farm) machinery at Sible Hedingham. . . . the next evening they collected in greater numbers, many parties having been observed to join them from neighbouring villages, armed with bludgeons etc., . . . the Halstead Cavalry made several charges on the mob but without effect. Early next day a party of 20th Dragoons arrived from Colchester."

The festering social inequities of the century continued. It was an epoch of child labour in the pits and mills of the industrial north and of deprivation in the shires and rural east. In 1830 another widescale outbreak of rick burning and machinery smashing occurred. The names "General Ludd" or "Captain Swing" are associated with this period. During this confrontation, three days of wage riots occurred at Ridgewell, Birdbrook and Stambourne—close to the roaring lorries of the contemporary A604. The rioters' demands were for a wage of two shillings a day. Six years later, the transportation of the Tolpuddle martyrs threatened the concept of labour guild and collective workers' action itself.

But the impulse to form a farm workers union was not to be indefinitely thwarted. In the second half of the Nineteenth Century, the extensive energies of men such as Joseph Arch[†] succeeded in establishing the forerunner of what has now become the National Union of Agricultural and Allied Workers[‡]. The fascinating story of the union's development is told in "Sharpen the Sickle", by Reg Groves, and records that in 1872 localised wage strikes occurred close to our Bulmer Furrow, in Wethersfield, Sible Hedingham, Newton, Boxted, Finchingfield, Cavendish and Glemsford. Weeks and months later, these disputes were to crystallize into a greater and recurrent test of will—the mens' "right to join a union", the principle of which was so fiercely resisted by their employers.

In 1893 a strike is documented from a more local source—Bulmer's neighbouring parish of Belchamp Walter. To appreciate its fermentation, we need to review the deterioration in agricultural profitability, which occurred in the late nineteenth century. This was largely a consequence of the importation of wheat from the American prairies, which precipitated a decline in domestic prices.

Wheat	1855	16s. 0d. cwt	1895	5s. 5d. cwt
	1875	10s. 6d. cwt	1905	6s.11d. cwt
	1885	7s. 8d. cwt	1915	12s. 4d. cwt

* From Essex Records Office: Essex Herald ref: ERO/24/A/169B.

† Joseph Arch visited and spoke at Sudbury Market Hill during May of election year, 1884.

‡ At the time of writing, to be amalgamated with T.G.W.U.

The number of farmworkers had already fallen by 111,000 between 1871 and 1881. Similarly, the area of land under cropping in England and Wales declined by 2,097,000 acres between 1866 and 1893. Land prices had plummetted. Moat Farm, Gestingthorpe, which had fetched £50 an acre in 1869, sold for £12 an acre in 1903.

But it was in 1893, at the lowest point in the cycle of flutuating prices, that the farmers of Belchamp Walter attempted to redress their own fortunes by lowering the wages of their employees, from eleven to ten shillings a week.

As a consequence, the men went on strike and the Suffolk Free Press* reported on March 1st, 1893:

"quite fifty men are standing off".

In the edition of March 8th, 1893, the headline to a fascinating account of social conditions of the time declared:

WALTER BELCHAMP
THE FARMERS AND FARM
LABOURERS

Wages Dispute: Lock-out: Union Meetings:
THE VICAR AS A MEDIATOR

The newspaper continues by vividly describing the village and the meetings between the farmworkers and the Vicar:

"Nearly the whole of the farm labourers of Walter Belchamp are this week in enforced idleness. The fields are deserted, the farm buildings silent, machinery stopped, flocks and herds attended by owners or comparative strangers, and field work at a standstill. In the village street, and at scattered cottages in the large somewhat straggling parish, men and lads are seen leaning at the door posts of their houses, talking in twos and threes at the gates to their front gardens, walking listlessly, with hands in pockets and short clay pipe in mouth, along the rough macadamized roads, or discussing parish affairs at mine host's at the Bells".

The farmworkers case and the cause of the strike was subsequently explained:

"From statements made by the men themselves, corroborated in the main by their employers, it appears that, about the middle of last month, five of the farmers simultaneously gave their men notice that their

---

* The same paper records a meeting at Gestingthorpe to discuss "the cause of the depression" the previous week.

weekly wages would be reduced from eleven shillings to ten shillings a week. The men were then working from 7 a.m. to 5 p.m., or two hours less than in the busier season. This being so, the men agreed to the reduction without any grumbling or expostulation with the masters. A fortnight afterwards, the men were informed that the following Monday morning they would have to go back to the longer hours usual in the spring and summer, and work from 6 to 6, being an hour's extension at each end of the day. The men responded that they had no objection to the lengthened day if they had their former pay, but they should decline to work twelve hours a week more for a shilling less."

So the strike began. But one of the farmers disputed the criticisms of low pay and insensitivity, declaring:

"They would not have made a reduction even now, had it not been for the miserably low price of wheat. Two neighbouring farms were going out of cultivation, and unless things soon altered for the better, this would be the case with other farms."

The two sides were clearly a long way apart. The farmworkers reaffirmed their position, refuting the farmers' exaggerated calculations of their harvest remuneration and other fringe benefits.

"The men appear determined to hold to what they consider their rights and to stick together, feeling confident that they will be backed up from the Union funds. They emphatically contradict the statement that they receive £8.5s.0d. as harvest money. They say they were only paid 12s. an acre, and each man took 11 acres, which would only tottle *(sic)* up to £6.12s.0d. instead of £8.5s.0d. They also state that only two men get 1s.6d. for threshing, and then the day must be an exceptionally long one".

The article continues with a sub headline proclaiming:

THE MEETING AT THE FIVE BELLS–
THE VICAR PRESENT AND OFFERS MEDIATION

The meeting of the farmworkers in the upstairs club-room at the Five Bells is then described:

"A fire burns brightly at one end, illuminating the eager faces of the smokers sitting nearby. A solitary lamp on the dull brown wall, (which goes out towards the close of the proceedings but is speedily re-lighted) just makes the darkness visible, so that the reporters have to write more by instinct than by outward material illumination. Round the deal table are two or three chairs, and a few forms about the room, which is full to overflowing, almost like the Black Hole of Calcutta".

Several speeches were made, and Mr Wager, General Secretary of the N.A.U., who had travelled specially from Warwickshire, declared that:

"They were prepared to meet the farmers personally to discuss the question with them (for they knew that these were hard times for them) or to submit their case to a board of arbitration" . . .

"Mr Wager went on to say that as soon as he heard of the present dispute, he wrote to their President (Mr Joseph Arch, M.P.). (Cheers). Mr Arch at once wired back that the men must be supported, (Cheers) for it was unjust to reduce the men at a season when they were going to be called upon to do ten hours work a day. (Cheers). The men said they would work ten hours a day for eleven shillings a week. (Cheers).

The article continues by describing the arrival of the Vicar, Mr. Pelly, and reports his speech, in which he offers to act as a conciliator between the two factions. After some introductory remarks, he continued:

"When he was curate at Belchamp, his heart ached many a time when he saw the misery around him. He used to think of an expression which a certain eminent writer of fiction applied to the poorer classes, that they were 'starvelings'. Many a time when he saw men with large families, he had been puzzled to know how they managed to get along and bring up their children with the wages that they received. He heartily desired the welfare of the working classes, and believed that but for their Union many of them would have been in a sad condition indeed. (Hear, hear). But they had to be practical men and find out some practical way of getting along. They all knew in their heart of hearts that this was a very bad time for both farmers and landowners. At the present time, the price of wheat, from the producer's point of view, was simply miserable."

The vicar concluded and the somewhat patronising tone of the newspaper report continues with the remarks of Mr Sage, Union Secretary for Essex, whose speech is a model of intent determination and lively resolution:

"Mr Sage said they only wished they could get more like these gentlemen (the Vicar) to speak to and for them. (Cheers). But he (the speaker) was a 'peace with righteousness' man, and must maintain that theirs was a righteous cause, and though they wished for a peaceful settlement, must not give up their just rights. (Loud cheers). The present dispute was the fault of the employers. (Hear, hear). Still he was very glad that this gentleman was willing to go as a mediator, and at the private meeting which would be held afterwards they could decide as to the terms they would agree to. They had been told that the price of wheat was miserably low; he maintained that it was gloriously low. Twenty years ago, when wheat was selling well and the farmers were making a big profit, they showed the same spirit as now, and the men were ground down by miserable wages ('seven or eight shillings a week' murmured voices in the room) and thousands emigrated to foreign lands, which they cultivated, and were now sending corn over here cheaper than they could grow it at home".

Ultimately, Mr. Pelly's offer of conciliation appears to have been successful for in the edition of March 15th, the Suffolk Free Press records, in a brief commentary, that:

"The wages dispute is arranged: the men returned to work."*

It appears that the farmworkers' cause had triumphed and their employers had been forced to relent and agree to the former wage of eleven shillings a week.

Doubtless the excitement at Belchamp Walter reverberated throughout the neighbouring villages; several Belchamp men at the time worked at Goldingham Hall and we can imagine the questing, probing conversations that occurred in the stable, stackyard and on the headland as the news of the altercation was passed along.

But recollections of the nineteenth century do not quickly fade. Repeatedly I was told of desperately hungry men walking miles to steal a few swedes which were clamped up near the Deal Nursery in Bulmer; of farmworkers being "sent off home together" without pay in wet weather, and of other men, pathetically reduced to taking wheat home in their pockets at night. In the twilight gloaming of cottages and retirement bungalows, the dark stain of bitterness that is the nineteenth century, has lingered on in the memories of grandchildren and descendants.

It was a hard century of austere disciplines: the "tied cottage" was often the only opportunity to find a home and there was little time for relaxation or diversion. "At Belchamp Otten" reports one source, "the men were allowed Good Friday as a holiday . . . but the master, who was like a Tin God, made them all go to church in the morning first".

* Microfilm copies of the Suffolk Free Press which carries the full account of the Belchamp Walter strike may be read at the West Suffolk Record Office, Bury St. Edmunds.

Another story, handed down from the Belchamp Otten of the eighteen seventies, told of a farmer who announced to his men that their wages would be cut from 8 to 7 shillings if he couldn't get a shilling a coomb more for his barley at market . . . "he went to market on Thursday and didn't get his shilling . . . but the wages weren't cut, because the 'old bugger' died the next morning in bed". Possibly it was a just and purposeful example of divine intervention.

Yet the final word on the nineteenth and early twentieth centuries must surely come from the two elderly farmworkers as we sat in the bar of a local public house. The first muttered sadly, "You didn't get a shilling if you were ill in those days", to which his companion replied, "You didn't get a b_____ sight if you worked!"

Village life at the time was completely dominated by agriculture. In the 1871 census, Gestingthorpe had a population of 766 of which 185 were farmworkers. A flourishing agricultural foundry was in existence, whilst associated professions included a carter, a miller, three wheelwrights, three blacksmiths, two thatchers and a carpenter. Over a hundred women are classified as straw plaiters. Both Bulmer and Gestingthorpe were obviously vigorous communities and Kelly's Directory of 1886 includes amongst Bulmer's commercial residents:

James Andrews: Beer Retailer; Henry Clover: Miller;
George Dixey: Beer Retailer and Carrier;
Thomas Firmin: Blacksmith; James Patrick: Baker;
Edward Plume: Birch Broom Maker and Thatcher.

The farmers of the parish at the time included Messrs. Burlingham, Byford, Coote, Gardiner, Nott and Payne whilst George English is described as "brick, tile, drainpipe maker, farmer and assistant overseer at Hole Farm". In addition, the village had a mole catcher. Doubtless the skins of his moles and locally snared rabbits were sold to itinerant carters who took such produce to be sold in the markets and shops of Sudbury, Halstead or Great Yeldham.

A final insight into the settled, diversified, labour intensive agriculture on the farms of our Long Furrow, can be witnessed from the Auberies Estate's inventory for their home farm in 1875. In that year the cropping and live-stock consisted of:–

"49 acres of wheat; 34 of barley; 16 of oats; 9 of peas; 2 of potatoes; 10 of swedes; 10 of mangolds; 4 of cabbages; 9 of clover for hay; 18 of red and white not for hay; and 110 acres of grass.
Livestock numbers were: 10 horses, 11 cows, 11 heifers, 7 calves, 220 sheep, 140 lambs and 30 pigs."

The impression it creates is of a well balanced mixed farm, governed by the limitations and disciplines of traditional agriculture: an agriculture that was so much part and parcel of parish life, that the Bulmer school book of 1874, reports: "at the beginning of August many children were away gleaning or taking their father's meals to distant fields." Whilst in April 1877, "eighty out of a hundred children were away picking up acorns to sell as pig feed."

It is with these snippets from "Bulmer: Then and Now"* that we will begin to look more closely at the fabric of rural and agricultural life at the turn of the century: for the Furrow that we have traced for so far and for so long, from the neolithic plot to the horse era farming of the nineteenth century has at last come to the boundary of human memory and personal recollection.

* "Bulmer: Then and Now" published by Bulmer W.E.A. 1979.

PART TWO

Seedtime and Harvest Remembered
1893-1960

CHAPTER SEVEN

Farmers, Farmworkers, Medals and Bibles

As we enter the twentieth century we arrive within the realm of living memory and grand-parental recollection.

Let us then meet some of our octogenarian contributors–born in 1903 or earlier–who have given so much to this agrarian history. We will start at Lower Houses, Bulmer, where Philip Rowe*, born in 1900, lives with his wife, Mary. He is a member of the remarkable Rowe family, whose questioning instinct for detail, has been of such value in both this work and "Bulmer: Then and Now". His grandfather was David Rowe, who lost one arm in a chaff cutter and a finger from blackthorn poisoning and whose children were so prominent in the Bulmer of the mid-thirties. Over several conversations, Philip Rowe and brother Tom explained the largely forgotten skills of hurdle making, thatching, brickmaking, stack-building, bird catching, rat trapping and corn dolly manufacture. Authorities on the domestic economy of the old countryside, they informatively described the many uses to which the produce of hedgerow and woodland was put in their childhood days.

It is to Harry Winch that we next journey.   Born in Bulmer in 1895, he today surveys the village in which he spent so much of his life, from his house which overlooks the church and village meadow. A man of many skills, he is a past landlord of The Fox Public House, was a chauffeur to the Reverend A. P. Pannell, worked on Armsey and the Auberies Farms and latterly undertook building and carpentry repairs. Like all of his generation, there seems to be no domestic or horticultural problem on which he is unable to offer productive and valuable advice. Yet ultimately with Harry Winch, any conversation must turn to those epic years, when he left behind the serenity of Bulmer, to become No. 26727 in the ghastly horror of the "Battle of the Somme" in World War One.

"I was on a machine gun crew and in the first sixteen days of July, before I was injured, my crew of four was replaced through injury or death four times. On one occasion, in the trenches, we were only fifty

* Philip Rowe died in September 1982.

yards from the enemy. According to what was going on we could hear the jerries talking to each other . . . You got what grub you could—if you got a biscuit you were lucky: but it's funny, in between times you would get the chance to have a nap and you'd have it and that was that. Next thing there would be bullets and shells flying all over the place."

Sixty years later and now President of the local British Legion, he is still able to repeat every detail in the procedure for loading and dismantling the Vickers machine gun that he used.

Some Bulmer families suffered crippling losses in the First War and the harvest fields of our Furrow in 1919 must have had a tragic emptiness amongst the gangs of pitchers and stackbuilders with the absence of old friends and good mates.

Several of our older contributors had military experience. The late Sid Rowe volunteered in 1914, and spent some of the quiet moments in the trenches making a beautiful miniature chest of drawers from the brass cases of spent shells. Daughter Gertie Coe treasures it to this day.

Born in Bulmer in 1892, wheelwright and carpenter Hazell Chinnery, served with the Essex Regiment. During the hostilities he was captured and later named his house in Bulmer Street "Warlins", after the prisoner of war camp in which he was interned.

Farmworker Ernest Lott, who was born in Bulmer in 1899, now lives on the Tye, (near The Fox public house) and was in France with the Norfolk Regiment in 1918. The following year the regiment was transferred to India, and he remembers being sent to Lucknow, before receiving orders to go to the North West Frontier. Here, amongst the arid, brown, boulder strewn hillsides, west of Peshawar, he did picket duty and after several skirmishes remarked, "You could always depend on the Gurkas". After his military contract had expired, he returned to the Bulmer of his childhood, where he worked again as dayman and horseman on the soils of our Long Furrow at Gentrys and Jenkins Farm. Sometimes in the cruel gales of winter, when plodding behind a horse and plough, he no doubt thought back to the days of imperial guard duty in the land of the Pathans and Afghans.

But our connection between farmer, farmworker and the Indian raj was to continue. Colonel Hugh Moule, who farmed fruit by the brickyards for 20 years, was also on the North West frontier and based in Peshawar; farmworker Cecil Smith of Wickham St. Pauls was on strike duty with the Suffolk Regiment in the torrid humidity of Bombay in 1922. Today he is silver-haired and 79 years old, and I was privileged to spend some delightful evenings in his bungalow, looking out across the fields, where twenty years previously we had first made our acquaintanceship when talking across the hedges of neighbouring farms.* Cecil and his wife, Hilda, were particularly helpful in the research for the chapter on the 'Horse Year' and that on the changing flora of the local countryside.

India continued to draw our contributors and in World War II, lorry drivers Tom Hearn of Wickham St. Paul and Dennis Rippingale of Gestingthorpe were both piloting their vehicles between the bullock carts, trishaws, goats, beggars and pilgrims of the Grand Trunk Road.

Another Gestingthorpe man, deserves mention. Douglas Hasler (born 1918) served with the Royal Marines in World War II in both the West African and D-Day landings. Today he suffers from the devastating and all-debilitating motor neuron disease. His considerable strength is wasted. Emaciated and afflicted, he is unable to walk or to talk. But his father was a thatcher and deeply imbued in parochial life. With only one finger, and one letter at a time, he has tapped out his memories for this history on an especially sensitive electric typewriter. Being able to publish extracts from his recollections has given a special sense of justification to the whole project. Today, Douglas Hasler and wife Freda provide an example of the humour that can shine through such adversity.

"What was it like, the month you spent with the specialist in the London Hospital?" I asked when I collected the latest sheaf of his notes.

He murmurs slightly and his forefinger slowly presses the letters of the word communicator which is ever beside him. For about a minute and a half it whirrs and clicks. Then there is silence and I tear the small slip of paper from the side of the machine. For a split second the words of his answer seem meaningless and mistaken. Then I hear a low hollow laugh, a small lump rises in my throat and the sentence becomes clear: "Nurses very pretty . . . enjoyed chatting them up."

A few hundred yards from the Haslers' home at The Crescent in Gestingthorpe, is a rutted cart track that leads to the glade in Oakley Wood, which from 1947 until 1981 was the caravan homestead of erstwhile horesman, piece rate worker and woodman Bob Daniells. Born in Erpingham, Norfolk, he left the county after the widescale introduction of tractors and subsequently travelled from one piece rate job to another. Spring would find him chopping out sugar beet, in summer he would "take a harvest", in autumn he might be found in the orchards and hop grounds of Kent, before returning to "pull the beet", he had chopped out in the springtime; later, in the depths of winter, he would be wooding or ditching by hand. Yet during the hours of conversation within the dusky warmth of his caravan, it

---

* Amongst many other memories of his 3 years in India, where he was also garrisoned at Bangalore and Wellington (near Ootycamund), he recalls, "Five of us privates banded together and hired a 'bearer' (servant) for 1 rupee a week each. If we paid an extra 3 annas a day (16 annas = 1 rupee) we could be shaved–whilst we were still fast asleep. I can tell you, when we were sent back to Gibraltar we hully missed him!"

was the rugged individuality and cheerfulness of character that was so memorable and which was epitomised by his farewell remark, in the howling gale of a leaf-strewn November evening:

"Blast me boy! I've had a lovely life!"

Some of the men beside our Long Furrow adopted erratic and eccentric lifestyles. There are stories of men "who live alone—with a dog and a ferret and never did anything regular". A few had double barrelled names and the fading vocabulary of a grammar school education. At least one Suffolk farmworker, piece rate "dayman" Sam Harvey of Whatfield in mid Suffolk had won the Victoria Cross in the first World War. Several like Bob Daniells, preferred the individualistic status and personal flexibility of being piece rate workers to the strictures of regular employment. Others suffered from disabilities, which in a harsher era were not sufficient to prevent them from working. One was "Dummy" Parker, who worked at Jenkins Farm and as the sobriquet suggests, was deaf and partially dumb. He was able, however, suggests Horace Elsie, to make noises that the horses that he ploughed with could understand. Two particularly interesting men were Messrs. Marsh and Cook. The latter, who had lost both hands, worked for Marsh, who ran a threshing tackle. Marsh himself had only one good hand. Cook, who is quite well remembered was fitted with interchangeable hooks. Bob Raymond remembers . . .

"He used to do a full day's work in spite of his disabilities. If you met him on the road he would be likely to say 'fill my pipe, boy', and you took his pipe from his mouth, his tobacco and matches from his pocket, filled and lit the pipe and off he went!"

Other injuries, include the chaff cutting accident and blackthorn poisoning of David Rowe; the loss of an arm and eventual death of threshing proprietor Scrivener; the wooden leg of "Marpy," and blacksmith Jeffries, who was killed by a horse in the forge at Bulmer Tye.

Today agriculture is still one of the nation's most dangerous industries and each year approximately a hundred people are killed on Britain's farms.

The present history is only possible because Dennis Rippingale turned up at the right place, at the right time, to drag a lanky teenage boy, from beneath a hydraulically supported cultivator which had collapsed on his back on the morning of Easter Saturday 1970.

But not all death is morbid or melancholy. The last decade has witnessed the funerals of three of the kindest and gentlest of men to have been part of our Furrow—farmer George Chatters; farmworker Roland Pearson; and agricultural contractor Lawrence Coe. Yet no passing can ever emulate that of horseman and farmworker Jack Mann—a person of colossal energies and determined enthusiasms who possessed an encyclopaedic knowledge of rural life. With the blood of the countryside palpitating through his veins, keen and alert to every sound of hedgerow, creature and field, he died; instantly; gun in hand, dog beside him, on the frosty morning of the twenty ninth of January 1972.

What we are trying to show then, with these brief portraits is some of the individuality and rugged resourcefulness of the old East Anglian. But how, one might ask, was this independence of character actually manifest in the fields, barns and stables of our Long Furrow? At his home in Long Melford, retired farmworker and farmer Tom Edgeley defines the rural East Anglian mentality . . .

"If you didn't know something, people might make a little harmless fun of you–but in their own way they would eventually come to help you . . . but, oh dear, if you knew too much and you would'nt be told, then very quickly things might become uncomfortable. On a farm years ago, people were always playing practical jokes on each other, and having small, harmless little "games". But for anyone who stepped out of line, it could soon get very nasty."

Another source told of "driving a six inch nail through a person's coat when it was hung on a gate-post . . . as a warning". Years later, we can imagine the conversation . . .

"Just pick your ol' jacket up bu' and we'll get some dinner" . . . . "Have it got stuck? . . . Huh, blast me! What's that? . . . Hell, look at that–there's a nail in here, bu' . . . Did you see anyone do that, bu'? . . . No, I never saw nath-an".

One respondent described how, "groups of lads would walk round on a Sunday and if there was an unpopular man on a farm, they would all lift up his plough and put it in a pond, so when he came to work the next day, to plough his acre, he would see the handles just sticking out of the top of the water!"

Boastfulness, in all its forms, was despised and resented. The following evergreen story describes how a few quiet words deflated one farmer:

". . . you know the sort I mean, he always had the 'headest' crops and was forever going on about himself. Funniest thing was this. They were all picking spuds one day, and he came across the hedge and said all boastful like:

'Those potatoes aren't very big.'

Well, this old farmworker looked at him, kind of quiet for a bit and then he say:

"No that's right enough. They aren't very big. See, we grow 'em for our mouths—not yours!"

The whole East Anglian approach to self proclamation is peculiarly introverted; if the new people that come into the village can't perceive your qualities and strengths—that's their bad luck—not yours. There's no point in wasting *your* time in trying to impress them.

Most communities had the occasional member whose mental facilities were underdeveloped. In return for the general protection and livelihood that the locality gave him, the man who was 'slightly slow' or 'a little bit backward', might well expect to provide a good deal of parochial amusement and farmyard mirth. From the north Suffolk village of Ixworth come several typical examples:

"Years ago they sent this man to the blacksmith for a bag of 'wire netting seed', and on another occasion he went to Pakenham for a tumbrel full of 'post holes'. But the funniest thing of all", continued my source, "was this man who made a hen coop, and was so encouraged by his mate—who was a wily old bugger, that when he finished he finally realised that he had nailed himself inside and had to dismantle it before he could get out!"

But there were other more harmless pranks as well. Jack Cornell (who else!), recalls of schoolboy days,

"If the mistress had been too strict at the village school, one of us lads, would run off, sharpish after lessons and put a stone between the gate latch and the top of the slot in the gate post, so that when this school teacher walked home, she couldn't undo it. Next morning, we'd take this here stone out, and all hide up behind the hedge. Well, sure as ninepence the old estate gardener would come hobbling out with his oil can and give it a few squirts. Then the school teacher would come along and try the gate and say, 'Oh, that does go better for a little of your oil'!"

Charlie "Pod" Martin recalls the activities of another Bulmer schoolboy in the nineteen forties:

"Well. During the summer, I'd got up to Upper Houses and chop some beet out of an evening. When I'd finished, I used to push the hoe between two bales that were part of a straw wall for a clamp. Course, one night, when I went to pull my old hoe out, it wouldn't come. Next thing,

Kenny Day comes toddling round and says, 'Let me see, if I can pull it out for you Pod'. Well, when I left off that night, I thought I'd 'cast my eye about' and I soon saw that he'd tied it onto a couple of pig troughs. So I thought I'd have a game with him. Next night I brought another hoe along with me and hid it in the hedge. Then I spent 'hell and all' amount of time having my bit of bread and 'measuring up'. Course when I was ready, I took the other hoe without using the one he'd tied up and been waiting around for me to pull out. So I got even with him that way. But he was a Ken—he was.

It would, of course, be naive to imagine that everything along our Furrow had been pleasant and harmonious. Indeed at times we might wonder whether they were anything other than contentious and problematical. But in the highly stratified career structure of the old agriculture, the altercations were as likely to be between the farm staff themselves as with the employer. A fairly common aphorism was that "a bad mate was worse than a bad master". Possibly within the rivalries of delegated responsibility we can witness a classic instance of "divide and rule".

One older farmer summed up intra-farm relationships of the early twentieth century with the following comment:

"That time of day", he recalls, "you often employed fifteen or twenty men on a farm. As likely as not, there would be one or two tough old customers who wouldn't get on together or there would be one man who fancied himself to be a lot stronger than anyone else. About once every six months, you'd come into the yard and suddenly there would be one hell of a shout go up. You'd think to yourself 'What the blazes is going on now.' Then you'd come round a corner and see everyone stood in a circle and a couple of men having one such hell of a domino."

Besides the tensions between farm staff there were still numerous memories of disputes and disagreements between employed and employer. Frequently, however, a sagacious and quick-witted reply averted a more deeply embittered argument. Jack Cornell provides a typical examply:

"We were threshing wheat one day and this old farmer came stumping out. He looked as miserable as sin, and when he noticed that the 'boy' couldn't handle the coomb (112 kg) sacks, he began to get a bit roilled and started to shout: 'When I was your age I could carry a coomb sack!' 'So you might', cut in a horseman sharply, 'but that don't make he no stronger!'"

Tom Edgeley, recalls a more languid exchange between an elderly gardener and the 'lady' of the 'big house':

"Sam," she said critically one afternoon, "you've got one pace, and it's a slow one". "Madam," he replied after a moment's rumination, "you pay one wage–and it's a low one!"

From a more local source we have a similar story.

"This farmer saw his 'day-ploughman' having his 'bit of bread' on the headland and he stormed out. 'I can't afford to have you standing about eating you know'. The day ploughman retorted slowly: 'When I can live without grub, I shan't want to worry over much about your wages'".

At one farm in Gestingthorpe, recalls Stanley Surridge, a farmworker handed in his notice in the early twentieth century and was told:

"You might be glad of a job here one day, you know". "No, master", replied the farmworker phlegmatically, "I might be forced to work here again . . . but never glad".*

More recently, a love-sick girl from the "land army" began to irritate her employer after receiving a letter from the "front".

"Well," my source recalled, "the boss went ahead at she something wicked . . . said she was moping about and wasting time and all that squit. Course one of the men who was stood close by, soon pipes up: 'Well, the old governor 'on't never die of a heart attack'.
How can you tell that?' asked his mate playing him along.
'Cos I don't believe he's got a regular b_____ heart to die on' came the reply."

With memories of the "land girls" and the Second World War, we are moving into the era of the Home Guard. Jack Cornell reminisces:

---

* War time and imperial service, as we have shown, took several of our sources to France, India and the Far East. Thatcher, Bertie Hasler (1882-1968) for example, served in South Africa during the Boer War, and after returning to England joined the 1914 Australian Gold Rush. Twinstead farmworker, Harry Rowe, spent four years in the United States, and most other families had relatives who emigrated to Australia, were "in service" in London or like Oliver Pearson, had moved to the industrial north to find work.
But despite having friends who had travelled the "empire and beyond" the mentality that sometimes emerged after centuries of manorial repression could also be expressed in more depressed terms:
"How deep was the Belchamp Brook years ago? one contributor was asked.
"Well", he muttered after a moments estimation, "I should say it was deep enough, so that you could have drowned yourself in it", came the not untypical reply.

"I remember once, we got sent on a 'quiet march' down Ballingdon Hill and up Sandy Lane. 'Quiet march' with your hobnail boots on that is! Anyway that was winter time and we'd all got fed up with parading about inside Bulmer village hall, so it didn't really seem such a cranky idea after all. Well, they sent us off at intervals and I was one of the last to go. Well, time I'd got to the housen at the bottom of Ballingdon Hill, I could begin to see, what you'd call half decent. When I came round the corner where the 'Kings Head' is, I thought, hello! that's the uniform of _____ going in there. So I thought, well if that's the game, I'll slip in and have a quick one as well. Course, when I went in, the blessed pub was nearly three parts full of Bulmer Home Guard! Anyway after a while, we all thought we'd better get this here 'quiet march' over with so we could get off home and go to bed. So off we all went clattering up Sandy Lane like a herd of cattle. I shall never forget the sergeant what had been sent to follow us, as we overtook him. 'Huh,' he say, 'I thought you'd been suffen quite together, as well.'"

For a final illustration of East Anglian humour, let us paraphrase a story which Tom Rowe (born 1902) told me beside Upper Houses on a fine evening of June 1982.

"When I was a boy, there used to be an old chap I worked with at odd times. He wasn't quite the ticket really. I remember one occasion when something had gone wrong, and he came stumping up the road, grumbling and cursing to himself. 'Huh boy!' he muttered when he saw me, 'that's a good job there's two sorts of luck in this world."
"What do you mean two sorts of luck?"
"Good luck and bad luck."
"Why?"
"Do else I wouldn't have none at all!"

But irrespective of the luck that a man had, and whatever his responsibilities in the old system of parochial agriculture, there was every likelihood that he would be given a nickname. George "Jute" Chatters, of Belchamp St.Paul declares: "Time was, when everyone round about had a nickname: if they were called by their proper names, I don't believe anyone would know who they were." Later we shall meet or hear of "Wag", "Jute", "Chick", "Happy", "Ginger", "Dickums", "Shorty", "Stumpy", "Baggy", "Pod", "Toffee", "Bot", "Tige", and "Schemer".

Several of our sources—whatever their nicknames—will also have played village cricket. There are warm memories of the matches that were played on Saturday afternoons and Wednesday evenings and which offered a little relaxation from the long hours of weatherworn work.

"In Gestup," recalls one source, "Farmer Frank Nott used to ride by on his horse and put a half crown, on top of a single stump and if one of us boys could bowl it down, we could keep the money. Of course, that time of day, before there was any television or many motor cars about, it was a regular competition to get into the village team and if you didn't show up for practice or do your bit to help with getting the pitch ready, they'd just as soon chuck you out again."

Many Gestingthorpe people still speak, with a mixture of pride and wry humour, of the matches that were played on the cow grazed grass of Tin Meadow behind Hall Farm. Others recall the mid week evening matches, when play often continued in quite dusky conditions. One source emphatically commented, "you'd find that the last two or three batsmen would 'get out' in a bit of a hurry, so we could get finished before the pubs closed". That time of day pubs closed at ten o'clock and they jolly well did close as well".

But even allowing for the quality of the pitches and the murkiness of the light, it was still surprising to be repeatedly told that an average pre-war village cricket score was 30 to 40 runs. A few back copies of the Halstead and Colne Valley Gazette from the summer of 1933 provided the reports of some local matches. Initially they did not auger well for an investigation into the noble tradition of Gestingthorpe's cricketing heritage. For on July 19th the village team journeyed to Belchamp Walter and were bowled out for 13 runs! "Gestingthorpe", reported the Gazette, "were all out in seven overs and three balls, Laver taking five wickets for eight runs and Chatters* four wickets for three runs." Belchamp whose team included George Chatters (top scorer with 19), Charlie Martin, Jack and Charlie Overill, Jack Laver and Harry Cansell, batted second and scored 59.

The return match which was played on the legendary Tin Meadow in September saw honour restored when Mitson and Felton bowled out the opposition for 41 runs. Gestingthorpe replied with a score of 102 with Dick Felton making 69.

During the same summer, Belchamp Walter who scored 27 were beaten at home by Wickham St. Pauls. Farmworker Cecil Smith opened the batting for Wickham, but was caught and bowled by Laver for 2. Later in the season, Belchamp ventured into Suffolk and played Glemsford. The visitors declared at 70 for 7 before dismissing the home team for 24. George Chatters, bowling with true Essex venom took 5 wickets for 12 runs.

Similarly in a mid week game between Gestingthorpe and Pebmarsh, "Drury and Mitson removed the 'homesters' (Pebmarsh) for 24". Gestingthorpe whose batting order included bookmaker Charlie Downs, carpenter Douglas Hasler, wheelwright Cecil Nears, farmer William Nott, baker

* All references here are to the late George Chatters of Belchamp Walter.

67

Dick Felton, blacksmith Dick Nice and farmworkers Stanley Surridge and Albert Finch, "replied with forty, thus winning a good game by sixteen runs." Top scorer for Gestingthorpe was Reg Mitchell, butler at Gestingthorpe Hall, who made 14. For Pebmarsh J. Rust took 6 wickets for 12 runs.

More recently, the home of Gestingthorpe cricket has been transferred to a new playing field beside the crossroads in the centre of the village. As a teenager I have pleasant memories of searching through Wilfred Prior's adjoining field of winter barley in an attempt to retrieve the ball, after one of Tom Elsdons rocketing sixes.

During those years of the late sixties and early seventies, George Cooke of Gestingthorpe Hall, annually produced a team of solicitors and lawyers from the offices of his London legal practice to challenge the village team on the afternoon of the Whitsun bank holiday. Generally he unleashed at least one fast bowler in the mould of Garner, Willis or Lillie upon the parish. This bowler was justifiably considered to produce more pace than anything that might normally be encountered in parochial matches. In the author's first Whit Monday game, all that stood between the reputation of Gestingthorpe and total cricketing humiliation was the inpenetrably correct defensive technique of Delvyns farmworker Tony Self, and the watchful, effortless strokeplay of carpenter Nicholas Stovell.

But no resumé of Gestingthorpe cricket would be complete without a brief mention of one time cobbler and crippled postman, the late Lennie Martin. With his white coat and walking stick he umpired for many years. The memory of his bright eyed kindly humour off the field and strict regime on it, will linger with Gestingthorpe residents and local sportsmen for many decades to come.

If personal individuality was expressed in nickname, sporting prowess and one's ability at work, the religious non-conformism of the village was manifest in the chaples of the Baptists, Congregationalists and Methodists. Bulmer, Gestingthorpe and Wickham St. Pauls each had their own chapels and dedicated congregations. In an age when one was either "chapel" or "church", many of the "chapel-ites" (non-conformists) were dependant on local lay preachers. In "Bulmer: Then and Now", John Dixey tells of Henry Payne who farmed Clapps Farm and died in 1922:

> "He often preached at the chapel and at the end of the sermon, he would say to one of his men in the congregation . . . 'Well, John, bor, we'll jist have one more hymn 'fore we go and feed they bullocks.'"

Farmworker and country sports enthusiast Reg Rippingale, ironically recalls the marksmanship of one local methodist minister whom he took rabbit shooting between Wickham Hall and Butlers farm shortly before his marriage. Reg explains:

"This parson was crazy to do some rabbit shooting. Well, the first time a rabbit bolted from a hole, he was so slow, that he missed the rabbit but shot the ferret which was just coming out. So that was one of my ferrets shot! Well, I advised him to be a bit quicker, and I put my other ferret down a hole and stood back and waited. Then all of sudden, he fired again! But this time the ferret had come out of a hole which didn't have a rabbit in it at all–but he'd been so blessed quick off the mark that as soon as he saw something move, he shot at it–and killed it. That was a tidy game, I can tell you! I lost two ferrets in one day!"

Later we will learn of other "doctrines" of the horse era. We will describe the "creed" of straight ploughing and drilling and enunciate the gospel of exactitude in stack building and thatching. It is a catechism whose single response was "perfection in all aspects of work". But the men and women whose memories we have recorded share an elemental distinction in common. It is this.

Simply expressed, they are the most competent generation of farmers and farmworkers who have ever been part of our Long Furrow. Their aptitude will never again be genuinely matched. Instinctively, they could farm again in the tradition of past ages with the horse, the hoe and the fold. Equally they can coax spluttering life into elementary tractors and crawlers. Finally, after only a few moments orientation, they can clamber onto the most modern of sophisticated combine harvesters and take over the controls once more. Cyril Philp in his eighty third year does just that. Many others made astute and constructive observations on the trends and developments of contemporary farming.

Today in the evening of life, these last members of the horse era generation look out across the farms, fields and undulations where so much has passed and been accomplished. It is amongst these meadows, hedgebanks and fields that they had tamed the savage stallion, "pulled beet" in the blizzard, beat the record when threshing, drilled gun barrel straight for weeks on end, and still, too, beneath a blazing sun, with sweat bathed shoulders, had scythed, tied, "shocked" and pitched.

CHAPTER EIGHT

The Twentieth Century

The Village and the Furrow: Sparrow Pie: Breadmakers and Brewers

We have shown in previous chapters how political and technological factors have influenced the land use of our Long Furrow across its three thousand years of existence. We saw in Chapter Six how the fields of Bulmer in 1875 were growing a multitude of crops and supporting a wide variety of livestock. The inventory of that year includes cereals, roots, vegetables, leys and pasture for horses, pigs, cattle and sheep. From our present day semi-monoculturist standpoint it is difficult to imagine such diversity. As latter day village dwellers, we are, in fact, almost completely detached from the genuine interdependence that once existed between countryman and nature. In this chapter we will explore the bygone cottage economy and the traditional parochial crafts that provided the village with its self supportive cohesion and diverse activities of life.

But as a prelude, to remind ourselves of that countryside and the agrarian systems that prevailed within it, let us imagine that it is 1905 and that we are walking along the rutted roads and tree-shaded lanes that led from Gestingthorpe ("Gestup") to Bulmer beside Goldingham Wood.

It is late summer. As we walk beside the jumbled hedgebanks, we see the bright red berries on the fading and straggling stems of black byrony. Poisonous cuckoo pint is partially hidden in the grass but in the bushes are the opening nuts of the orange coloured spindle berry. Passing Goldingham ("Gogum") Wood, we see bullace, sloes, blackberries and hazel nuts amongst the trees of hornbeam, elm, oak and ash. Walking on, we observe a curling thread of woodsmoke, and then the caravans and outside cooking hearth of travelling gypsies, peg-making from the hazel that is coppiced.

We are passed by the rattling donkey cart of a local carrier and on "40 Acres" is the smocked and bearded shepherd George Barrell, crook in hand, leading his flock like some biblical shepherd of old. Some ewes have had the "tup" (ram); there are red raddle marks on their fleeces. From the hillock we see swedes, mangolds, and potatoes ridged up, hand-hoed and weeded. In the valley where now grow willow trees are the horse and bullock meadows with their meadow cranesbill, fleabane and purple loosestrife. The ash grove is newly planted and in the distance are the myriad of greens amongst the park by Belchamp Church, whose spectrum is ever changing and ever infinite.

We walk on: towards the "slade". Two men are spreading muck by hand, a third approaches with another load in a tumbrel. Hurdles for the fold are standing in the gateway and just beyond the headland are the field-built corn stacks with their hazel "springels" and perfect finish.

Opposite, in "Dysters", are the chattering, happy gangs of gleaners; mothers, daughters and young sons, whilst in Mill Field, the solitary sheaf still stands as prohibition that no gleaner may yet enter. In the distance, the sun reflects upon the horse rake's tines as they sweep across the stubble with the combed up rakings. We pass Lower Houses, with their gardens of vegetables, herbs, apple trees and bee skips; and there in "Carters Hawk" is horseman Alfred Pearson, and as he calls "Wurdy-Wurdy", the horses turn obedient to his command. Climbing the hill, comes the heavy "road" wagon of 30 coomb sacks with the horses groomed down, sleek coated and the brasses so proudly displayed.

At the corner of the twisted, overhung lane to Upper Houses is 'old' David Rowe, with his single hand of only three fingers, marching along with the letters of his postal round. In the stables and barns of Griggs Farm, farmer Courtney maintains his own smithy and thinks of buying a binder to hasten his harvest for another year. But we continue walking and pass the long skirted women of Bulmer Street, with their pails of water drawn from iron hand pumps, as their children in "once a year" new harvest shoes scamper and play in the road. Pausing between the red brick Chapel and the Cock and Blackbirds, one hears the whistling industry of Corders Wheelwright Shop, where Hazell Chinnery has commenced his apprenticeship. Possibly he is learning how to repair a farm cart, renew shafts or "shrink" the iron tyre (rim) onto a wheel. More likely, as the "boy", he will be turning the lathe by hand for the "knave" of a waggon, and when it gets dusk, his elders will light the candles and oil lamps by which they work.

Further on, we reach the crossroads to the Tye. At Smeetham Hall, the Hyde Parker family are newly arrived. Turning to the right is the rotational and balanced livestock husbandry of the Auberies and its tenanted farms. In the distance, the sound of a traction engine thumps out across the parish as the beams for another farm building are split within the estate's own saw pit. A young man with leather boots walks by with a horse for the black-smith near the "Fox". Children rush past in pursuit of acorns, Harry Winch or Ernie Lott may well have been amongst them. Beside the road are the heaps of stones for road repairs garnered up by their mothers at a penny a bushel.

But at this moment a young girl walks towards us as she goes to her domestic duties as a parlour maid at Goldingham Hall. Her name is Emily Hearn. She is the youngest daughter of "old" David Rowe, and like many other girls of the era, she is "in service".

*   *   *

Today, aged 92 (born 1890), Emily Hearn lives in Maplestead. She is the oldest participant in our survey but from the sprightly manner in which she opens the door and the way her eyes light up with enthusiasm for the pro-ject, she could easily be the youngest. Several Sunday afternoons were spent discussing her duties as "parlour maid" and her years as landlady of the "Blackbirds". But of special interest were her recollections of the brewing, breadmaking and cottage economy of her distant yet so vividly recalled childhood.

"Father used to brew once or twice a year, and always in the early part of the summer" she explains. "It was a long day's work; he had to get up pretty early and get on with the job. There was the best beer and the 'small' beer, which was like the seconds. It wasn't as strong as the best beer and was used at harvest time and went into smaller containers. But it still made a very nice drink. The malt and the hops came from Balling-don in big sacks and the copper that he used to brew it in was next to the bakehouse."*

"Ah yes, the bakehouse . . . so how often would your parents have baked bread?" I asked.

"About once a week. Mother used to have a big bread trough and when she had made the dough, she made the loaves up on the table. Then we used to help her carry the table from our back door up to the bakehouse. Whilst all this was going on, my father would have heated the oven ready for the bread. Every winter he 'had' a fence (hedge) off one of the farmers. He preferred whitethorn for baking, as it burned well and gave off more heat."

---

* Bert and Stanley Surridge of Gestingthorpe explain that "you were only allowed one sack of malt a year. So you used two bushels (half a sack) in the first brew which made 35 gallons and the rest later in the year. Like the late Sid Rowe of Bulmer, they would put a "withe" or a birch broom handle in the beer when it was working and provided this piece of wood was then kept under cover, there would be enough yeast on it to work the second brewing. Charlie "Pod" Martin of Goldingham Hall recalls that "sometimes we let the beer feed on greengages; and when it was ready it tasted almost like wine."

"How did he know when the oven was hot enough?"

"Well, I don't rightly know, but I think it may have had something to do with the colour of the bricks. Anyway, once the fire got down to ashes, they would sweep them out and put the bread in and that was how they baked."

"Did they have to keep heating the oven?"

"No, although Mother would sometimes put some ash in front of the oven door . . . so what with his bees, home made wine, beer brewing, bread baking, and the postal round he did, my father was kept quite busy, despite only having one hand . . . and then of course he had the pigs to look after. You know he used to say that 'he had two pigs in the sty and one up the chimney'. We had a huge chimney in those days, with little inglenooks where we could sit when it was cold."

"And would the pigs be sent away for slaughtering and butchering?"

"Oh no! It was all done in the back garden by a local man—a Mr Rippingale—who was the expert at pig killing and butchering. And on the following day, he would return to cut it up. Mother used to cook the fat and lean pork and we would eat it with turnip tops or any other vegetables. The rest of the pig was pickled with brown sugar and salt, and when ready the hams and bacon were covered up and put up the chimney. In fact, neighbours used to put their hams up our chimney as well because it was so large."

Eighty five years later, the house where Emily Rowe watched her father bake bread, do the brewing and place hams up the chimney is now occupied by nephew Tom Rowe. In the process of time, the fireplace has been reduced in size but a colossal beam still testifies to the width of the original hearth front.

Together with brother Philip, he continued the explanation of the rural life of their childhoods and described the home-made traps, snares and bee skips, that were part of the skilful armoury of rustic lore, that the old countryman of our Long Furrow possessed.

"In those days, farmers would pay a farthing for every sparrow that you caught," relates Philip Rowe. "Well, my father (Emily Hearn's brother) made a 'clap' sparrow net, which he sold to his brothers for 7/6d. Anyway, they went out at night and placed a lantern behind the net and then a thorn hedge was 'driven' towards it. There must have been thousands of sparrows about in those days, because they reckon that they paid for the net in one night, which means they must have caught 360 sparrows, if not more!"

Another contrivance was the "brick sparrow trap", remembered by many older contributors. Threshing contractor, Jack Cornell, describes the techniques:

"Make a rectangle of 3 bricks and prop a fourth one up with a piece of gartridge (dogwood) with a twig on top of the crosspiece to the brick; when a sparrow stands on one of the gartridge forks, it upsets the twig and the brick falls on top of it. Actually retrieving the sparrow without it then flying away is more than a little difficult. But the principle can be used for other birds, and if you want to catch a blackbird, you can 'bait' it with a piece of apple and you can also use the same technique for catching field mice."

BRICK SPARROW TRAP

12 sparrows were reckoned to make a meal. The most difficult task was to catch the sparrows when the brick had trapped them, without the bird flying away before the brick was lifted off.

As a boy, Jack was sent by grandfather David Rowe to cut some gartridge because the equal double crotching is ideal for the cross piece on which the sparrow will perch, before "tripping" the mechanism.

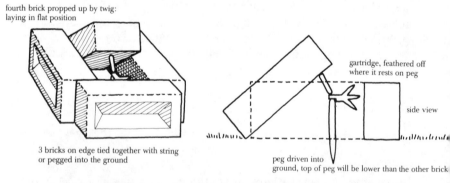

fourth brick propped up by twig: laying in flat position

3 bricks on edge tied together with string or pegged into the ground

gartridge, feathered off where it rests on peg

side view

peg driven into ground, top of peg will be lower than the other brick

Several of those who were visited testified to the tastiness of sparrow pie. It was estimated that about a dozen were needed to make a helping; others had enjoyed blackbirds–and one contributor confirmed that "the breast makes a nice little meal". Skylarks were also considered a delicacy and were snared with horse hair, whilst hedgehogs held a perpetual attraction for the itinerant peg-making gypsies who would ask "Have you got me a pig?" (i.e. hedgehog), and whose meat is considered by some old horsemen to be the explanation for a gypsy's good health. But thrushes or "mavis"

74

were not eaten and Hazell Chinery observes that cats decline them as well. Rook pie, however, was a seasonal dish, and older contributors will recall the farmers collectively shooting in the rookeries, during the second week of May. "This is the only time of the year (the 12th of May became an annual date in some parishes) that the young rooks are edible," explains retired farmer Bob Pinhey of Liston.

It was also during the early twentieth century that urban bird fanciers used to purchase goldfinches, linnets and chaffinches from the rural hedgerows of Bulmer and Gestingthorpe. A mastic called "bird lime" was available to facilitate the trapping. One octogenarian recalls:

> "It was a sticky substance and these old bird catchers used to smear it on the bigger branches of the trees, especially fruit trees. Then they would put a 'coy bird up there, and possibly use nets as well. Goldfinches are more difficult to catch, however. They roost on a different bush each night and you can go several nights with your nets and not find any at all."

One creature that required a vigorous policy of control was the rat. Without the poisons now available, they represented not only an agricultural and household aggravation, but also a source of extra income to farmworkers who were paid a penny a tail for the killings. Philip Rowe describes the manufacture of a rat snare for domestic use and we have an illustration of the relevant items.

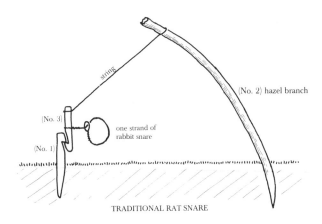

string

(No. 2) hazel branch

(No. 3)

one strand of
rabbit snare

(No. 1)

TRADITIONAL RAT SNARE

"First of all," he explains, "drive a peg, like a small tent peg, into the ground (1), then push in a 3 foot hazel branch about a yard away (2). At the end of this piece of hazel tie a string about a foot long. At the other end of the string, tie a piece of cleft wood (3) that will notch beneath the 'tent' peg. On this cleft stick tie one strand of a rabbit snare (4). When the rat is then caught in the snare it will shake the cleft stick from the 'tent' peg and the hazel branch will spring up and strangle the rat before it can bite its way loose."

Individual farmworkers had their own methods of trapping rats. The late Bob Daniells reckoned that he had caught hundreds with a half filled barrel of water which is reached by an inclined board supporting a sprung end. A piece of fish is suspended over the furthest end of the incline.

Yet there was no place on the traditional farm to compare with the corn stacks for "ratting". At threshing time "the sheaves absolutely seethed with rats", and there are several stories which indicates that it was not unusual to kill a hundred or more in a day. Traction engine driver Jack Cornell, reminisces with a typical anecdote:

"I had a mongrel dog which rode on the tank of my motorbike. One day at Spencer Coe's it killed 150 rats in one stack of canary seed. Just think of that . . . 150 rats in one stack! Then he got so excited that he fell in a cess pit and I had to pull him out. Of course, you know what a dog does as soon as he gets out of a pond–could I get away in time? Did we stink!"

Whilst the rat could be snared, caught and killed by any member of the community, the rabbit was often the special privilege of the horseman. Indeed, on some farms the rabbiting was let to an outside warrener who paid a rent for the "rights". But the "clean killed" rabbit has always represented an immediate source of nutrition or extra income to the countryman of our Long Furrow.

One horseman, Charlie "Pod" Martin, who "had the rabbiting" at "Gogum" (Goldingham) Hall in the thirties, explains:

"When wages were thirty shillings a week, I could occasionally earn nearly as much again with the rabbits. I had some luck on "Dysters" one weekend. I put 24 new snares down–they hadn't even had time to get dull–and I caught nineteen the first night and five more on the second night."

But "Pod" Martin also maintained another traditional attribute. For he was a dead shot with a catapult, and several of the village's older residents testify to his ability to shoot the cigarette from a man's hand:

"I used to keep a catapult the whole time and I'd grow a crotch on a hedge . . . if it wasn't quite the right angle, I would tie it across and let it train itself into shape."

He concluded an entertaining evening with an amusing anecdote of pigeon shooting one Saturday afternoon:

"I arranged with my mate to meet him at the back of Gogum Wood one Saturday after dinner. The pigeons were coming in on a lot of laid barley, that the binder hadn't picked up. Well, I got there first and I thought, 'hello! there's a nice one up that tree', so up with the gun, and bang! Then my old mate walks up, looking at me kind of peculiar and he says: 'Can't you see that's a 'coy bird you've just shot the head off up that tree!' He'd put it up there with a long pole."

A far less frequent, but equally acceptable means of "gleaning a lunch" for the horseman at plough, was explained by the late George Chatters on a hare shoot when he identified to the author that the screams emanating from the willow plantation, was of a "stoat killing a rabbit" and that if one could locate the stoat, it was a useful way to "catch a rabbit clean".

During the Victorian and Edwardian era, hares, which a particularly skilful person can "mesmerise",* were considered to be game, as were the manorial partridge and pheasant. With many others "Pod" Martin declares:

"There were far more partridges than pheasants in those days—almost all the true old fashioned sort. We put up nearly a hundred brace in one drive at Gogum in the late twenties."

But if game birds and hares were the preserve of the landed gentry, moles were a legitimate source of income to all. In the late nineteenth century, Bulmer had its own mole catcher and Bulmer Parish Council chairman, John Dixey, retells an amusing story:

"When the cottages on the Tye were burnt down, Jim 'Cappa' Carter was watching the fire and someone picked up a bucket of what they thought was water, and threw it on the fire . . . but it turned out to be the skins of molecatcher Harry Dixey!"

* The principle of mesmerising a hare—and catching it, involves circling a long stick over one's head when approaching. This has the effect of disorientating the animal's panoramic vision. In an alternative technique, suggested by one source, the approaching person, would take off his jacket and leave it on the ground in front of the hare and then walk slowly around to the back of the sett. Whichever system was adopted, and there are other variations, it was only the most skilful who would succeed in killing the animal.

Within the rural domestic economy, allotments and fruit trees would assume great significance; so, too, did bees. There were reckoned to be many more swarms about in those days than now. Philip and Tom Rowe described the manufacture of the traditional straw skips whose bands were tied together by hazel bark binders and which preceded the contemporary wooden hive.

Bee skip made from wheat straw and hazel binders

But the bees were often killed in the "smoking out" and before the introduction of "extractors" the combs had to be smashed . . . "they were then put in a cheese cloth and the honey run off; what wouldn't run out was soaked out and became mead" (water and honey boiled up).

"We used to float an egg on it," interjects Philip. "If the egg would float, we knew that the mead was strong enough. But it's strange stuff . . . you don't realise that you've been drinking it . . . until it's too late!"

With memories of mead, we are moving into the realm of home made wines and preserves. Douglas Hasler (born 1918) of Gestingthorpe provides the following memoir:

". . . apart from brewing beer, twice a year, my father also made home made wines. These included parsnip, dandelion, sloe, rose-hip, wheat, elderflower, potato, elderberry and rhubarb. Sugar was 3 pence a pound and 3½ pounds to the gallon was the usual quota, so a 4½ gallon cask could be filled for less than five shillings (25p).

Wife Freda, whose father, Harry Everitt, was a horseman at Hall Farm, adds:

"They didn't have any expensive bottles, just large earthenware jars. The wine was left a fortnight to ferment and was then syphoned off and theoretically left for a year. But it was often drunk earlier. My father arranged his wine making so that as one lot finished another variety would be coming on. Quite often, though, wine would be mixed with beer to make it go further."

Dennis "Chick" Rippingale (born 1922), reiterates the traditional approach of:

> "Making what you could from the hedgerows as the seasons of the year came round. Mother used to make ketchup from the big summer mushrooms whilst dandelion wine was regarded by the old people as being as good as medicine . . . especially for weak stomachs and small complaints."

Yet amongst the warm and cheerful memories of home-made wines, sloe gin, mead and beer, let us remember that in the early twentieth century, the provision of that most elemental of liquids–water itself–frequently involved a strenuous daily routine. Ernest Lott, who plodded eleven miles behind a horse to plough his "acre a day", then walked several miles to and from the fields to his home, and finally completed his daily routine by carrying two pails of water for a quarter of a mile to his house on the Halstead road. At Twinstead, Harry Rowe, who worked at Hill Farm and Sparrows Hall, walked through an ash grove and down 72 steps (and up again!) to collect the water for his household. "Jute" Chatters philosophised:

> "You wore hoops to stop your legs knocking the buckets and you didn't think it a mucher if someone went and tripped over the bucket when you had just got home! Of course, in those days everybody had soft water butts and one old man round here used to catch his water from a nearby land drain."

Tony Self of North End, Little Yeldham, and Tom Rowe of Upper Houses, Bulmer, both recall that:

> "Sometimes people would 'deeve' out their water from spings near their houses."

Not surprisingly there was also ill health. Smallpox, with its midnight burials, lingered in Gestingthorpe until 1874. Typhoid struck one Bulmer family in about 1905.

But despite the limited diet of the farmworker, it was an age of tremendous physical exertion. Feats of individual strength and muscular prowess were recognised with reverence and admiration.

> "You had to be 'more than a little strong' to put two 56 lb iron scale weights above your head and then bang them together," quips one retired farmworker of the competitive activities which would take place in the barn, the 'dresser shed' or the blacksmith shop."

Horseman and tractor driver, Jack Mann (1908-72), a person of intense fitness and agility, walked from Belchamp Walter to Ipswich market and back—a journey of nearly 60 miles—in a single day. Fifty years later the first girl home in the Sudbury Fun Run on the morning of Good Friday 1982, was granddaughter, Sheena Mann.

Jack Cornell recalls being told of the 'colossal strength' of George Hearn:

"I've heard different ones say," continues Jack, "that before the war he got in a muddle one night at Clarks Farm, Belchamp Walter, with a double shaft road wagon that was full up with sacks and it got tipped on its side. Well, the governor came out and he swore at him and said what a lot of extra work he had made for them all for the morning. But an hour later, when the governor came out, George Hearn had tipped the wagon back over and loaded it all up again. And those wagons would weigh nearly a ton."

A similar recollection of physical strength is provided by retired farmer Bob Pinhey (born 1903) whose father farmed Lamarsh Hall until 1922:

"We used to take some of the wheat by barge from Pitmore Lock on the River Stour. When we loaded these barges, we only had a couple of planks to stand on, but a man called Fenner, our stockman's brother, would pick up a coomb sack (2¼ cwt: 112 kilos) under *each* arm and walk from the waggon onto the barge like that. You know you've got to be a strong man to carry one sack like that, let alone two."

Competition existed in all aspects of physical fitness, horse control and perfection of work. In one village, about 1880, a young farmer walked for one mile with a coomb of wheat on his back to win a shilling bet—and more importantly, a good deal of parochial respect.

Another competitive test was to place a sixpence on the underside of a man's upturned wrist. By clenching the highly developed muscles in his fist, World War One veteran Harry Winch, was able to "spin" the sixpence right over from the head to the obverse until the last years of his life. I wonder if any of our readers can do the same thing with a new 20 pence piece?

But it was the endurance and fitness of all those who worked in the Furrow of that era that is so astounding. Ernie Lott of Bulmer Tye, like many of his contemporaries, never weighed more than nine stone, but unremittingly carried the coomb sacks of wheat, beans and clover (18, 19 and 20 stone, 110-125 kilos). When placed in the barn the sacks were stood vertically on the ground with a horizontal middle row and a third tier placed vertically on top. He continues:

"For the final row, two of us clasped hands together and a third pushed to gain height."

A ubiquitous and unpleasant memory was of "carrying 19 stone of beans on your back and then you go and tread on some—it's like walking on oiled ballbearings!"

But as we leave this review of the early twentieth century, let us recap with some of those enduring memories from childhood long past and activities otherwise forgotten.

For Gertie Coe, of Brickwall Farm,* born in 1906, it is of her father, craftsman and thatcher Sid Rowe, "playing the accordion on Boxing Day as the young chaps danced over the broom stick" . . . and of the harvest "horkey" at Jenkins Farm, for which her mother cooked the pork, and the memory of killing the pig with the resultant "blood puddings" and "pork cheese", (brawn from the head), of an animal of which nothing was wasted except for the "shriek". Whilst of school years, she instantly laughed: "Oh, acorning—a shilling a bushel"; and of the old people talking of "old time and new time, or the Lord's time and those silly fools in London's time" when the clocks first "changed" in World War One.

For Gladys Billimore, the memories of childhood were centred on "gleaning at harvest" and "taking people's milk in the mornings", from which she earned her pocket money for the Sunday School treat to the seaside. Later, she described the old men, stopping for "victuals", dressed in their buskins, leather boots and "westcots".

For Janet Cooper, the first recollection of youth was the fear that her bout of whooping cough would be treated with the traditional cure that she heard whispering relatives recommend outside her bedroom door. She would have been far less alarmed had she not overheard their comments, for the traditional cure was to eat fried mice. Luckily she recovered without having tasted these benefits of hedgerow medicine.

Jack Cornell, however, whose observations are seldom less than jovial, recalls wryly:

"I remember waking up in the morning and hearing the hobnail boots of Walter Eaves, (Albert Rowe's horseman) clumping down the road at a quarter to five in the morning and thinking—that's a rare start to the day!"

For all our contributors, they were decades of hardship, frugality and yet humour and happiness.

* Visited by Arthur Young, see Chapter Five. With true rural irony, the "wall" of Brickwall Farm is in fact made of flint!

81

Emily Hearn remembers "we used to love blackberrying and nutting". It was an age when crab apples, sloes, bullace and hazel nuts were all part of the rural diet. So too were the earth nuts* that were occasionally dug up and eaten by children.

Alice Self recalls buying sixteen walnuts for one penny from Charlie Downs who owned the trees beside Gestingthorpe crossroads.

For some there is the recollction of making broth from the sheep's heads that were sold for sixpence each, whilst Yvonne Jeggo laughs at an old joke: "They said that if you left the sheep's eyes in the broth, it would help to 'see you' through the week."

For Oliver Pearson, whose father kept the Belchamp Otten Red Lion†, the memories of the late nineteenth century are of his father's public house being opened as six o'clock in the morning, to serve people on their way to work, and of the farmworkers sitting up all night to brew their own "harvest beer" at Red Lion corner.

From some there are the lingering memories that have been passed down of the nettles and horehound that were added to hot water to "flavour it up a bit" in the centuries before tea became widely available. From a few, there are the more recent recollections of placing burnt toast in the teapot when the family budget was depleted and spent.

But as they developed from childhood to maturity, through the ever hastening seasons of life, so too did other observations become of importance. For Emily Hearn, it was the "strict adherence to Sunday, in even the wettest of harvests"; for "Jute" Chatters, it was of women stone picking at three ha'pence a bushel. Woodsman Bob Daniells recalled the once a year, after harvest, purchases of leather boots and the sixpence a week that was paid back to the cobbler, whilst the late George Chatters emphasised the importance of preserving the investment, in an age before the wellington rubber boot had been invented:

"These leather boots had to be worn in all weathers, but my father, who was a horseman, kept two little bags of oats above the fire and whenever his boots got wet, he put these bags inside them to absorb the moisture."

Yet the most frequently recurring memory of all, was of the villages being vibrant, self-contained, self-supportive communities. Bert Surridge, who worked for 52 years at Parkgate Farm, Gestingthorpe, enumerates the bygone trades of the parish:

* Pig nut, earth nut: Conopodium majus: family Umbelliferae.

†Today, Archibald Pearson, Oliver's son, maintains the family tradition and keeps the Batt Hall Off Licence.

"Gestup (Gestingthorpe) had everything in those days," he declares, "you never had need to leave the village in your life. In this parish there was a pub, 2 off-licences, two bakers, two shops, a post office, a school, a bicycle repair shop, a blacksmith, a carpenter, a wheelwright, a cobbler, a foundry, a brickmaker, pottery works and also an undertaker, so you didn't have to worry about travelling very far—even when you died!"

By comparison, Gestingthorpe today has only the blacksmith and public house remaining. Similarly, life-long farmworker Roland Pearson (1900-1973) remembered the days when "Belchamp Otten School (now deserted), was a busy throng of 60 children". When Roland left the school at the age of thirteen, he spent his first year working on the bottom rung of the rural career structure, as a backhouse or "back'us" boy at Otten Hall.

Another one time "back-'us" boy was George Finch (born 1895) of Gestingthorpe:

"They used to call me 'Rover' because I was always chasing about, cleaning the boots, getting the milk, chopping up wood, and one thing and another."

Later he was to obtain a nine acre small holding which he kept for fifty-two years.

"I was my own master for the greater part of my life," he exclaims. "I kept one cow, calves, pigs, chickens, ducks and black rabbits for their skins. I had enough corn for about one day's "sheening" (threshing ma-"chining") and the other smallholders came and helped each other out when the threshing tackle came. I cut my corn with a scythe, right up to 1973 and I carted and stacked it all by hand."

But there are other, sadder, grimmer memories as well. For Oliver Pearson (born 1889), the oldest countryman whose recollections are recorded, the most haunting memory of all, repeated only hours before his death in 1973, was of the

"old men, with terribly hunched backs—some almost bent double and hardly able to walk. When they finally retired they got eighteen pence a week from the village. If they were single they also got a small loaf of bread; and couples got a big loaf. These old people lived in absolute terror of being sent to the workhouse. It was terrible for them!"

But as we leave the old rurality, let us remind ourselves of that greatest single childhood memory, of which all of our sources and respondents have spoken with such genuine happiness and pleasure. It is possibly the most deeply felt recollection of all; it is of scything and sheaves, of waggons and stackbuilders and of "yellums" and thatchers. It is of harvest itself! It is this we shall investigate next. We shall start our journey far away from the fields of Bulmer on the estates of Czarist Russia. It is here that Tolstoy describes the early principles of reaping and harvest . . .

CHAPTER NINE

Harvest Time: Horkeys and Thatchers

"Have you ever seen a reaping machine?"
"How do they work?" asked Dolly.
"Exactly like a pair of scissors. A plank and a lot of little scissors.
Like this . . ."
Anna took a knife and fork in her beautiful white hands, sparkling with
rings and began to demonstrate . . .
"What a pity it does not bind, too! I saw one at the Vienna exhibition
that bound the sheaves with twine," said Sviazhsky.

(from "Anna Karenina")

Whilst Leo Tolstoy was writing of fictitious Russian estate owners, in his great works of world literature, the very real and still very much alive Emily Hearn, now 92, was walking home from her duties as parlour maid at Goldingham Hall, when she saw her first binder.

"It *was* a novelty," she recalls. "A McCormick . . . owned by Mr Courtnell . . . although with the binder there were far less losses for us to pick up when we went gleaning."

It is important here to establish the distinction between the "reaper" with which Emily Hearn was familiar and which was a horse-pulled cutter bar depositing untied straw in heaps, and the "binder", a later machine, which as its name implies, not only cut the crop, but also tied the corn into bundles or "sheaves".

But development of harvesting technique has not been limited to the past century. We observed in Chapter One how the first neolithic "garden farmers" of our Long Furrow would have simply plucked the ears from the standing corn. Later, flint, bronze and eventually iron sickles were used. The Romans, who arrived in our Gestingthorpe Furrow about 43 A.D.

improved and balanced the straight Celtic sickle, by putting a curve into the design which made it easier to use. Simultaneously, they developed the scythe for mowing grass, although this implement did not replace the sickle for cutting corn until the early nineteenth century, when the "cradle" was attached.

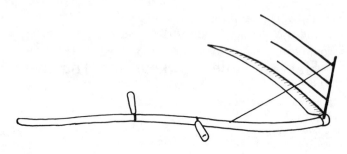

Scythe with 'cradle' attached

The next logical process was to attempt a mechanisation of this laborious task. Joseph Boyle of London secured the first patent for a reaping machine as early as 1800. Experimental work continued for half a century, and a notable prototype was designed by the Reverend Patrick Bell, a clergyman in Scotland. At the Great Exhibition of 1851, interest in reapers was intensified by the display of McCormick's reaper which incorporated several improvements and was imported from America. By 1869, at the Manchester 'Royal' Show, a record number of 84 reapers were demonstrated.

To bind and tie the cut corn was the next development and, in the late nineteenth century, manufacturers experimented with several alternative patents. By the early twentieth century, these improvements were becoming common. Most of our oldest contributors recall the local introduction of "binders" to replace "reapers". Harry Winch considers that Bulmer's first binder appeared at around 1908 and this would corroborate the remarks of Emily Hearn.

"The 'Home Farm' on Auberies estate," remembers Harry, "did not purchase a binder until 1915 and at about this time farmers began to cut barley mechanically as well."

Yet even the revolution that the reaper and binder brought to the harvest was only a temporary phase of transition. Within half a century of Bulmer's first McCormick binder, observed by Emily Hearn seventy four summers ago, the entire village would be harvested by combines—a job which itself becomes increasingly robotized with the passing of each year.*

In a traditional harvest, scything was only the first of many activities that had to be performed before the harvest was "safely gathered in". For after the rows of mowers had passed through a field, the swaths had to be tied up into "sheaves" with straw from the swath which was twisted round into "bands". These sheaves were stood into groups or "shocks". Later the sheaves would be "pitched" and "loaded" onto a waggon or "harvest buck". A lad would lead the horse and possibly a "trace horse" (front additional horse) back to the stackyard, where the waggon would be unloaded and built into a stack by the "stacker" and ultimately thatched.

But how, it will be asked, was this vast programme of work to be orchestrated, organised and delegated? And what was the terminology used? What were the local words and colloquialisms that were heard within the fields of our Furrow? And which, moreover, of the old harvest traditions had survived? Is it possible that any of the archaic, pagan, Celtic and Saxon customs of fertility goddesses and mother earth had percolated down through the heady centuries to linger on in to the twentieth century?

In "The Horse in the Furrow", "The Pattern Under the Plough" and "The Farm and the Village" author George Ewart Evans, provides the answers to these questions from memories and surveys obtained in North Suffolk. He describes the "Lord and Lady of the Harvest", "beever" (tea time), "elevenses", "fourses", "largesse", "horkeys", "wetting the scythe", "glove money" and the traditional rite of placing a green bough on the last waggon load of sheaves at the end of harvest.

But at this point we must ask ourselves: did the same rituals and customs prevail, forty miles away in the handful of villages which we are here investigating?

Answering this question provided an exciting opportunity for genuine research amongst a "target source" whose numbers are dwindling by the year. Interviews were conducted in farmworkers' cottages, retirement bungalows and isolated farmhouses in Bulmer, Gestingthorpe, the Belchamps, Wickham St. Pauls, the Maplesteads and Castle Hedingham, and the general answer would appear to be affirmative. Yet within this, there are several variations. Of more direct local interest is the difference in these

---

* But it is not only the machinery of harvest that has changed. So too has the crop itself. During the last eighty years, the science of plant breeding has ensured that varieties of wheat have become progressively shorter. In a binder and scythe harvest, varieties such as "Little Joss", "Rivet" and "Squareheads Masters" frequently grew to six feet or more in height. Emily Hearn declares that the crops, "were often six feet high and far taller than me". Today, the genetic descendants of these varieties, have been crossed with a dwarfing (or shortening) gene and some contemporary wheats now only grow to about eighteen inches high. Similarly, the fields which now benefit from the application of chemical herbicides were often infested with thistles, charlocks, docks, mayweeds, crows onions, bellbine, grass weeds and poppies, such as are depicted in the landscape paintings of the time.

To Borley
and Foxearth

Mill

BRUNDON

SUDBURY

Mill

Smeetham
Hall

Batt
Hall

Kitchen Fm.

Blackbirds

BULMER

Kings
Head

Triggs
Farm

am

†

Sandy Lane

Amsey
Farm

Ballingdon
Hill

The Auberies

To
Middleton

Upper
Houses

Clapps
Farm

LT. HENNY

The
Grove

ery

Jenkins
Farm

The
Fox

BULMER
TYE

GT. HENNY

rm

Parsons
Wood

To Lamarsh
& Alphamstone

Gentrys Farm

ler's
all

utler's
Wood

TWINSTEAD

Hill Farm

To
alstead
A131

To Pebmarsh

Miles

1   0   1   2

89

expressions, and dialects between the Belchamps and with Bulmer, which adjoins Sudbury and carries a main road. Older men from neighbouring parishes reckon to be able to identify each other's village of birth by their differing vernacular.

Despite these differences, the contemporary expressions of "elevenses" and "fourses" were commonplace. But "beever", a colloquialism for tea-time and frequently used in mid-Suffolk, is not a familiar local word. "Glove money", paid by farmers to the gangs who tied up the swaths of corn, is a phrase and custom which none of the older respondents of our Long Furrow (who did the job) can remember or had ever heard of. In fact, on several occasions older farmworkers quipped what a, "lousy old job tying the bands was, because the fields were full of thistles in those days and your arms and hands got scratched all over". Nor has the phrase "wetting the scythe"* been enunciated in our many hours conversations, but several Belchamp sources used the prefix of "wetting" (i.e. an excuse for a drink after a traditional accomplishment) in identical situations (e.g. "wetting the harvest", "wetting your whistle", "wetting the waggon" (last waggon)) and agreed that it was the sort of thing that might have been said.

The after harvest feast, known as the "horkey" (hockey) was, however, clearly remembered. But, possibly as a result of ecclesiastical pressure to establish the harvest festival, the actual ritual of the horkey was only main-tained on about half of the farms by the First World War. ("Well, yes, we never had one but my brother worked for . . ." etc.) Gertie Coe (born 1906) clearly remembers her mother preparing food for the Jenkins Farm horkey but recalls that little of the genuine horkey survived after 1919. Moreover, by this time, and in subsequent years, the horkey seems to have been in-creasingly paid for by the farmer and the requirement of the head horse-man and "Lord of the Harvest" to beg "largesse" from tradesmen, black-smiths and wheelwrights had begun to diminish. (Those who were associated with agriculture were expected to donate a small amount of money towards the horkey celebration). Yet the concept of harvest "largesse" had not completely disappeared. Threshing contractor Jack Cornell, who worked within a five or six mile radius of Bulmer in the '30s and '40s, was quite familiar with the term. He further explains that the reduction in the authority of the "Lord of the Harvest" was a gradual one but can be dated from the coming of the reaper and then the binder.

But here, too, there is tremendous variation between individual farms, let alone neighbouring villages. As recently as the late nineteen forties, the concept of "Lord of the Harvest", "largesse" and "horkeys" co-existed beside other farms which had last used the expressions two or three decades earlier. The fascinating but fading tradition of "sticking an oak bough" in the last load home followed an identical pattern. At Armsey

---

* Not to be confused with "whetting"—the use of a sharpening stone.

Farm, Bulmer, reports Harry Winch, "It was talked of, but not actually done after the First World War". But at Goldingham Hall, just a mile to the west, the tradition lingered on for another twenty-five years. Interestingly, at Belchamp St. Pauls, George "Jute" Chatters had no recollection of this custom at all, on the farms on which he had worked and taken such an interest in for the past sixty years. However, our three respondents who had mid-Suffolk childhoods (H. Cooper, F. Billimore and H. Elsie) all had vivid memories of "the horkey bough". It is also relevant that the bough had to be from an oak tree and the contrived conversation: "I've heard they used to put a hazel branch or something in the last load" brought a very rapid and assertive: "No, you're wrong there—it would have been an oak bough they put on the last load."

What is certain is that this fascinating practice—originating in which murky phase of pagan history we cannot tell, was continued on many farms of our Furrow well into the twentieth century.*

In some instances, a "hockey bough" was placed on the final stack of harvest, whilst at Jenkins Farm, Bulmer, a variation of a "guy" or some such thing was put on the last waggon load.

But there was no great mystery or esoteric ritual involved. "It was," said Philip Rowe, in reply to my question, "just a good excuse for a jollification" and a lot of beer at the end of harvest."

The last of the expressions from north Suffolk, "the Lady of the Harvest", being the man who was second in command to the "Lord" survives in neither memory nor ancestral reputation in our north east Essex Furrow. It is possible that such a 'lieutenant' may only have been needed on a very large farm. Possibly it disappeared with the introduction of mechanical reapers which would have led to a diminution of his duties.

There is evidence, however, that the shadowy figure of the "Lady of the Harvest" had existed in the area. Explaining the rite of "hen beer", "Jute" Chatters provided an old ditty from Belchamp St. Pauls:

"A man called 'Shorty', was scything by himself, and he came to a cottage whose chickens had strayed onto the field. He went to the door to ask for the 'hen beer' and when he was asked how many were in the scything gang, he replied (being in fact on his own) that:
There's the lord and the lady,
Front man, back man,
Little old Shorty and me!"

In the ditty at least the "Lady" is recognised as belonging to the gang.†

---

* The tradition could possibly be compared with a similar paganistic custom that many of us enjoy at Christmas—kissing beneath the mistletoe.

† Shortly before going to press, Bert Surridge, who worked for 52 years at Parkgate Farm, referred to the "Lord" and "Lady" of the erstwhile harvests on that farm. The "Lady" was the "Lord's" assistant and his familiarity with the term again illustrates the difference of tradition that existed between one farm or village and another.

"Hen beer', as the tale indicates was demanded by the scything gang where chickens had tramped down the crop and made their job more difficult. Charlie "Pod" Martin remembers that:

"We all stood at the back of the garden going 'chuck, chuck . . . chuck, chuck' in the manner of a hen . . . These old men had an excuse for beer in every activity they did, but the work was hard and they needed it as much as food."

Another widely remembered tradition is "nailing the colt", or "wetting the colt", at harvest time. This is not to be confused with the "half gallon of beer" the horsekeeper and the blacksmith drank when a colt was first shod. Alfred "Happy" Meekings explains:

"They got up to all manner of capers in those days. In harvest time they used to 'shoe a colt'. This would be a young chap who was 'taking the harvest' and 'in the gang' for the first time. They would grab hold of him and 'make out' they were going to drive a six inch nail in his foot until he cried out 'beer!' and then he would have to buy them a gallon of beer."

This custom has several corroborations and one wonders in which century this act of initiation first originated. A similar tradition was that after "taking the harvest" with the farmer, a token bond of a shilling was given to the employee. The late Fred Ratcliff remembered that "this sealed the bargain . . . once you'd accepted the shilling you were committed to working for that farmer".

"Jute" Chatters continues:

"Well, this money was then all collected up and given to the 'Lord of the Harvest', who bought a barrel of beer with it. On the first day, the men would cut a few yards into a gateway and then sit down and drink this beer for the rest of the day; then the next day, they were full swing and really into it . . ."

In Chapter Eight, Emily Hearn described her father brewing the harvest beer. Many of our contributors have similar memories, and recall that the brewing was often done at night, because, "it was a long job and the men never had much time off by day". During the harvest the long hours of manual labour produced some good thirsts. One Bulmer octogenarian took his father, "a five pint jar of beer three times a day and there was a 'niner' (9 gallon barrel) in the field as well".

One method of financing the supply of beer on some farms was from the sale of harvest rabbits, which would be caught by onlookers and workmen as the field was cut.

"Every evening, these rabbits would be sold in an auction to the village people by the Lord of the Harvest and this money would go towards 'harvest beer'*, recalls 'Pod' Martin of Goldingham Hall, Bulmer and Stanley Surridge of Delvyns Farm, Gestingthorpe.

But what exactly was the "Lord of the Harvest", of which we have written so much, and what were his responsibilities?

Farmer and steam enthusiast Cyril Philp of Castle Hedingham, who assisted in his first harvest in 1911, when he led the horse drawn harvest bucks from the field to the farm and back explains:

"Harvest at that time of day for a farmer was the next best thing to a holiday. The farm staff would appoint a 'Lord'–a foreman, or call him what you like. All the farmer did was to tell this elected boss of the workers what he wanted done and the 'Lord of the Harvest' would see that it got done. The farmer would say, 'Look, tomorrow I want you to go and do that field,' and the 'Lord' would get out his gang, see how many he wanted, and generally do the directing. And when it came to the carting and stacking, he'd do the same thing."

In Bulmer, the first confirmation I had that this system of delegation existed in the principal village of our Furrow, was provided two and a half hours before midnight, on a frosty, snow-clad Christmas Eve, in a traditional low-framed thatched cottage, when retired hurdlemaker, Philip Rowe enquired:

"Did I ever tell you that my father used to be Lord of the Harvest on Jenkins Farm?"

"No!" I replied excitedly, "but I didn't think he was a head horseman."

"You didn't have to be. In fact you often weren't. It was principally the person who was best at scything. He had to lead the gang and set the pace. You see, a gang of mowers have the same formation as geese flying, so the man at the front has got to be a good one. But my father, the Lord, he also had to be something of a scholar. If they were cutting a field of

---

* An additional local custom to raise beer revenue was a "fine" paid by a member of the harvest gang who opened his "shut knife" before the "Lord" had opened his at a meal break."

one crop or one variety, the Lord had to work out how many acres there were to come, how many loads of sheaves that would be and how large the stacks should be so that the stack matched up half decent to the quantity there was to come. Of course," he continued, "you *could* always make a stack up with straw, but you didn't want to have to do too much to it."

"What about the tying up? When was that done?"

"The wheat was tied up right behind the scythe, and it was always mowed into the standing corn, which would help to hold the cut wheat up so the 'mower's mate' could tie it easier. There were always two. For every mower, there was one man tying up behind him. I can remember ten mowers going in a line and they all had their mates with them.* Barley of course, might lay a day or two and be carted loose like hay."

Rates of work with a scythe varied with the condition of the crop. Charlie Chatters estimates that:

"one man could mow an acre of barley in a day . . . the crop swaths were then left, although if they became wet, they might be turned.

From Belchamp Otten, Oliver Pearson recalled twelve men cutting eight acres in a day, whilst at Kirby Hall, Castle Hedingham, Cyril Philp enthused about one record day when eighteen men had mown twenty five acres between sunrise and sunset. But that was an exceptional achievement and these figures corroborate the remark of Charlie Chatters that to "mow an acre was a good day's work."

An interesting aside to the subject of the manual harvest is provided by Oliver Pearson whose son, Cyril, is now choir master at Bulmer Church. In 1900, at the age of thirteen, young Oliver was requested by Mr Gardiner, who farmed Little Yeldham Hall, to harvest some beans by sickle. It took him a week's work, for which he was paid the agreed wage of five shillings.

Reg Rippingale remembers that:

"Because the beans were only 'set' (sown) in every second or third furrow and then 'ploughed in', you had to cut them with rips (sickles),

---

* George Finch (born 1895), recalls that a frequent comment heard amongst a scything gang was "keep your heel down!" This referred to the heel of the scythe, as if one mower cut higher than the others, his neighbour would have more to cut. "My father," continues George, "was 'Lord of the Harvest' and there were often nine men mowing in a line behind him; they'd do a bout and then come back to the hedge for, 'a little lubrication'. When I was a boy, I sat in the hedge and poured the beer out for them from a niner of beer." He also variously describes a band as a 'withe' and a shock as a 'traves'. Reg Rippingale (born 1899) remembers that when oats were mown, the man with the scythe also made the bands.

stacking. The headlands of wheat fields had still to be "opened up" by scythe to allow room for the horses to walk, when they pulled the binder. "Jute" Chatters remembers that tying up around the headland was a "poor old job", especially if there were a lot of thistles scratching your arms and hands. Fifty years later he demonstrates the knack of making the straw "bands" that were used for tying the sheaves together:

"You pulled out two scuds of straw," he explains, "and bent back the heads. Then you spliced the two bands together by hooking the heads under each other and twisting them up. You then had one long band and you pulled this round the sheaf and then tied the ends together."

We have an artist's representation of this form of "sheaf binding", for the sheaves which stand close beside Mr and Mrs Robert Andrews in Gainsborough's portrait, to which we have referred so often, are tied by the "straw bands" that were used until the introduction of the binder. Harry Winch (born 1895), who was to work on the same gentle slopes and neat fields that Gainsborough includes in the painting, remembers, "up to 20 people,'tying up' behind two reapers on Armsey Farm".

Later, Harry was to drive a six foot binder and reckons that he could comfortably cut 12 acres a day. Here again, crop density, weed problems or "laid" areas could quickly slow a binder down. Contributors to our survey report that between eight to fifteen acres a day might be accomplished, and twelve would appear to have been a good average.

When the binders were working, they sometimes required maintenance and adjustment. One task which is ruefully remembered, "was holding the horses when the men changed a 'finger' or the knife in the binder". Farmer Harold Cooper, reminisces:

"The trace horse on the binder was often ridden by a young lad, and it would be his responsibility to hold the horses at these times. I often did this job as a boy. It wasn't much fun standing there holding the trace horse and trying to keep the flies away, when the men were changing a 'finger' or straightening a 'section'. The horses only had to jump forward about half a pace, and one of the sharp, pointed 'fingers' could easily gash a man's leg—then if you were the boy you wouldn't be very popular for a few minutes!"

The horses who pulled the self-binders were quickly tired and it was considered to the the hardest work that they endured. They would usually be changed at midday and quite frequently at two hourly intervals. In either event they had to be given periodic rests. Three horses were normally required, although on the very hilly land of Hill Farm, Twinstead, up to five were known to have been needed by horseman Harry Rowe.

One astute observation, was that the quantity of string used by the binder, gave an elementary guide to the numbers of sheaves and possible yield of the field.

"A ball of old fashioned binder twine an acre, was reckoned to be a good crop," reports "Happy" Meekings.

The size of the sheaves which were bound by the "binder twine" could be adjusted to suit conditions. As they fell, latterly in groups of five or six, they would be shocked (stood up together) and allowed to dry. "Pod" Martin, who saw 47 harvests at Goldingham Hall, describes the technique:

"It's no good just standing the sheaves together, do they'll fall over in a gale. The first two sheaves you drive hard in the ground and twist the ears together, then you can lean the rest up on to them as easy as you like."

Harvesting with binders could start two or three weeks earlier than with combines. "Jute" Chatters explains that:

"A farmer would do the biggest part of his cutting before carting the sheaves and building the stacks; only a big farmer could cut and cart at the same time."

Moreover the crop might need time to ripen and dry out:

"Oats were meant to stand shocked for 'three church bells' (i.e. three Sundays). Wheat (which has a husk) and beans could be pitched or loaded onto a waggon and stacked first thing in the morning with a 'heavy dag' on it, but barley had to be completely dry."

"Shocking", pitching, loading, stack building and thatching were all labour-intensive and skilful operations. Horace Elsie remembers a typical scene in a field of ripe wheat with four people shocking, two pitching and one loading. But farmer Driver, for whom he worked, could load, (arrange the sheaves as they arrived on the cart) for three people at once "he had vast hands and was a master-loader" recalls Horace.

The Reverend Trevor Howard, rural dean and rector of Bulmer, Belchamp Otten and Belchamp Walter, described the traditional garnering, in his harvest festival address at St. Andrews Church on a Sunday evening in late September :

"The smells and the sounds of the countryside, the shocks glistening in the moonlight, the men in belts and braces, with their pitchforks and the calls of 'hold ya' to the 'loader' on the top of the waggon when the horses that pulled the buck went forward".

"Actually loading the waggon," says Freddie Hunt of Bulmer Street, "was also something of an art: the objective was to load it 'inwards', forming a natural cohesion between the waggon and the sheaves. Moreover," he recalls, "the 'pitchers', who forked up the sheaves, had to present them 'ears first' to the 'loader'–do else they'd just as soon get tossed back at you!"

When the waggon was loaded and sometimes roped down, it would be taken back to the stackyard at the farm. Often a young lad would lead the trace horse and be responsible for this task. Cyril Philp, Bob Pinhey and blacksmith Frank Nice of Gestingthorpe, each recall the boy-hood process of taking the waggon back to the farmstead, and returning with an empty harvest buck.

But before we leave the harvest field, let us remind ourselves of the collective social experience that harvest work involved. Let us imagine any one of the fields of our Furrow in the early thirties, where so many of our contributors were at work.

Here, in any summer ripened field, is the stationary harvest waggon as a couple of men pitch and another one loads. In a neighbouring field, a horse-drawn binder is at work driven by the head horseman, proud and efficient. Several men with shirt sleeves rolled up over sun-burnt arms are "shocking" the sheaves, whilst a gang of lads, armed with sticks, are waiting at the corner for departing rabbits. Freddie Hunt, Dennis Rippingale or Ken Day might be amongst them. At this moment, farmers Nott or Miller may have ridden past to inspect the progress, and from the farmyard along the rutted track, with its overhanging hedge, comes the empty harvest waggon with the trace horse led by some youngster in his first years harvest work.

"Those harvests were full of fun and games," recalls one old campaigner. "Often there would be women, girls and children in the waggon bringing out the harvest food* and when they passed 'old ....' stumping along, they all hid up and then threw handfuls of straw and chaff all over him . . . grumpy old 'darvil' he was!"

Further on in the harvest field, they jump out and with happy laughter unload the dinners accompanied by bottles and cans of cold tea.

---

* Several Bulmer women walked to Sudbury and back to buy meat before cooking it and then taking it out to their husbands in the fields.

As the harvest gang paused beneath the sun, passed on the flagon and rested aching limbs, so, too, would the conversation turn to the bantering jokes and agricultural observations of village life:

"So and so, they've finished . . . but poor old .... he be in the headest muddle out–but there again, he always was all over and behind."

"They say his wife has kicked over the trace", comes the informative reply.

"She always was 'on thorns', I know her of old" a buxom matron murmurs.

"He ain't very cute", mutters the harvest lord dismissively, whilst a 'pitcher' quips, "They never got no 'thistleing' done at all last year–old Bob what 'fed' the threshing drum, he got so many pricks in his hands, that he say there wasn't room for any more."

"He's a Bob–he is!" chuckles a horseman, whilst another laughs at the harvest 'colt' and asks:

"You dus'nt let them 'shoe' you then?"

Beside him, an older man slowly counts out the grains from one large head of wheat and mutters, "That be a tidy crop he's got there . . . used a ball of string and more an acre, so they say."

"Why, you look tired!" declares the young man to the older, who sucks a straw and answers with equanimity "Tain't so likey, boy."

"Are you fit, then? Come along together!" calls out the Lord of the Harvest."

The men return to the fields and in the farmyard the stackbuilding continues. This job, and the thatching of the stacks were skilful tasks and a matter of much pride to the craftsmen involved.

Moreover, as the authority of the Lord of the Harvest declined, with the advent of mechanisation the same man frequently took on the responsibilities of the "stacker", who built the stacks in the corner of the field or at the farmyard.

The research for stack building and thatching has been greatly assisted by the remarks, comments, explanatory drawings and anecdotes of erstwhile thatchers and stackbuilders: Philip and Tom Rowe, Freddie Hunt, Charlie Chatters, George "Jute" Chatters, Alfred "Happy" Meekings, Charlie "Pod" Martin and Douglas Hasler.

During these conversations, it was explained that a two foot base of straw was laid on the ground onto which the sheaves of the corn stack were placed. But by the time the stack had reached eaves height (8-9 layers high), the weight of the sheaves compressed this straw base as rapidly as the stack was raised, and "for a couple of layers you simply wouldn't gain any height". On top of the stack there were three men; one to take the sheaves from the elevator (or pitcher) and pass them to the 'binder' and the 'stacker'. The 'stacker' was the most important man of this operation. He laid his sheaf down and the 'binder' then positioned his, to overlap it in. It was emphasised that it was vital to keep the middle of the stack 'full', otherwise during the natural sinking that occurred during the year, a hollow would form, allowing water to penetrate the thatch. As the stack reached the roofing phase, a 'stage hole' was left, in which one man could stand. This man would be expected to catch the sheaves from the elevator or "pitchers" and pass them on to the stacker.

"But what happened if there was too much for one stack and there was no more of that crop or variety to be harvested?"

"Well, you tried to get it right and calculate it all out. You could always make it up with straw if there wasn't enough, but if there was too much we would build a little stack on the side: we used to call this the buttery or buttry."

Before we leave the stacker, however, let us remember that although it was not infrequent to have to prop up one side of a stack,* the story of "old ...., who built a stack and it fell down as soon as they took the elevator away . . ." caused only the utmost amusement and friendly derision.

Once the stacks were built, they would need thatching. This was a distinctly skilled operation and may have been performed by outside contractors, such as Philip Rowe senior and his two sons, who thatched the stacks of Goldingham and Smeetham Hall. Again, from the various conversations, a picture of the thatcher's requirements begins to emerge.

Freddie Hunt recalls that the late Sid Rowe with whom he worked was a "master thatcher" and remembered passing up the "yellms" or "yellums" (prepared straw bundles) to him in a crotched stick.

"You passed up enough for one complete run, but on a round stack, the thatcher had to calculate out all the geometry to get the overlaps right as he got closer to the top."

Tom Rowe declares that:

"Few farmers had 'tilts' (stack covers) in those days and my father was in a desperate demand as he thatched at two places . . . they both wanted him at the same time. After a very long day, his fingers would start to bleed from straking out the straw."

---

* Engineered with a crotched pole and a crowbar.

As the thatching progressed, the yellms would be bound in by the "springels" which would generally be cut out of the hedges from hazel or, less suitably, willow or elm. These "springels" were then tied in across the yellms with string or occasionally wood. The thatching ladders were usually of 40-44 staves in length, and Tom Rowe recalls that:

"Smeetham Hall had a thatching ladder of 44 staves, which was built like a battleship—only one man could move it on his own, and he had colossal strength.

The staves on these ladders were designed to be 9 inches apart so that the "second stave from the one you stood on would 'notch' into your knee". By comparison, a ladder to carry sacks of wheat up to a tumbrel or granary had closer staves to reduce the muscular exertion on the man's legs.

It was vital to have a good assistant or thatcher's mate, and it was suggested that he worked harder than the thatcher himself and was often as skilful. It was the mate's task to prepare the yellms for the thatcher, ensure that he had a steady supply of straw for this task, and carry up or pass up the yellms as required. Making the yellms was quite complex but "Happy" Meekings enumerated the process:

1. Shake out as much straw as you anticipate will be required with a 2-tine fork. This is called the "bed". It was best to make the bed as big as possible.
2. Splash water on straw, to "wet the bed".
3. Give straw time to absorb the water (ideally about 2 hours).
4. Draw straw out of the bed, straightening out by a rapid movement of fingers, which would remove some short straws ("snaffly bits").
5. After "fingering it out" and "squaring it up", the yellm was ready for for the thatcher to lay.

For this service the thatcher and his mate would be paid a shilling a square* in the early part of the century and half a crown (2/6d) by the nineteen thirties. A thatching "square" measured ten feet by ten feet (i.e 100 sqare feet). An average stack might be about 15 square. A stone was thrown over the top of the stack with a piece of string attached to measure the distance of the diagonal slopes. A good example of a thatching account is provided in the pencil written notebook of Bertie Hasler (1882-1968). By 1945 his rate per square is three shillings and sixpence (17½p): The statement for that year for Mr. Prior of Hall Farm, Gestingthorpe, reads:

---

* For "straw stacks", the rate was ninepence a square (figures from Priestfields Farm Year Book).

Wheat 44 x 40 (feet)	17.60 (square)
37 x 40	14.80
Oats 40 x 34	13.60
Barley 37 x 42	15.54
	61.54 (square)

At the end of harvest, he had thatched a total of 263.08 square, at Hall Farm for which he was paid £46.1s.4½d. Meanwhile he had also thatched 162 square for Mrs. Gardiner of Delvyns Farm.

Son, Douglas (born 1918), now disabled, has typewritten the following memoire:

"Thatching stacks at harvest time was very hard work for besides thatching at Hall Farm and Delvyns he also worked for Mr. Wallace at Oddwells Farm and Mr. Williams at Chelmshoe House Farm. As the thatch only had to last a few months, he used binder string and a few springels . . . He cut the latter out of Oakley Wood, from long hazel poles which were about one and a half inches in diameter. He took them home in a tumbrel, cut them into lengths of two to three feet and then split them into four."

Douglas concludes with a few remarks on the high level of physical fit ness which a lifetime's thatching had developed in his father:

"He'd been thatching since he was eleven years old and couldn't understand what hard work was. Shortly before World War Two, he got the order to thatch two barns, almost opposite Belchamp Walter Hall. It was a big job and I helped him for a fortnight, but the pace nearly killed me, although I was 20 years old and considered myself strong– Ripper's timber factory seemed like a rest camp after working with him! On one day, I had to 'draw' the straw near a big patch of nettles . . . I complained, but he muttered something brusquely and picked the nettles as if they were grass. They didn't sting him because years of thatching had made his hands too hard . . . in fact, until the end of his life he could pick up a red hot cinder and light his pipe with it."

Returning to the harvest stacks that were thatched in the farm's stackyard, the farmer would normally be expected to provide a water butt and he would have deliberately kept some straw stacks for thatching from the threshing of the previous year. Wheat varieties being considerably taller than at present, it was not unusual to have yellms of four feet or more in length. Later, in the autumn, when time allowed, the thatcher would return

to these stacks and "trim off" the ragged ends with a pair of sheep shears.*
Possibly a corn dolly would be twisted into the apex of the last stack.

Rates of work obviously varied according to the size of the stack. Charlie "Pod" Martin spoke with great satisfaction of the day in which he had thatched two stacks and the impression prevails that this was an exceptional day's work.†

But the greatest fear of the farmer during the interim period between stack building and the "settling of the thatch", was that a strong gale would either disgorge the unthatched stack, or lift off the thatch where it had been laid. Thomas Hardy writes of this in "Far from the Madding Crowd", and in the film version we have an epic scene, as Gabriel Oak struggles to pull the "tilts" over the stacks before the storm and Farmer Boldwood's later depair when he sees his own stacks truncated and drenched.

But bad harvests and disruptive seasons are not simply the preserve of the writer of fiction and director of celluloid. All of our older contributors recall one particularly wet year in the early part of the century, when sheaves were carted on Boxing Day. At Reeves Farm, Belchamp Otten, they were immediately placed on a muck heap. Sid Rowe, then working at Jenkins Farm, Bulmer, was amongst others who finally settled up for "taking the harvest" in the January of one year. Half a century later, he used to declare in the manner of a riddle that, "he had been paid for two harvests in one year", and then ask coyly "now how did that come about?"

In wet seasons, the shocks would need re-arranging to facilitate drying and individual sheaves would be turned round. More recently, in one exceedingly wet season during the nineteen fifties, Dennis Rippingale reports that: "Crawlers had to be hooked onto the front of combines and two tractors were required to pull each trailer".

But in other years, it was the memories of drought or the heat which have been passed down to posterity. Oliver Pearson remembered that around 1910, the men of Belchamp Otten were forced to leave off in the middle of the day, because it was too hot to work. In 1921, another very dry summer, smoking in the fields was prohibited and in John Cornell's threshing book, we read that new cut wheat was being threshed by the end of July. Several sources suggested that the harvest gang would suck sloes, or "bits of chalk" in those severely hot summers. Bert Surridge recalled that older men utilised whitethorn stems or little black pebbles" for the same purpose, whilst Reg Rippingale reminisces of one countryman who had an alternative method of "cooling down":

"If we were mowing, or opening a field up, on a hot day, anywhere near some damp ground like down in Brook Field, this old chap would

---

* Front page of "Bulmer: Then and Now" shows Sid Rowe, doing exactly this on the thatch of a building.

† C. Philp, "a 10 or 12 square of stack would take the best part of a day."

keep his eyes open and if he saw a frog in the grass, he'd catch it and tuck it in his shirt front and leave it there. But that was the small frog that I'm talking about—we used to call them 'Jakeys' in those days".

There is more of interest in this recollection, than the rather quaint means of refrigeration of the hardened old mower. The twist concerns the "jakeys" or frogs themselves. It is now fifteen year since I last saw a frog in the lush grass by the Belchamp Brook.

But if the frogs have disappeared, the climatic fluctuations still occur. In the severe drought of 1976, harvesting of all cereal crops was completed in July on many local farms, and the potentially abundant prospects of spring-time had materialised into a mediocre and disappointing harvest; the price of wheat fluctuated accordingly, reminding individual farmers who had "sold forward" in the expectation of good yields, of Hardy's words in "The Mayor of Casterbridge," that, "more money is made—and lost—by gambling on the potential of the crops of the green fields of England, than on the green baize of the casino card table."

Today, with all the resources of mechanisation and sophisticated equipment at one's disposal, one might imagine that some of the tension, urgency and frustration associated with harvest had finally diminished.

It is the reverse. Horace Elsie declares:

"There were many more smiles about years ago."

But harvest for the years of research in our Long Furrow has come to an end; the last sheaf is pitched, the oak bough is on the waggon, the binder is returned to the barn, the "Lord of the Harvest" has begun to "settle up", the thatcher's mate prepares the last yellms, and, as dusk falls, the cool mists of autumn rise up from the Belchamp and Stour Valleys to the lingering men in the fading sunset as a portent of autumn's approach.

It is time that we looked at the horse year: at all of the operations from raking to ploughing, from seeding to "thistling", that precede and prepare for the harvest of the following year.

In a few moment's time, we will start our investigation. We will take our short ear bags and knives and join the gleaners in a Bulmer field of our Long Furrow, but before we do this, we will find our best suits, wash the grease from beneath our fingernails and go and give homage at the annual harvest festival.

CHAPTER TEN

The Horse Year

Bulmer Church commands wide views and stands upon a little knoll. Beside the gravel path lie the unmarked graves and ornamented headstones of the former farmers and farmworkers of our Furrow. Here, beneath the gentle grass and soft moss of the consecrated soil are those who also rest, unrecorded, but who cut, stored and threshed the last 800 harvests of our village.

How many others, one wonders, have also been involved since the hand of man first worked the plot, the farmstead and the manor? What were they like, these men who have been part of this same process and who "stetched" the land, lambed the fold, coppiced the spinney and flailed the sheaves? Beneath this grass they lie; those who have carried the beacon for 800 years. They have fuelled it with their purpose. They have been short on words but long on wisdom; they had little education but were large of craft. The baptism was a rural trinity of backache, harvest and hoe.

For one brief moment in the gale strewn gloaming of the late September harvest festival, one thinks of those who have gone before. Here, then, lie the erstwhile farmers, proud impatient and strong; the head horsemen, perfectionists, dedicated and precise; the smock covered shepherd; the day rate worker; and the Lord of the Harvest who had set the pace with his scythe while his mate tied the bands behind.

It is a strange and mysterious inheritance and the soil of our furrow holds yet the secrets of their passions, aspirations and beliefs.

The bell tolls out from the flint walled tower and I leave the unsung resting place of so much toil and experience for the warm decoration of the harvest festival. Here, amongst this reverie, the Reverend Trevor Howard declares with the direct simplicity that makes it one of the half a dozen sermons I will remember for a lifetime:

". . . just as the farmer expects a harvest from his fields, so, too, does God expect a harvest from the field of your life."

We leave with the "harvest home", and the farming year of the horse age is ready to start once more.

As the last of the sheaves of the harvest were carted away and the final stacks thatched, so, too, did the women and children of the village embark upon gleaning the scattered ears that remained in the fields. This was often a family activity and Bob Raymond recalls of his schoolboy days:

"My mother used to go with several bags and take an old kitchen knife and a stone "rub" to keep it sharp. We used to pick up the corn in bunches and Mother used to cut the ears off and leave the straw behind."

Like Gladys Billimore, Gertie Coe and Rose Chatters, he would have worn a "short ear bag", which was tied around the waist, whilst the ears on long straws were held in the hand. Later, the accumulated gleanings would be flailed or drum threshed and fed to chickens at the bottom of the garden*.

On most farms, the fields would be raked before gleaning commenced. But most contributors (including some farmers) doubted whether raking actually paid for itself: that it continued into the 20th century was a part of the frugal philosophy of "waste not, want not" so prevalent in Victorian England. What is certain, however, is that the quantity of unshocked ears declined considerably with the introduction of the scythe in the early nineteenth century and the development of the reaper and binder continued this process.

But on all farms, irrespective of the means of harvesting, gleaning was prohibited prior to raking. To signify that a field was "out of bounds", the farmer left a single sheaf in the middle of the field. Harold Cooper of Elmsett recalls that this was the "policeman", but only George Finch, (born 1895), our oldest farmer, recalls this expression in the local villages of our furrow. Similarly, in some villages, the church bell was rung in the morning to indicate that gleaning could begin. This allowed all families, irrespective of the age of their children, an equal opportunity to glean the maximum possible. We have records of this from Belchamp Otten, Gestingthorpe and again Elmsett, but not from Bulmer itself.

Whilst the work of the gleaner, farmer and horseman continued, so, too, did that of the threshing contractor, who, with his steam engine and threshing drum, would have tried to keep busy from the first days of stackbuilding at harvest. Similarly, the "steam contractor" would have visited the village during the summer and autumn with his mole drainer, deep cultivator or plough to work on the fallows and stubbles.

Steam power had been introduced into agriculture from the mid nineteenth century and vigorously championed by I. J. Mechi, a leading farmer

---

* In earlier times the number of heads picked up was larger and the gleanings may have gone to make flour. George "Rover" Finch recalls of the pre-binder era, "In one year, my mother gleaned enough wheat to fill a sack of wheat–after it was threshed."

of Tiptree in the 1850's. Three decades later, John Prout of Blounts Farm, Sawbridgeworth, near Bishop's Stortford, became notable as an equally enthusiastic advocate and published his theories in a book entitled "Profitable Clay Farming" (3rd edition 1881).

The standard use of steam in eastern England involved the engines remaining on the headland and pulling mole drainers, ploughs and cultivators across the field by means of a wire rope.

Tom Rowe remembers the small field by the Sudan poultry farm being mole drained. A traction engine stood at one end of the field and he had to tow the mole drainer back to the other end with a horse. When he got to the further headland, he stood on the mole drainer to steer it, as the engine winched the implement back towards itself. In most situations, however, the engines worked in tandem with one on either side of the field. Cecil Smith, recalling the engines working in unison explains:

> "At Wickham Hall, where I worked, they used to do some steam ploughing every three or four years. When the ploughs were going through hard ground, it would certainly make the engines pop and hiss, and if the engine drivers wanted to pass a message from one side of the field to the other, they would give a 'pip' on the steam whistle."

It was whilst I was researching the era of "steam cultivation" in the Long Furrow of our fields that I was repeatedly recommended to make contact with a farmer of 83 years of age. One source had described him as, the "most well-informed and mechanically knowledgable of the old generation of farmers that you'll meet". It was thus with a certain degree of apprehension that I journeyed one bright, snow-lit December evening past the shadows of Castle Hedingham's great Norman keep and along the snow walled, sunken lane to Kirby Hall. Here, farmer and steam preservationist Cyril Philp, enthusiastically devoted a couple of evenings to discussing the horse era, the great depression, tithe war, early mechanisation and the principles of the "steam engine" operation.

> "The steamer in its day was the salvation of this heavy, wet land—which can be quite productive if you get the water off by mole drainage or deep cultivation," he explains.

"And steam was the only thing that would cope?"

"Well, there wasn't anything else, was there?"

"Were horses ever used for mole draining?"

"Yes, you *could* mole drain with horses but you would need at least eight and you would only pull it to about 12 inches. But with a 'steamer', you could get down to a proper depth (24 to 26 inches), and still do 15 acres a day."

"How much could they plough?"

"If a contractor could do 20 acres a day, then he would be *more* than happy.* That was long hours, mind—daylight to dark, non-stop. But the big advance with a steam engine was that it made contracting possible on arable farms. There had never been land work contractors before. It simply wasn't feasible with horses, but if a farmer got behind with his ploughing in the late 19th or early 20th century, all he had to do was whistle up the steamers and they'd get him up to date again."

"How many people were there in a steam gang?"

"Five. A team consisted of two drivers, one on each engine, one man to steer the plough, one to pull the plough down on the end, and a boy who ran about, made the tea and relieved the other men so they could have a break in sequence."

"So you mean they didn't stop?"

"No, once they started, it was flat out."

"I've heard say that the man on the water cart had a busy day . . ."

"Oh yes! he did. On this heavy-going land, a steamer might need up to 200 gallons an hour when mole draining on a steep pull and the water-cart man had two engines to fill up and probably only a hand pump to fill his water butt with!"

"Jack Cornell, who helped me write the chapter on threshing machines, reckons he burnt about 7 cwt of coal a day on that job. How much would you need for steam ploughing or mole draining?"

"About 15 cwt for each engine."

"And the safety valves lifted off if the pressure was exceeded?"

"Yes, every engine was built for a certain pressure. The first portable engines were built for 50 lb a square inch. But by the nineteen thirties, most had been improved to a specification of 180 and even 200 lb a

---

* At the same time two horses and a man, were expected to accomplish an "acre a day".

square inch. A good driver can keep his pressure on the mark all day long without letting the safety valve blow . . . of course, not all these old stagers were angels and if they came to a stiff old pull or a tough patch, they would screw the safety valve down a little to give 'em more power. It's the top ten pound that's got the most pull . . . but that *should not be done* . . . the safety inspectors would look at you sideways if you got up to that kind of caper . . . if you did too much to it, the boiler could explode; the thing is built for a certain specification and if you overtax it then something's got to give."

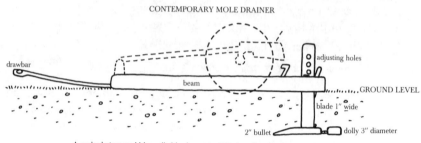

CONTEMPORARY MOLE DRAINER

A mole drainer could be pulled by horses to 12 inches. Steam power enabled the bullet and expander "dolly" to make its semi-permanent 2 or 3 inch drainage channel in good clays at a depth of 20-24 inches. Mole draining continues on local arable farms and still requires the most powerful of tractors or crawlers to make a satisfactory job.

Although the steam traction engine represented a colossal advance in a farmer's ability to "open up his land", the arrival of steam tackle was not always greeted with the same degree of enthusiasm by the farm staff, who had to cart the water.

"Work with that water butt? More than a little I did . . . I don't believe we had a spare minute all day long," recalled one farmworker.

But the most chilling memories are those of the dedicated older horse-keepers whose job it was to "roll" or cultivate behind the steam tackle. With considerable feeling and great sensitivity for their animals, it was repeatedly pointed out to the author that:

"The horses would stumble around as best they could. No, that was a poor ol sight, to see 'em hobbling across them jagged old clods getting bruised and bleeding as they went.

For the horseman himself, the prospect of walking over "concrete hard clods the size of a motor car wheel and bigger" suggested an unpleasant, irritating and tiresome day's work.

"Steam cultivators! Don't mention those b____ things to me! No! some of them old time farmers didn't give a damn for man nor beast when they were about"

was one fairly typical comment.

Irrespective of whether the "steamers" were being used on a farm, the great majority of work would continue as normal. The steady routine of ploughing in preparation for winter sowing, "ducksfooting", or light cultivating, drilling and harrowing, all proceeded in the normal season.

Most jobs had expected rates of work per day. On Bulmer's generally easy-working soils, the ploughman would be expected to accomplish "an acre a day". On the heavier soils of Belchamp Otten, he would want to plough "about" an acre a day, whilst on the heaviest clays of mid-Suffolk, the employer's expectation was reduced to three-quarters of an acre a day.

Other jobs had more standard daily averages:

Ducksfooting–3 horses	10 acres a day
Drilling–3 horses	10 acres a day
Harrowing–2 horses	20 acres a day
Rolling–1 horse	10 acres a day

Drilling (seeding), which now starts from the first week in September, did not usually commence before early to mid October. Several farmers followed traditional dates, of which October 11th was the most common. The "ploughing in" of winter beans, was often the first seeding operation and this might take place a little earlier, during the first week of October. It has more recently been established that this date is conducive to the spread of the devastating fungus–"chocolate spot". But it was explained by retired farmworker "Jute" Chatters that:

"being as the 'ploughing in' of beans was a bit tricky, the farmers liked to get it done first."

Of the other autumn sown crops, he remarked:

"We didn't start drilling until we had had a few rains and showers. We had to wait until the middle of October to allow the weeds and volunteer cereals to "chit" first. Then we could kill them by ploughing or harrowing them about. Nowadays," he continues, "you've got weedkillers and your weed control is much less governed by your cultivations than it was in the days of the horse."

Irrespective of the date of the operation, accuracy in "matching up" and straightness of line were not only essential requirements, but also a gospel and a doctrine unto themselves. "Jute" Chatters continues:

"With the single exception of beans, crops were drilled 'over wart' and you had to cross the furrows 'plumb'. If you were a bit on the cut or 'on the huh', part of the implement would be out of the ground when crossing."

Drilling, which began to replace broad-casting in the eighteenth century, initially required three and even four men and up to four horses, but as implement design improved, two men were latterly able to manage.

As the year progressed, so too did the weather deteriorate. The horseman's life became grim. Some jobs, like drilling, would require finishing, before autumn gave way to winter.

"Mud sticking to your boots like footballs," recalled one old horseman in the Belchamp 'Plough', "and you'd go trudging up the field in the rain and sleet . . . then maybe you'd try and cover yourself with up with a couple of corn sacks." He paused and continued frivolously, "but even the blessed sacks had your boss's name written on, so if you stood still, everyone knew who you worked for."

Thankfully, when we have had to "muddle wheat in" during the storms of recent autumns, it is from the comfort of a tractor cab. But there is still an inherent sense of concern at the sight of a tractor skidding and winding itself up hills, with mud "balling off" the front wheels and water shedding off the perspex. In a squalling gale on October 15th, 1976, the Rector picked his way into Dysters Field, Bulmer, to ask doubtfully:

"Are you sure your coulters aren't getting blocked, Ashley?"
"Well, I try to keep my eye on them."
"You know seed time and harvest never fail."
"Maybe, but we get a good run for our money at times."

Traditionally the strictness of the "no work—no pay" ethos was such that several men remembered getting "soaked before lunch, soaked after lunch and soaked again when we went back to feed the horses."

One source, who worked for a particularly money-conscious farmer ("a tight ol' _____ ") during the depression of the nineteen thirties, recalls:

"He used to come out to pay us on a Saturday morning and he'd say: 'How much time have you lost?' If you said 'half a day this week', he'd mutter, 'All right'; but if it had been chronically wet and you'd lost a day or a day and a half, he'd say 'That's good'. Well, my mate soon got tired of this and piped up: 'So it might be good—good for some, but it's no _____ good to we!'"

With the advent of winter, other tasks such as threshing, ditching, hedging, "brushing out" (clearing the light wood and grass from the banks of streams and ditches), would be interspersed with seasonal tasks such as mangold and swede picking, help for the shepherd, fence maintenance, mucking out and littering the yards ("itself a worser job than ploughing in the wet") and muck spreading, which was sometimes placed out on a contract basis in the 'twenties at 1½d. a heap. A similar task was "turning muck", instigated to relocate the internal heat which killed weed seeds. To ensure that a heap was properly forked over, some farmers would bury a chain in the middle, which they wished to inspect at the completion of the job.

One fascinating book to come to light in the search to illuminate our Long Furrow, is the "Farmers Labour Account Book" from 1908-1915, belonging to Mr.S.J.Philp,then of Priestfields Farm, Castle Hedingham. In this, the farmer has filled in a meticulous daily account of his thirteen men's work. We read, for example, that in the month of January, 1909, the farm staff were ploughing, turning muck, dressing wheat, barley and beans, ditching, threshing, carting bushes, wood, chaff, litter, muck and corn, stripping mangold seed, and occasionally ferreting. Whilst on Saturday, January 23rd, one employee, a boy, went spreading mole hills. The men are paid the going rate of between ten and fourteen shillings a week.

There are several fascinating revelations in the book. The beans for seed were being flailed as late as 1912. George "Jute" Chatters remembers that this practice persisted even longer in Belchamp St. Pauls and explains that a "threshing drum was reckoned to crack too many for seed".

Priestfields Farm appears to have been a pleasant place to work. There are no expamples of men being sent home in wet weather. From the detailed entries, however, we can establish that the afternoon of December 6th, 1915, was unpleasantly wet. We read under the headings for that date, that the two senior horsemen, W. Laver and C. Collar, spent the morning ploughing and the afternoon "cleaning harness", whilst the under horse-men, H. Collar and E. Turner spent half a day ploughing and half a day carrying chaff. A particularly interesting entry is that of August 6th, 1914. It is the day after the First World War broke out. We can imagine the farm-workers, in their waistcoats and buskins, removing their clay pipes as they pondered upon this grave development that was to bring so much suffering to their fellows and friends. On this occasion, the entire farm staff spent the morning "setting up corn", whilst in the afternoon they were "threshing oats".

One major task for the horseman would be the carting of the wheat from the farm to the local mills at Sudbury, Brundon, Cornard, Belchamp Walter and Batt Hall.* For these journeys, a stronger and heavier road waggon, capable of taking two horses abreast, would be used. Charlie Chatters took wheat from Belchamp Walter to Cornard Mill. Aged 15, he walked in front with the trace horse. Carrying between 20-35 coomb sacks (2-4 tons), carting must have been an almost full time job on some of the largest farms. It was certainly an occasion for which the head horseman would polish the horse brasses (which belonged to him and not the farmer) and endeavour by "various means" to ensure that his horses were seen at their best.

"These horsemen, they'd try to beat one another with the way the horses looked–and they would often spend an hour of their *own* time before going out on the road, getting the horses ready, putting on the horse brasses and getting the coats to shine," says "Jute" Chatters. Wife Rose corroborates the point:

"My father *was* a head horseman and Mother had all the brasses hanging up in the corner of the living room. They were *really* beautiful. Of course, we had to clean them up for Dad, but those horses did look lovely when they were 'dressed up' and going out on the road."

Several farm supplies, such as flour, seed corn, cattle cake and coal would be brought back on the return journey. "Jute" Chatters took wheat to Clover's Mill at Sudbury (now The Mill Hotel), with two horses and a trace horse and brought back flour on the return journey.

Horace Elsie could manage two loads a day from Bulmer to Cornard carrying 30 coomb sacks on a double shaft waggon, which itself weighed nearly a ton.

"But on one or two occasions I had to come *up* Ballingdon Hill with a full 30 coomb load (67½ cwt) but if you didn't have four horses you could get in a muddle. I came up the hill once with 3 horses and they had to go down on all four legs and I had to go across sideways to get started again. Of course, there was always a wooden roller with a few nails driven in, which you would hang behind the wheels when you went up a hill. This trailed behind on the road; if you could run the waggon back onto this beam you could give the horses a rest. But they only ever made me come up that hill with three horses once. Next time with a full load it had to be four."

* Another destination were the maltings to which the most suitable barley was sent. There were maltings at Sudbury and Long Melford in addition to those at Upper Yeldham Hall and Sewells Farm, Little Yeldham.

An alternative method of transport was provided by the barges which plied between the towns on the River Stour. Bob Pinhey (born 1903), whose father farmed Lamarsh Hall and Newmans Farm, recalls:

"The barge was pulled by a tow horse which walked along the bank. From Lamarsh Hall, we would take our corn down to Pitmyre Lock and load the barge up. From there it would go to somewhere like Colchester or Manningtree. But the day of inland water transport was quickly coming to an end and I don't believe that we moved any more wheat in this fashion after about 1915."

The atmosphere and mechanical apparatus of the Pitmore Lock barge loading, must have been similar to John Constable's famous oil painting, now hung in the Tate Gallery, of a horse, towpath and barge near Flatford Mill in the early nineteenth century.

Bob Pinhey describes what happened to the remainder of the farm's surplus wheat and barley:

"Well, most of it went to Bures. In those days, the road from Lamarsh was only made of rough stones, and it was so hilly and narrow that we mostly used tumbrels to cart it. We used to have three tumbrels, which would take eight sacks each and required two horses to pull them up the inclines. We reckoned on each tumbrel doing two loads a day."

As a further interesting aside to the "horse year", Bulmer Parish Council Chairman, John Dixey, points out that:

"A considerable number of horse waggons were sent to meet the train at Sudbury, and on market days," he continues, " the cattle and the sheep were driven quite freely from the market ground, right through the centre of the town to the railway station. Yes, they certainly *did* cause some havoc and pandemonium as they passed amongst the stall-holders and shoppers–especially if one got on the rampage!"

One crop which came to be commonly grown in the fields of our Long Furrow and which was taken to Sudbury Railway Station as described by John Dixey, after the First World War, was sugar beet. First introduced into the country in the late nineteenth century, it was not grown extensively in north east Essex until the nineteen twenties. Harry Winch saw his first sugar beet crop in World War I when serving with the Machine Gun Corps in France. "What the darvill are these things?" he wondered. Farmworker Cecil Smith, returning from India and Gibraltar with the Suffolk Regiment in 1924, saw what he thought were "colossal parsnips", when he first saw the East Anglian countryside after an absence of four years.

For a few decades, sugar beet were grown with considerable enthusiasm and were regarded by many farmers as "a highly profitable cornerstone to the arable farm". Today, the crop is in decline in Essex and its acreage is retreating to the lighter and easier working soils of Suffolk and Norfolk. But sugar beet themselves are also of historic interest as representing the last of the old "piece rate jobs", that were based on physical rather than mechanical labour.

Retired Bulmer farmworker Frank Billimore, who spent his early life near Bury St Edmunds, describes how the system worked:

> "In the autumn the sugar beet were loosened in the ground by a horse plough and then a gang of four of us 'took on' the job of pulling them by hand, knocking them (banging the beet together to clean off the dirt), and topping them. We had a hundred acres to do and it took us about ten weeks. I was paid 9d. a 100 yards for pulling them. In the spring I got 3d. a 100 yards for chopping out and 1½d. for second time work."

Pulling sugar beet by hand must surely be one of the most physically arduous tasks of the horse era. "Pulling", "knocking" and "topping", all done in a series of swiftly synchronised movements, certainly strengthened a man's wrists, but in ice cold, windswept, sleety conditions, it cannot have been a very pleasant occupation. Wide shouldered, piece rate journeyman, Bob Daniells reminisced:

> "I used to bind up my arms and wrists to give them support. When it was rough and cold I just carried on with the job and after a while forgot about the discomfort."

Farmer's son and haulage contractor Ken Day describes an older farm-worker "pulling beet" at Hilltop Farm, Bulmer in his youth:

> "He used to pull them out in all weathers. He seemed to become completeley absorbed in the job. He wore an old sack round his stomach like an apron and put all the beet into perfectly rounded heaps, and if there was a likelihood of a frost, he would carefully cover each heap up with a few tops",

But if the job was unpleasant for men, it was also arduous for the horses who "ploughed" them out. Cecil Smith described the horses falling, stumbling and slipping over on the frost and ice, when on this job.

Later, during the fifties and sixties, the crop developed almost "cult" proportions: "Have you got your beet hoed?" ... "Did you get an acreage increase?" ... "How is it the chap next door gets all the lorry permits?" were the comments of both farmers and farmworkers, whilst the latter would take a particular interest in the crop establishment and the "going rate" for "chopping out". Similarly, when the lifting of the crop started in the autumn, local hauliers vigorously competed to be first to arrive at Felstead Sugar Beet Factory. Haulage contractor Ken Day explains that:

"If you were first in the queue, you might get an extra load in, so you earned a little more that day. But lorry haulage of beet hasn't been going on all that long and even when I was a boy, some beet were still going to Sudbury railway station."

An example of the movement of sugar beet by railway is provided by Stanley Surridge, who worked for 63 years at Delvyns Farm, Gestingthorpe and recalls:

I've carted sugar beet to the railway station at Hedingham twice a day for weeks on end. The horses which I used were shod every fortnight on this job and in winter we had the blacksmith put in frost-nails, although they often broke off in icy conditions. Well, when you got to the station, everyone was allocated a separate truck and we had to load and unload everything with an old beet fork. Yes! if someone got a high truck, they'd hully get onto the porters."

But technological, political and economic circumstances are in a state of continuous flux. On 2nd February, 1981, the news reader on Radio Four's evening bulletin, crisply announced that the Felstead Sugar Beet Factory was to be closed.

For those young farmers who had so enthused about the crop in the early seventies, it was a salutary lesson. The only constant factor in British agriculture is that it is ever mutating. We have witnessed already the transformation from the sickle to scythe from reaper to binder and from binder to combine. In later chapters we will investigate the decline of sheep, the transience of the threshing machine and the replacement of the oxen for draught work by the heavy horse and tractor. Sugar beet, similarly made a brief entrance onto the Long Furrow of Bulmer and Gestingthorpe. Today they are already making their exits.

Despite the bleakness of winter, the work of the farm continued. Most holdings in the multi-dimensional, interlocking agriculture of the mixed farm had a yard of bullocks, a shed of turkeys, a meadow of chickens, sties of pigs and stables of horses. Swedes and mangolds were grown specifically as winter feed, and the horses would require exercise if not in full employment.

There were also the newly sown crops to protect, and young lads were paid to go bird-scaring on the slowly emerging fields. In the nineteen thirties, Frank Billimore was paid a shilling a day for this task, and like so many of these past agricultural customs, a vivid description of bird scaring can be found in the opening chapters of Thomas Hardy's book "Jude the Obscure".

Ditching, hedging and "brushing out" continued throughout January and February in an age before the mechanical ditcher and hedge cutter so revolutionised these activities. We may well imagine our "day" labourer, or horseman of old, standing among the damp clay of a four foot ditch with a spade or a "brushing rip" in his hand. Before the introduction of wellington boots, the job must have been bitterly unpleasant if the leather boots had split or cracked. Horace Elsie suggests that one technique was to stand on small wooden boards when digging out existing ditches. Where clay drainage pipes were being laid, horseman Charlie Chatters reckons that:

"You could dig a chain a day . . . but you had to work hard".

After the pipe had been laid in the bottom "spit" of the trench, black-thorns, brushwood and straw were utilised as "permeable fill", although these were later replaced by clinker and now stone. Hector Finch, who recently retired from driving the trencher for Waspes Land Drainage Company from Cockfield, where he sometimes achieved 60 chains a day, reports that:

"Years ago men sometimes dug their 'chain a day' beneath the weatherproofing of thatched hurdles . . ."

Sometimes on a streaming wet winter's morning, as I puggle round the ditches with a drainage spade, I still come across the occasional nineteenth century land drain, which is still delivering water. The clay pipes were locally made by the Rayner and English families of Bulmer and Gestingthorpe. The men who made and trenched them into the fields of our Long Furrow are forgotten now and lie buried beneath the mossy grass of local village churchyards.

Oddly; watching the murky water gushing out, from the clay pipes into a steep banked ditch is one of the most satisfying if esoteric of pleasures that I experience in the farming year.

But the cleaning of ditches, the "brushing out" of banks and digging of land drains, is all "dunton" old work, and men must have yearned for the lengthening of days, the sight of the "hazeling furrows" with the "nubbly clods" and the "tilty mells" of springtime.

With the arrival of dry March and April weather, seeding would commence again. It was particularly important that the rows of seed were "set" perfectly straight, for when the crop emerged the "horse hoe" would run between the ridges of corn, killing the competing weeds. "Jute" Chatters used a Barnett & Lake steerage hoe.

"One man drove it and one man walked behind to keep it in the rows."

"Was there anywhere to sit?" I asked naively.

"Hell, a bit!" came the reply from the other side of the bar. "They didn't know what seats were in those days!"

Horse hoeing was a highly skilful task requiring intense concentration. This was especially so where one-man hoes were in operation. The job was also of critical importance to the "tidy" farmer.

"Mr. Stennet at Armsey Farm" relates Harry Winch, "tried to hoe two or three times . . . but often in a wet spring it didn't all get done."

One older farmer remembers:

"parting the poppies in a corn field to look for the wheat."

Several other contributors recall the "huge heaps of poppy heads and weed seed"that were separated out by the threshing machine. "It wasn't unusual to grow as much weed as wheat" was one comment. It was the last era of an age, whose farmers had never known herbicides or chemicals and to whom "thistling", "docking" and "roguing" were important and necessary weeding operations. Oliver Pearson for example, earned 6/- a week pulling charlock for Mr. Gardiner at Yeldham Hall in 1905. Another contributor described how "cut throat razors were tied on to sticks to cut the tops off thistles". "Thistling", more frequently performed, however, with a weeding prong or hook, was also an important day rate supplement to village women. The efficacy of the job, however, depended on its execution at the right time and farmer Cyril Philp provides an old ditty which is still of botanical interest to gardeners and horticulturalists:

119

cut thistles in May

   . . . they'll grow the next day;

cut thistles in June

   . . . you're a month too soon;

cut thistles in July

   . . . and then they'll die.

Other weeds presented similar problems and opportunities for labour. Docks were dug out by hand with a docking iron–a narrow two tined fork, and charlock heads were sometimes "swigged off". The latter, like poppies, are observed to be particularly numerous in certain years.

This then, was the horse era husbandry with its well balanced mixed farming, which was governed by the limitations and pleasures of traditional agriculture. It was this agriculture with its lambing, shearing, breaking-in of horses, seeding, rolling, horse-hoeing and hay harvest that is so clearly remembered by our oldest respondents and which has so changed, as a consequence of the twentieth century.

Yet across these transformations and developments there is a slender lingering Hardy-esque thread of continuity. One older horseman in our survey, in a jovial mood, late on a summer's evening, was explaining the importance of a fallow and the traditional requirement of ploughing "rested" land five times. I imagined him for a moment, in his buskins, leather boots, corduroy trousers, "westcot" and cap, with his "dinner bag" hung in the hedge.

"What did you think about, occupy you mind with, when you were hobbling about behind a horse all day?" I asked.

"What the hell does any young man think about in a damn great field when he's all by himself for days on end!" he roared back with a vast grin on his face and a wink in his twinkling eyes.

There it is then. We leave him fresh-faced and supple-limbed, standing on the headland with his two horses and wooden plough those sixty odd summers before. He touches the rein and utters the command, and the sleek-coated horses move onward with the majesty and power that is history itself. He eases the rein and squints into the sun, across to the distant hedgerow as he straightens the line and mechanically gets into his stride.

Suddenly a warm smile creases his face and he remembers the pretty girl whose eye he had caught at Gestingthorpe Fete. Quietly repeating her name between his lips, he walks on, along the endless furrow with the warmth and expectation of springtime in his heart.

And whoever it was that he thought of, it seems that he finally chose well. For from among the older contributors to the "Long Furrow", we have celebrated 7 golden, 14 ruby and 21 silver weddings.

But with these thoughts of springtime, and expectation, it is time that we enquired into the shepherd and his sheep, the stockman and the hurdlemaker.

CHAPTER ELEVEN

Shepherds, Stockmen, Drovers and Hurdlemakers

We have seen in previous chapters how the agriculture of our Long Furrow was considerably more diversified in the year 1900 than in the present era. At that time, on a journey from Gestingthorpe to Castle Hedingham, one might expect to see at least twenty alternative crops growing in the fields, whilst the meadows and pastures would be grazed by pigs, horses, cattle, fowl and sheep.

It is the latter animal, "the golden hoof" of the fold, and the shepherd that we will investigate in this chapter. Across the recurring seasons of our Long Furrow, they have played an integral part for at least 2000 years. The first positive evidence of sheep in our villages is from the Romano-British farmstead village on the Bulmer and Gestingthorpe boundary. From here, we have the animal's bones and imprint of a lamb's foot pressed into a clay tile only moments before it was baked.

Continuing our search amongst the fading manuscripts of the Record Office and the dusty documents of private collections, we learn of the sheep population at the time of the Great Survey in 1086.

At Overhall, Gestingthorpe, there were 80 sheep, whilst at Goldingham Hall, Bulmer, 200 are counted. Later in this chapter, we shall meet Charlie "Pod" Martin, the last shepherd of Goldingham Hall before the final flock was dispersed in 1936 after an unbroken fold of at least 850 years.

Throughout the Middle Ages, the economic importance of the Golden Hoof was manifest in the vicinity with the building of the spectacular wool churches at Lavenham, Kersey and Long Melford. We know also of the importance of the weaving industry to towns such as Halstead, Earls Colne, Glemsford and Sudbury.

However, the wool industry was to suffer a decline, and in 1571 a law was enacted that, "those under the rank of gentleman are to wear a woollen cap on Sundays and Bank Holidays". We recall from Chapter 3, how the young men of Sudbury resisted this regulation. Similarly, a hundred years later in the reign of Charles II, a statute decreed that "the dead are to be buried in a woollen garment". Yet despite the decline in the cloth trade, sheep continued to form an essential cornerstone to the rural and domestic economy of our villages. Weaving provided a vital supplement to the meagre incomes of many village families in the seventeenth and eighteenth centuries and in Gainsborough's portrait of Robert Andrews, we have the clear representation of sheep, grazing in a neatly enclosed rectangular field, in the valleys that slope away from the Auberies towards Sudbury and the River Stour.

Finally, we saw in the last chapter that the same fields of the Auberies which Gainsborough portrayed, were still carrying sheep 100 years later, for in 1875, the inventory included 220 sheep and 140 lambs. At this time we may safely assume that sheep were maintained on all of the large local farms. Smeetham Hall supported a flock until the First World War, whilst at Jenkins Farm, they lingered on like a living white requiem to a bygone glory, until 1962.

Today, there are just two sheep on Bulmer's 2759 acres, and to discover the lore, craft, skills and memorable incidents of a shepherd's career, I had to locate yet another man whom I had never met, but about whom I had heard a great deal.

Born in 1905, Charlie "Pod" Martin spent 47 years as a horseman, shepherd and eventual foreman at Goldingham Hall, Bulmer. He left the village on his retirement in 1970. It required a series of telephone calls to identify his friends and former colleagues and then attempt to establish his whereabouts. Now it was a June evening. After knocking on several wrong doors as the search continued, I began to wonder, as I had so many times before when I had made fresh contacts, how the erstwhile shepherd would receive this comparatively young stranger with his incessant questions, biro and notepad.

"Can I come in?" I enquired hesitantly.

"Can you come in? I should think you can," he beamed with the same warm encouragement that I had received from forty other strangers on forty other doorsteps during the summer research of the Long Furrow. It is a hospitality that had made this section of the journey and this phase of the investigation so pleasurable and rewarding.

"How are you getting on with the old farm, then?" he asked.

"We go from one muddle to another," I jokingly replied, "but it's you that I am interested in. I am trying to learn a bit about the old-time farming, when you were a shepherd there."

For one moment he paused. The lorries and cars on the Sudbury to Bury St. Edmunds road roared past. And then, without another second's hesitation, he launched into an account of the shepherd's year, vividly describing each season and task, as if it were only yesterday that he had shorn his last sheep and lambed the last ewe. It is the lambing with which we start:-

"I had a shepherd's hut near the barn and I lambed 'em down between the buildings and the pond; I had a couple of hurricane lamps to hang up and one to carry about. When it was cold, I took a bottle of home-made blackberry or sloe wine to keep me warm on. I had a Tortoise stove in the hut and as the hours of night went by, I could hear the striking of the clock on Belchamp Church, across the valley. I had a bed in the hut, but on some nights there wasn't much time for sleeping–you'd just about get one ewe comfortable and things sorted out, and then another would be coming along."

Of the 70 farmers, farmworkers and members of associated occupations who were interviewed in the research for this book, it is only the shepherd, Charlie "Pod" Martin, who could return to a mixed farm today and carry on, almost exactly where he left off nearly half a century ago.

Shepherding is the least changed of all the rural activities within the intense transformation of the twentieth century. The techniques in principle are identical and the practical changes only minor. Rubber rings have replaced the burning iron, that older contributors remember being used for the removal of tails and the same procedure can be adopted for castration, although the burdizzo or nipper of Charlie Martin's day is still widely in use. But some expedients may never change.

"Sometimes I would have to milk the house cow in the middle of the night, to feed an orphan on. Of course, with orphans and triplets I would skin a dead lamb and put it over the orphan, to encourage the ewe to think it was her own. Anyway, come to the finish, when they were sold I would go with Cyril Cornell to somewhere like Braintree Market and then I'd settle up with Mr. Miller who I was working for. I was paid a bonus of sixpence for the first lamb from every ewe and ninepence for the extras. In my best year I marketed 415 lambs off 250 Border Leicester ewes. They used to call it the 'shepherd's harvest'".

But the shepherd's year does not end with the lambing. Charlie Martin continues with memories of his dogs.

"The first bitch I had was a little wonder. She must have saved me miles of walking. The guv'nor bought it for me off an old drover. She

124

would catch lambs for me that had got through the wire, and separate them out a treat, if I wanted to trim the feet up or look at them special."

"When you moved from field to field, or along the road did you walk behind the sheep to drive them?"

"No," he answered vehemently and proudly. "I used to walk in front, the dog would be at the back . . . all the proper old shepherds could lead their sheep as well."

I thought of the open wheat fields with the intense fungicide and chemical attention that I now devote to them and attempted to imagine the same land five decades previously when Charlie Martin had lambed, pastured, shorn and "flushed his ewes" there.

"You know, in those days, we would drive them over wheat," he continued, "never for very long, mind; there would always be a boy there to keep them on the move, and after very frosty conditions, the hooves would help to press the roots back in the soil again."

"And then after lambing you'd come to dipping and shearing?"

"Well, later on, yes. I sheared them all myself, although I'd have a chap to help me. I used to 'clagg' them first and shear them later. The skill in that is to put your knee underneath and keep the skin tight, so you don't cut them."

Like the head horseman, the shepherd was skilled in many spheres; part vet, part farm worker and part nutritionist.In an age before the arrival of instant communications he had to ultimately rely on his own experience and ingenuity, to provide the solutions to many of his problems. The point is corroborated with further memories:

"Mr. Waters, the vet from Halstead, gave me a needle and some silk to stitch them up with. Sometimes a lamb broke a leg on a hurdle, so I would get a bandage and put splints on for a couple of weeks. Another thing that we had to keep a watch for was Black Gargett. This develops if a lamb bites a ewe by mistake and results in the udder filling up with blackish water. We had one ewe get it right bad. I drained this liquid out by cutting the teats off, and then I had to disinfect it three times a day. But could I get it to eat afterwards? I tried everything– sheeps parsley, the lot. I had it in a fold of its own and I just couldn't get it to take anything. Then I tried a little sprig of ivy and that was the first thing it took."

Another aspect of shepherding, was the "puncturing" of sheep who have "blown", (swollen with gas from too vast a consumption of rich, lush food). The art of puncturing was an attribute of both shepherd and countryman. On one local farm of our Long Furrow, sheep were driven over charlock, which was growing on a fallow, and within a couple of hours they had "blown". As with so many of our memories of rural lore, descriptive examples can be found in the works of Thomas Hardy. Cinema-goers should look out for Alan Bates as he plays the role of Gabriel Oak, portraying the exactitude and exertion of puncturing with a narrow, sharp lance, in the opening scenes of "Far from the Madding Crowd".

Another of Hardy's characters was Diggory Venn, the "reddle man", and hero in "The Return of the Native". The "reddle" that he purveyed across Egdon Heath was a red dye used for the marking of sheep. Although this occupation had been superceded by the late 19th century, a similar need for dyes exists in shepherding today, to identify those ewes which have "had the ram", during the "tupping" season. This identification marker is now placed in a belt around the ram which subsequently colours the ewe's back when mounted. Charlie Martin continues by describing the earlier methods.

"In those days, we hired five Suffolk rams from Lord Ellesmere. I divided the ewes into five flocks of fifty and put one ram with each lot. After three weeks, I changed the rams from one group of fifty to another. Those rams were devils, though—they'd rush up and bash into the back of your legs, and that was more than a little painful, I can tell you! Anyway, every day I had to put this red ochre on the rams' stomachs, so I used to feed them in a special place and catch their legs in my crook when they weren't looking."

But what of the shepherd himself? From all accounts, he was a respected, independent man within the parochial community. His claim to recognition was based simply upon the job that he did. "Jute" Chatters deposed:

"Those shepherds loved their sheep; they would do anything for them and they literally lived for them."

Emily Hearn recalls of her childhood:

"It was really *something* to be a shepherd in those days."

One shepherd of that era, at Hengrave, near Bury St. Edmunds, was Benjamin Billimore. Today his son Frank (born 1912) has become part of our Long Furrow in Bulmer. Over several years, when we worked together, I came to appreciate his warm hearted cheerfulness and keen perceptive interest in the agricultural trends and developments of the past century. Here he enumerates some of his father's shepherding duties and explains:

"In fact, both my father and grandfather were shepherds. In those days to be a shepherd meant that you were virtually your own boss. My father had to treat for all the diseases and foot rot. On a farm in those days, there used to be a big place like a chemists shop, where all the medication was kept. But a lot of the remedies were kept private to the shepherd and they wouldn't tell you much, although if a ewe was queer, it was fairly common to give it a little bran mash with a spot of whisky in it".

"I've seen one or two films and read odd books about drovers driving the livestock from the farms to market: was this still going on in your father's day?"

"Yes, it was. My father used to drive his lambs from Hengrave to the markets at Newmarket, Bury St. Edmunds and Colchester. When he brought them to Colchester he would stay the night on Melford or Cavendish Green. He always stayed out with the sheep and his dogs would be with him, half asleep and alert. Of course, you could hire drovers to take your sheep for you, but my father preferred to take his own."

The subject of droving, with its connotations of self contained reponsibility and open, traffic-less roads, began to fascinate me. Farmer Cyril Philp describes how the arrangement worked:

"Now, if you went to market and bid for some livestock, you never needed to worry about getting them home. On no! You'd see these men standing about in small groups leaning on their sticks, with their clay pipes on, and their dogs beside them and when they saw you put in a "nod", they'd soon come up and ask you if the job was accounted for or not".

One professional drover of the late nineteenth and early twentieth century was Charles Jeggo, who worked for Charlie Hearn at Pearls Hill Farm, Gt. Maplestead. Today, one of his eleven children, Tim Jeggo (born 1909), recalls his father's lifestyle:

"He had a big black and white collie and he was often away from home for a couple of nights each week. He used to walk to Bury St. Edmunds with a drove of bullocks in front of him and the sheep and his dog behind."

"Would he always go alone?"

"Oh yes: all except for when he was starting out: us boys would fight amongst ourselves to help him, rather than go to school, but once he'd gone a couple of miles he'd tell us to be off home, and after that he'd be alone."

"So where would he stop on the first night?"

"He'd try to drove 'em as far at the Bradfield Manger, public house, on the road to Bury St. Edmunds. Once he got there, he'd put the cattle on the meadow and sleep in an old shed and stop the night. As likely as not there'd be a lot of old tom cats meowing around about, and he'd holler and shout at them. The next morning, he'd be off again and drive the sheep or cattle to Bury Market."

"And then he'd come back home?"

"Well, according to what Charlie Hearn bought or arranged, he'd drive some more on the way back."

"It must have been very exhausting work."

"It was! You know, about midnight one evening, my mother heard him coming through the village . . . course, that time of day the only thing you'd ever hear at night was an old vixen fox calling out for an old dog fox and all such as that . . . Anyway, she heard him coming through

---

Above: Dick Nice (1892-1968) beside the forge in Gestingthorpe Smithy. Notice the cavity where the silver sand was kept.

Below: "shoeing a wheel" or "shrinking a tyre".

"Father, would be up at five in the morning, to light the fire and he'd start the job at about six, so that he could avoid interruptions. He used to try and do about half a dozen wheels at the same time to make it more worthwhile. On occasions, if he only had one wheel to do, he might do it in the forge itself. Cecil Nears, who was a wheelwright and carpenter, would often come and help him. It was very skilful work. If the tyre (iron band) was too tight, it would be allowed to burn into the wheel a little way before being dowsed with water (which led it to contract and remain tightly on the wheel). We had to pump the water up by hand and we dug a hole to catch it in so it could be used again. The fire was made from straw and wood. Years ago, the wood came as faggots and was purchased from local farmers."

In the photograph, Dick Nice stands beside the iron tyres, which are being heated. In the foreground is a wooden wheel on which the tyre will be placed.

Photographs by Frank Nice

William Humm. Stockman and carter. Both the beard and donkey became a feature of Bulmer life.

Tom Rowe, standing beside the chimney (now bricked in) at Upper Houses, where Emily Hearn had watched her father "putting hams up the chimney".

Village Hall—home made entertainments. Harry Winch as Charlie Chaplin, Gertie Coe as Piernette, Connie Dixey as Queen of Clubs. Also on the photograph is Edie Younger (née Rowe).

George Bunn with wooden plough (doing his acre a day)

Albert Rowe (we think) driving a 15 horse power Ivel tractor at Bulmer in 1915.

Charlie "Wag" Winch, beside the 295 horse power Ford F.W.30 tractor which he drives for Auberies Estates today.

Alastair Tuffill—Photography

Alastair Tuffill–Photography

George "Rover" Finch (born 1895). George was the last of Gestingthorpe's genuine smallholders.

Dennis "Chick" Rippingale, at the controls of a combine harvester on the same fields where his ancestors passed with sickle and scythe.

Walter Eaves, at Griggs Farm, Bulmer.

"Old" David Rowe (1842-1931)

An intermediary "bagger" combine of the mid fifties with Lawrence Coe, Jack Hunt and Wally Pearson.

ALASTAIR TUFFILL PHOTOGRAPHY

The "feather" in the pin that was taken out, to allow a "threshing" traction engine to use its winch.

Alastair Tuffill–Photography

Threshing Superstar . . . Jack Cornell!

Threshing at Smeetham Hall. The tackle belonged to Joseph Coe and includes a Robey engine and Marshall drum. On the photograph are "Dad" Mansfield (driving the engine), Toby Felton (cutting the "bands" on top of the drum) and "Scrudger" Deal (taking the sacks off). We think that the photograph was taken either during or just before the First World War as there is no "self feeder" on the drum.

Horace Elsie

Below:
Gertie Coe, with the miniature chest of drawers that her father, Sid "Schemer" Rowe, made from brass shell cases during the First World War.

Emily Hearn. No it is not a misprint. She really is the oldest living contributor to our survey, and was born (believe it or not) on July 1st, 1890.

Below:
Bert Surridge standing on the footpath where he walked to work at Parkgate Farm for 52 years.

Right:
Frank and Gladys Billimore
Frank's old horse brasses hang on
the wall beside him. They were
purchased for 9d each from Hobsons
on Bury St. Edmunds Market Hill
in the late nineteen twenties.

Centre:
Charlie and Mabel Chatters
Charlie was a head horseman at
Waits Farm, Belchamp Walter.
Mabel's father (Alfred Pearson)
was farm foreman at Goldingham
Hall after the First World War.

Below Right:
"Jute" and Rose Chatters
of Belchamp St. Pauls.
Jute and Rose are one of at least
seven "golden couples" to have
contributed to the "Long Furrow".

Below:
Ken Day of Hilltop Farm, Bulmer.

Alastair Tuffill–Photography

Alastair Tuffill–Photography

In the spirit of Coke and Arthur Young, ADAS officer John Llewellin supervises the trials combine, as it cuts and weighs out the experimental plots on Goldingham Wood field.

Discussing early drilling, take-all disease and nitrogen requirements for wheat, at a farm open day on June 24th 1982. Cyril Philp is in the foreground.

the village, but then, he didn't seem to get any nearer—and do you know what? He was so tired that he'd sat down and then, half asleep, he'd walked back to Monks Lodge before he woke up and knew where he was, so then he had to turn round and come back home again."

"How many sheep and cattle would he take?"

"Oh, he'd drive 50 cattle and 100 sheep. He didn't always take them the whole way together, mind. And there's another thing, you know. I'll tell you this—my father could neither read nor write, but where livestock were concerned he could hully count."

Droving itself was not only a rigorous outdoor occupation. Tim Jeggo recalls that his father was "always slightly on the trot" and as he moved, he would keep calling out "Hup, hup, hup, hup, hup!" to keep the livestock moving. Similarly, there were occasions when the job continued in the foulest of weathers, when a cold or rain-soaked drover might be miles from home.

We leave the Great Yeldham home of Tim and Yvonne Jeggo with a final story that reminds us that not only has the system of animal transportation been transformed, but so, too, has the height of the wheat crop to as little as a quarter of its pre-war length:

"My father went to Melford Hall one night, after a flock of sheep that he had to take into Bury. What happened I don't know, but somebody had left the gate open to the field where those sheep were—it was getting toward harvest time and the wheat was on full ear. Well, it poured with rain that night and these sheep all got out into this bit of wheat. Next morning, when him and this chap from the farm found them, they both got drenched up to their shoulders getting the sheep out of that wheat, because it was so tall, and then they still had to walk them to Bury Market."

But the Jeggo family's connection with farming did not terminate with Charles Jeggo. Son Tim worked on the same Maplestead farm for much of his later life and, appropriately, in view of his father's occupation, spent some years at the wheel of a motorized cattle lorry, covering in a couple of hours the distances which Charles Jeggo had accomplished in a day and a half's walking. Meanwhile, amongst the severely depleted labour force of contemporary arable farming, there are still Jeggos at work on local farms. At weekends, the eye that looks down the barrel of a twelve bore shotgun, at the pigeons on the field of oilseed rape or peas, may well be that of Philip Jeggo, who now works at Wickham Hall, the great grandson of Charles Jeggo, who had driven the bullocks and sheep along the same laneways now eighty odd years ago.

Not all livestock, however, required taking to Bury St. Edmunds. Several older contributors recall droving bullocks and sheep to the local markets of Halstead, Braintree, Great Yeldham and Sudbury. Similarly, other consignments were driven to Sudbury Railway Station and then conveyed by train to further destinations. Bert Surridge, who worked for fifty two years at Parkgate Farm, Gestingthorpe, describes the system:

"What we did was this . . . we used to drive the sheep down to Sudbury of an afternoon and leave them on the meadows on the right hand side at the bottom of Ballingdon Hill, somewhere behind where the brewery used to be. Then on the next morning, we would get up early and get down to this meadow and drive the sheep through Sudbury and along the Cornard road until we got to a narrow lane, near to where Arlington's garage is. Well, this alleyway led down to where the cattle and sheep were loaded up on the train.

In the previous chapter, on "The Horse Year", we read of Horace Elsie's three horses struggling up Ballingdon Hill. Throughout this "living" or "workingman's" history, we have tried to invest the everyday features of our contemporary journeys with a new dimension. The twisting lanes will be recalled for their awkwardness to the threshing tackle, and the road to Grove Farm, Henny, for the place where "the cow got stuck under the threshing drum". As we travel to Braintree, Great Yeldham or along the Cornard Road, we can visualise Bert Surridge or his brother, Stanley, herding the bullocks and sheep to the market or railway station. Finally, as we journey through Long Melford, Cavendish, Bury St. Edmunds or possibly the Bradfield "Manger" we will imagine drover, Charles Jeggo or shepherd, Benjamin Billimore, droving their sheep along the roads and the highways where the juggernauts and traffic now roar.*

Another activity of the shepherd, was that of shearing. We return with Frank Billimore to the days of his Hengrave boyhood, when he helped his father to perform the task. He explains:

"My father used hand clippers at first, although later on he also had the mechanical shears. As a boy, I use to turn the handle and tie up the fleeces. We started at dawn and carried on for fourteen hours or longer until it began to get dusk. My father stood on a low platform and had one

---

* The ability to perform long distance perambulations has not declined in the Billimore family. This year, thirteen year old John Billimore, great grandson of shepherd and drover Benjamin Billimore, completed the 26 mile Cardiff marathon in just over four hours.

man to catch the sheep, one to turn the handle and one to roll up the fleeces. He did all the shearing himself; he had about eighteen score to do, and it took him about five or six days. I know at night we were so tired that we used to sleep in the barn with the wool rather than walk home."

Another man to have local experience of shearing is George "Jute" Chatters of Belchamp St. Paul. He reminises:

"I helped a couple of men do three hundred one year. I used to tagg the sheep for them . . . take all the mucky bits off the back end and then bundle the fleeces up. But round about this way, most of the shearing was done by the Rowes from Bulmer."

Half a mile away from where Charlie "Pod" Martin was shepherding at Goldingham Hall, and approximately six miles from the Belchamp St. Paul's home of George Chatters, brothers Tom and Philip Rowe were living at Upper Houses, Bulmer, when they went contract shearing in the nineteen twenties.

"Shearing with hand clippers is notorious hard work . . . but we sometimes did forty a day," remembers Philip. "It was exhausting though, and a lot of shearers almost swam in beer to keep themselves going. But after a few years we found that tea made us sweat less, although we still worked up a terrible thirst."

Later the brothers progressed to mechanical clippers and one man was required to turn the handle which drove them.

But the relationship between the Rowe family and the sheep industry did not terminate at the conclusion of shearing. For at other times in the year, the family would manufacture the wooden hurdles that were so necessary to the shepherds whose sheep they had helped to shear.

It it Tom Rowe (born 1902) who explains the art of hurdle making:

"My father used to buy a load of sweet chestnut from Pannells Ash at Hedingham. There was a wood there which was coppiced and sold off by auction; then there was some willow sold in Castle Hedingham and we bought some there as well."

"Chestnut was better than ash?"

"Yes, you can't beat sweet chestnut really; it will last almost as long as oak. Willow was all right. It was nice and light to cart about. Old shepherds would put half a dozen willow hurdles on a stake over their shoulder, to carry them from place to place."

"Did you make all the hurdles here in Bulmer?"

"No, we made some in Wiggery Wood, near where the Roman Village has been unearthed, and another time we made a lot at the Leys Wood at the back of Gestingthorpe Hall for Mrs. Oates."

"Why would people buy wooden hurdles rather than iron?"

"Because they were cheaper and lighter! Iron hurdles sold for £1 each, when we sold our wooden ones for one shilling a piece. In fact we had to pay for the wood, the nails and a penny for the "hank", out of that shilling, so we reckoned on two of us needing to make about a dozen a day."

"How exactly do you go about making a wooden hurdle?"

"We used to split the poles three or four times and we reckoned that the splitting helped to preserve the wood; moreover, if you take the bark off, the wood lasts even longer still. There's quite an art in splitting hurdle wood and for this job we used a writhing iron. We then made and morticed the heads on before putting the nails in."

The seasonal working of the Rowe family, is indicative of the openings then available to the rural craftsmen and which brought a full year's piece rate employment to the family. With the advent of summer, they were sheep shearing on a contract basis, earning 6d a sheep. During the summer, when the shearing was over, the brothers might go "straw tieing" or "hay cutting".* As an evening pastime they might make the "binders" required to tie together the straw coil in the manufacture of bee skips. Father, "old" Philip Rowe, had also collected oak bark to be sold as tannin and as we explained in Chapter Eight, had been a one-time "Lord of the Harvest" at Jenkins Farm before the advent of the binder. After this development, he continued his seasonal interest in the harvest and with his sons "thatched" the stacks of Goldingham and Smeetham Hall. Finally, with the harvest home, the stacks thatched and the sheep sheared, the brothers might have done a spell with a local threshing tackle before the cycle began again. Tom Rowe estimates:

"We hoped to make thirty shillings a week on the jobs like hurdle making, at a time when farmworkers were earning about a pound a week. But in the shearing season the rewards would have been greater."

* During the horse era, there was a colossal demand for straw and hay in towns and the 36 lb straw and 50 lb hay trusses would normally be destined for a big city via the railway.

Ultimately, however, it was economics and the increased technology of fertilisers, weedkillers and cereal mechanisation that spelt the death knell of the sheep industry in Bulmer. For any of our forefathers to return to our contemporary furrow, this absence of the "golden hoof" would be as difficult to understand, as any of the other more obvious trasformations that have occurred in the past eighty years. But when John Reid of Jenkins Farm emigrated to New Zealand, and sold the last flock from our furrow in 1962, it represented the termination of a continuous theme, which originated with our Celtic homesteaders and persisted through the Roman, Saxon, Manorial and post-Reformation farming systems of our village. With the fall of the auctioneer's hammer, an element of rural life was dispersed into the vacuous eternity of all that is past, and with it went all that was once held sacred by generations of hurdlemakers, shepherds, drovers and shearers.

With the passing of years, so too have cattle numbers declined. Bulmer's last "great" cattle man was, in fact, a Scotsman, Mr. Col MacDonald Bain, who bought Goldingham in 1936 and subsequently aroused considerable interest by bringing his entire herd of 45 tuberculosis-tested Friesian cows, 40 young stock and three horses by train form Castle Douglas, Scotland, to Sudbury Railway Station. Jim Hastie of Foxearth recalls that his father was head stockman for Col Bain and was one of the nineteen people who migrated south with him. He also explains that the milk from Goldingham went to a dairy in Wickhambrook, and Bailey & Goates, builders from Sudbury, installed the relatively modern innovation of milking machines. But in 1947 Farmer Bain sold the farm and the dairy was discontinued. The Hastie family, however, continued the tradition of stockmanship and today Robin Hastie is herdsman at J. O. Brand's notable Foxearth herd of red and white Friesians.

Yet Goldingham was not the only farm in the village to have cattle. World War I veteran, Harry Winch comments:

"Most farms had a yard full of bullocks for the winter, and they fattened them up on swedes, mangolds and chaff. At Armsey Farm we had Jersey cattle as well, and there was a milk round to the neighbouring parts of Bulmer and Henny. From Kitchen Farm," he recalls, " they arranged deliveries in the Batt Hall area."

In the neighbouring village of our Furrow, there were dairy herds and milk deliveries from Hill Farm and latterly Parkgate Farm, Gestingthorpe. Many of our older contributors recall collecting the milk, on the way back from school or work, from the dairies or smaller farms where "a couple or three" house cows were kept. In Belchamp St. Pauls, "Jute"

Chatters describes the art of manufacturing home-made butter and remembers:

"We used to put the cream in a Kilner jar during the war (Second World War) and shake it up. I used to hate this job. I used to sit here and shake it of a night–some nights you didn't want to shake it very long, but other nights you'd shake it until your blessed arm very near fell off, before it would form."

But the delivery of milk and rearing of bullocks was not limited to the larger farms of our Furrow. Alice Self recalls smallholder, Will Hart of Brook Farm, Belchamp Walter,

"He brought the milk round in a pony and trap and ladled it out of a churn with a jug if you wanted to buy some."

She also recalls the provident manner in which Will Hart, and many other smallholders, supplemented their supplies of hay:

"In the summer, he would go round with a scythe and cut all the grass verges beside the roads and farm lanes; then he made it into hay by turning it with a pitchfork and later he picked it up in a tumbrel. The farmer had the benefit of getting his banks mown, and the smallholder got free hay for his bullocks and cattle."

Today our Long Furrow still maintains a few bullocks, kept on the meadows of Smeetham and Nether Hall, but there are no more local milk rounds. The nearest commercial dairy herd is about three miles away and the milk that reaches our doorstep, like the bread that one buys in Sudbury, may have originated from a destination that is forty of fifty miles distant.

As a final comment on the transformations that have occurred to the self-sufficient mixed farming, that had been an indivisible element of our Furrow for over two thousand year, let us take a journey with Ruth Steed (née Miller), to the farmstead of her childhood at Goldingham Hall. She remarks nostalgically:

"I will never forget the atmosphere and the sounds of the farmyard at night, and watching Pod coming out of his hut and going about on his rounds, as he looked over the new born lambs and the waiting ewes. My father took a great interest in Suffolk horses as well. Alfred Pearson was head horseman, and with the house cow, the bullocks and the extensive poultry, the whole farmyard had an aura of life, vitality and vibrance that permeated through the darkness of the stable to the yellow light of the wind blown lantern . . ."

Half a century later, the stables, piggeries, cow byre and sheep fold are deserted, empty and quiet. The bales, hurdles, hurricane lamps and shepherd's hut that Charlie Martin used for lambing have disappeared into the ebbing tides of passing time. They have been replaced instead, by the air conditioned combine, the 200 horse power tractor and the cereal trials work that is of such fascination.

Now, a couple of purpose-built, lofty-roofed, asbestos buildings, suffice to store the grain that is grown on the fields where the sheep and horses once grazed. At night-time the atmosphere amongst the rusted half doors and unfilled hay racks, is one of a lifeless ghost world, whose tales of ingenuity and humour, and of hard work and endeavour, can only yield up their secrets in the fading twilight of an old countryman's cottage.

There is an urgency to do this, lest future generations do not understand, or will not believe the depth and inspirational strength of all that is past.

CHAPTER TWELVE

Horses, Horsemen, Stallion Leaders and the Village Blacksmith

Many books have already been written on the independence and resource-fulness of the horseman, of his hours of work; the local commands; and the secret concoctions for "calling", "jading" or curing illness. In this chapter we will include examples of individual "horse keeping" with the memories of the head horseman, under-horseman and day ploughman, who have been part of our Long Furrow.

Unlike sheep, whose populations we examined in the last chapter, agri-cultural horses were not particularly numerous until the fifteenth, sixteenth and seventeenth centuries. There is evidence of cavalry or riding horses at Roman Gestingthorpe, but at Doomsday (1086), the manors of Overhall and Goldingham only carry four "rouncies", or farm horses, between them. These were far smaller than the "heavy horse" of contemporary times, which itself was developed in the middle ages, to carry the armour-clad knights of battle.

Our enquiry begins at Gestingthorpe crossroads, where the nineteenth century iron foundry had once produced ploughs and pig troughs for the farmers of our village. It is a few yards from here that one sees a row of retirement bungalows; they overlook the swings of the playing field with its scampering children, cricket matches and pensioners who stroll beneath the chestnut trees, with the red brick church tower behind. This is where we meet Charlie Chatters, 82 years old, bright eyed and wide shouldered. He extends a broad forearm and shakes my hand with a powerful grip that was forged in seven decades of hard, manual work.

Over several Sunday afternoons he described the horseman's life and philosophy:

> "Horses," he says bluntly, "respond to kindness; the kinder you are to them, the kinder they are to you."

He continued by explaining the first phase in the working life of a horse, that of breaking it in:

"It took a couple of days; we had to put a collar on for a start and then we used to put a log of wood behind on a plough trace. Two men held the lines during this process and when the colt was ready it would be put alongside a steady old horse and for the first half day one man would lead it and another drive the team.

"What about ploughing with horses?"

"Well, once your horses were properly broken in, they were quite O.K. Plenty of good horsemen were able to plough all day without needing a line at all."

"You mean that they could control their horses with nothing more than verbal commands?"

"Yes, that's right. Of course, on jobs like marking out the 'stetches', it was different, because these tasks required the greatest skill and accuracy. It was terribly important to get everything dead straight, especially on 'running land'. If your furrows didn't meet up plumb, you'd soon be the laughing stock of the village. You see, in those days," he continues, "there wasn't any television or motor cars to take people away from their work. Farmworkers did a full six days then, and on Sundays you would see the older men go for a walk and pass judgement on the standards of other people's work. That time of day, a good horseman was a recognised and respected member of the community. It was the head horseman's job to mark out the stetches, draw the first furrow and do the drilling—in other words, all of the most important and skilful jobs. When I marked out, I put the sticks up and paced the 'stetches' out and then when I drew the first furrow, I would follow the sticks and between them, keep an eye on a piece of straw, a clod or a stone which was directly in line."

"So when you'd finished marking out, what sort of a depth and furrow width would you get with a horse drawn plough?"

"The ploughing that I did was with a 9 inch furrow about 3 or 4 inches deep on an 8 yard stetch, although, of course, some people used wider or narrower stetches."*

* In the Colnes on very wet land, stetches were reduced to 7 feet to assist drainage, and the horse would walk in the furrows when they pulled the drill; but this was exceptionally close.

137

What is of interest is that, with one single exception, all the older horsemen that I interviewed preferred to use wooden ploughs, "because they pulled easier" than iron ploughs which did not always need holding. But, irrespective of the type of plough he used, the horseman of Bulmer and Gestingthorpe would be expected to accomplish his "acre a day".* Agricultural custom and farmers' severity ensured that a man who could not achieve this work rate would soon be short of a job. As a point of interest, the horseman who ploughed his acre, would walk eleven miles along the furrow. Including the other journeys—to and from work, to the allotment or water pump at night, it is evident that several of our older contributors were often averaging 18-20 miles a day.

Although the head horseman may have perfromed the most skilful operations, he had other obligations as well. He was expected, for example, to feed the horses on Sundays and on weekday mornings, arriving at work at five o'clock. This was two hours earlier that the day ploughman and derived from the belief that the horse must have two hours for eating and digesting before commencing work. For this, the head horseman (normally one to each stable of six horses) was paid more and might enjoy the special privilege of "having the rabitting". Traditionally, head horsemen were also paid an extra ten shillings a year for lighting and whip money.

During the early twentieth century, when Charlie "Pod" Martin first worked at Goldingham Hall, his direct superior was head horseman, Alfred Pearson. Today, Alfred Pearson's daughter, Mabel is married to Charlie Chatters at Gestingthorpe, and she recalls:

> "When we lived at Belchamp Walter, my father had to get up every morning at four o'clock, and then he walked the couple of miles to work. Later, when he became foreman, we moved to the farm, and on one occasion when my father was ill, his horses would not feed until his employer, Mr. Miller, requested that he went to them."

Years later one can imagine these men, professional, dedicated and competent, striding through the darkness of night, past the tower of Belchamp Church, across the misty meadows of damp grass, over the gurgling Belchamp Brook and up through Long Smallbridge Field to Goldingham Hall, carrying, as they walked their dinner bags of bread and cheese.

When Alfred Pearson at Goldingham and Horace Elsie and his brother, (the latter was head horseman at Jenkins Farm), had finished feeding their

---

* On the heaviest land in Suffolk, the expectation was reduced to three quarters of an acre a day. The limiting factor was, of course, the horses, who would rapidly tire on the stickier clay soils.

horses at six o'clock, they would then have their own breakfast until the other "day ploughman" arrived at seven.*

Traditionally, on a large farm employing several horsemen, there would be a strict order in the departure of the horses from the stables. I have been unable to find any memories of this system in our Long Furrow of Bulmer and Gestingthorpe. Doubtless such an order of precedence had at one time been enforced, but there was a general feeling that such direct manifestations of the horseman's hierarchy had begun to break down after the First World War. But Frank Billimore, who was working at Hengrave, near Bury St. Edmunds, describes the system of stables, horsemen and precedence from as late as the early thirties:

"I was on a farm with eighteen horses. They were divided into three stables of six horses. Each stable had a head horseman. I was under-horseman in the stable of the senior head horseman. Being only an under-horseman, I didn't have to arrive at work until seven o'clock, but I always had to be fourth in the procession as we left the stables. Later on in the morning, the head horseman would tell one of us under-horsemen to light a fire where we could have our breakfast. Of course, I was only young then, and the senior horsemen often said that it wasn't built right, but because of the order of things, they would never build one themselves."

Another difference that Frank Billimore describes between the practice at Bulmer and that at Bury St. Edmunds was in the arrangement of the day. With certain variations, the horsemen of our Long Furrow in Bulmer left the stables at seven and returned at some point during the day for dinner and to feed the horses. This was normally at eleven or twelve o'clock and lasted for an hour. They would then return to their ploughing, until three thirty or four o'clock, before bringing the horses back to he stables to brush them down, rack up for the evening and help the head horseman prepare the bait. By comparison at Bury St. Edmunds, Frank Billimore's day was regulated by the countywide "Suffolk system" of "working right through".

"We left the stables at seven, had a bit of breakfast about nine (nineses) and then carried straight on until about half past two. We got back to the stables at three o'clock and then had our dinner until four o'clock. When we came back, we strawed up, brushed them down and got the food ready for the morning. Of course, ploughing was the main job for the under horseman and in the autumn, you stuck at it for days on end."

But not all the ploughs were traditional single furrow models. There were

* Longer hours before World War I.

139

also two furrow ploughs suitable for lighter, "kinder" soils. Goldingham Hall, Bulmer, had two double furrow ploughs in addition to the single furrow versions.*

"Pod" Martin describes his first day's work on the farm where he was to remain for another forty-seven years.

"All the horses there were Suffolks at that time of day," he relates, "and I had to take a two furrow plough out onto Church Field with three horses. There was a 'bowl' wheel on the side which the plough rode round the headland on. One of the mares was in foal and I was told to let it have 'a good blow', at the end of each bout. Later on, I did the whole range of jobs–rolling, harrowing, ducksfooting, made potato ridges, used the slicer†, did the drilling, inter-row hoeing and drove the binder."

Whilst "Pod" Martin was walking behind his Suffolks at Goldingham, Horace Elsie (born 1908) was at work at Jenkins Farm, Bulmer. Today he lives near the old blacksmith's shop and in a quiet, humorous manner, we spent seven and a half hours discussing the horse era and the coming of mechanisation. Taking notes as fast as I could write, I quickly came to appreciate the remark that one of his old friends had used to describe him.

"Hory Elsie? The most capable person I know–that man could do anything."

Here he reminisces about ploughing and horse behaviour:

"I used to love ploughing. When you go from field to field, the plough was put on a little sledge to cart it around. Ploughshares normally lasted about two days and a well set wooden plough should not need holding. There are three mechanisms to alter a plough to set it up right, and only if it was very hard should you need to raise the handles to get it in. Of course, we all had our tricks. When I was ploughing mustard in, I would hang an old share on the back to help bend the stalks under."

"Would the horses speed up on the last bout of a "stetch", or just before dinner?"

"No, but they'd go like the clappers around the outside furrow of the headland, when the field was being finished."

---

* Beside requiring three horses for two furrow ploughs, there were also occasions, when three horses might be used on a single furrow plough in wet conditions on heavy land.

† Used to kill weeds in potato and root crops. The slicer passed beneath the potatoes set up in baulks and cut the roots of weeds, especially thistles. Arthur Young describes one such slicer and ridge skim on his visit to Bulmer around 1800, where he saw it at work on the farm of Mr. Hale of Goldingham Hall.

"Did you always come back for dinner, or did you sometimes go "Suffolk" system on the further fields?"

"No, we always stopped for dinner. But if we were a long way from the farm, for example, up near the Deal nursery, we might take a truss of hay with us for the horses and make a fire for ourselves from a few sticks. We'd have a warm up around it and have our own dinner at the same time. Then we'd go and finish our acre. Of course, when we finished in the afternoon, we didn't just switch off the tractor and rush off home like you young 'uns do. We had to brush the horses down, feed them and generally look after them. At Jenkins Farm, it was my job to pump up the water for the livestock–I had to turn the handle on the pump three hundred times every evening. When we'd finished the horses would be let out into the yard if it was wintertime, or put onto the meadow during the summer."

"I've heard that these horses got very agitated when the hunt went by–is that right?"

"I should think it is. They could hear the hounds miles away. We had one horse at Jenkins which smashed a fencing rail and jumped clean out of the yard to join the hunt. And another time, on Stoonhams field, a horse completely took off with a cottis hoe, when the hunt was nearby. George Turps, the horseman, simply couldn't hold it."

"What other things would irritate horses?"

"Oh, lots of things. You'd get certain colts or horses that couldn't abide the touch of a chain on their legs. We had this one horse, Smarter, her name was, and before we found this out and covered the chains with bags, she'd jumped right over a ditch and low hedge with a manure drill behind her! I was in the other field and I thought, 'that's a rum 'un, that manure spreader going out of this gateway!' But after that, we tied some old sacks round the chains and it never got wild again."

It was the horseman's responsibility to look after his animals if they suffered from illness or infection. Shire breeds and Clydesdales, which had "feather" on the fetlock were susceptible to "grease" which was a swelling up around the "feather". It was sometimes cured by disinfectant although Horace Elsie observes:

"They seemed to have more 'go' about them when they had the 'grease', and I believe that for a short while they even pulled better. But it wasn't unusual to see a farmer with a 'greasy' horse, pretty soon put it into a local market."

A remarkable fatality is reported by Hilda and Cecil Smith:

"Years ago a horse was killed by an adder in the marshes at Henny. The snake bit the horses tongue and the subsequent swelling choked it before anyone could get there and save it."

But the concern for an animal's health, was not limited to horses alone. As a lad, Frank Billimore, had watched over a donkey for two weeks, after the vet had instructed that if it lay down with double pneumonia, it would never again get up.*

Remedies which were common in the stables and farmyards of the Long Furrow, include the following:

"If a cut is going septic, put a poultice on, made from the leaves of comfrey and mixed with bread.

For a horse with pneumonia, apply a hot mustard paste between two sheets of brown paper over the horses lungs and wrip it up in a horse bag.

For 'strangles', put hot bran mash in the bait bag and let the horse breath the steam."

Controlling inherently difficult horses also required craft and expertise. Paul Mann, grandson of a long line of local horsemen, tells of a horse

"which reared every time it was put in the shafts of a tumbrel, so they pushed the tumbrel into the barn and positioned the shafts beneath a low beam. Then they put the horse in the shafts and it reared up . . . but it learnt never to rear up again."

Tom Edgeley commented:

"Sometimes a horse would get 'hard pad' in the mouth, making it difficult to control. But, if you rub an elder twig through the roof of the mouth, it would soon soften it up. Some people would also put a twig of elder in the horse's bridle to keep the flies from its eyes."

Yet if these are the everyday expedients of the day ploughman, what of the head horseman's tricks? And what of the agents and properties with

---

* Donkeys at the time were quite widely used by carriers, carters and independent contractors. Philip Rowe senior had gone from Bulmer to Alpheton, mid way on the road to Bury St. Edmunds, by donkey cart to fulfil a thatching commission. Son Tom, who accompanied him, recalls: "A donkey walks terribly slowly, but if you can get it into a run or gallop, or it follows a mule, then they're not too bad.

which these older horsemen were reputed to have exercised their mystical powers of control?

Many, of course, have died with the older generations. Others have been retained and discreetly preserved by historians. Doubtless, where horses are in wide use today, the same understanding of scents, smells and the concoctions which provide them are still remembered and utilised where necessary.

Let us, however, quote a few remarks and personal memories to illustrate how the experience and secrecy of the dedicated senior horseman, who had spent a lifetime studying his animals, was to manifest itself in the stables, the meadows and fields of our Long Furrow.

"Calling" agents for horses were quite common. Horace Elsie described one horseman who . . .

"could call horses from 200 yards and then they would follow him down the road like a flock of sheep . . . but he was a master horseman."

Another source, "Pod" Martin, tells of an incident in his youth on a farm near Borley:

"The farmer told the head horseman to get a pony back from the meadow. No-one else could get near it, and we couldn't do anything with it at all, but the old horseman walked down the lane to the meadow and got out a little bottle, no bigger than a matchbox, and put some of this scent on his handkerchief, and that pony came up to him as docile as a kitten. Of course, being nosey, I wanted to know what he had used. He let me look at the bottle but he wouldn't tell me what it was."

"Another time," he continues, "we had an old horse that we had to put a waggon on. You'd think the old thing hadn't got any strength at all, it was so old and knocked up, but this head horseman would 'chemicalise' it up somehow, and for a few hours it would be just like a colt again."

Far less common than calling agents, but much more effective in establishing a head horseman's inviolate position amongst the farm labour force were the "jading" or "stopping" agents. These "jading" agents again depended on a horse's highly attuned sense of smell. Although they could be used for harmless reasons (e.g. to make an unruly horse stand still), they were also utilized in farming disputes. As yet we have no memories of jading agents in our Long Furrow. Frank Billimore, however, is able to provide an example from Hengrave, near Bury St. Edmunds. He remembers:

"The old men said that years before, when the neighbouring farmer and the head horseman had had a row, the head horseman was made to leave, but the next day, when the other men came to work, they couldn't get his horses out of the stable, even though there was nothing physically wrong with them."

An alternative method of rural revenge on a harsh employer was to induce abortion in livestock. This could be contrived by mixing special preparations, such as the root of hemlock or urine into the ration. In Gestingthorpe, lifelong farmworker and one time horseman, Bert Surridge, repeats a story from the turn of the century:

"Years ago, they had a lovely mare on a farm in this parish, but she wouldn't come into foal. After they had tried her twice, the farmer went up to this old head horseman and said: 'If you can get her into foal, I'll give you two weeks' wages.' Well, next time she had the stallion, it got her into foal. Later on that year, the Master came round and said: 'I've got two weeks' wages for you here, but tomorrow you can pack your things up and leave this farm and don't you come back here no more!' 'Why?' asked the horseman, 'the mares come into foal.'

'Yes,' replied the farmer, 'and you were the rotten bugger that stopped her before.'"

But after the First World War, these altercations between farmer and horseman, and more frequently between horseman and day ploughman, considerably declined, and most horsemen concentrated on the turnout and appearance of their horses.

"Linseed improves the coat," remarked one, "whilst the root of bryony will fatten a horse up and improve its looks . . . but bryony is funny stuff and I should think it's illegal. If you do too much to it, you could kill an animal; we only spread as much on the bait as we could get on a three-penny bit. Of course," continued my source, with the knowing and comprehending discretion which he preferred to maintain, "these old horsemen, they knew what they were doing; they had their ways and they had their habits—it didn't pay to upset them, but if they wanted to they could do almost anything with a horse."

The horsemen vied with each other in perfecting their horses turn-out and performance. "Jute" Chatters reminisced:

"Now if you had two head horsemen on one farm, they would each have their own locker of grub for the horses, and they were so suspicious of each other that they jolly well kept it locked up, too. You know, Ashley," he continued, "These head horsemen simply lived for their horses and if one was ill, they'd think nothing of staying up with it all night, and if the farmer asked them to do so, they would feel that he had insulted them for ever questioning their dedication."

It was at this point in our search, as we discussed medication and illness, that a fascinating booklet from about 1890-1900 was brought to light. It was produced from a deep recess in a farmhouse bureau, and lent to me by retired farmer, Philip Lawson (born 1901), of Ixworth. It is a lined notebook in which a one time farm manager and veterinary assistant, Michael Holden of Bradfield St. George, has written, with the neat handwriting of Victorian England, the cures and preparations which he advised and administered to sick horses and cattle. The index runs to fifty items and includes:

No. 4   Jaundice.
No. 5   Thick winded horses.
No. 7   For stangles in horses.
No. 11   To make a horse follow (a man).
No. 16   To cause a stallion to cover.
No. 17   To cause a horse to submit to be shod.
No. 27   Worms in a horse.

Amongst the fading pages, one reads of treatments that can only have been discovered as a result of a lifetime's observation, and at least one generation's worth of trial and error. Moreover, for the farm foreman or head horseman, information such as this, would have been essential to him in winning and keeping his job. Upon one's skill in the furrow and ability in the stable, by whatever means, depended one's livelihood and prestige.

Across the now browning pages, one reads of the diverse constituents which would have been surreptitiously obtained from the chemist, the grocer, the confectioner, the garden and the hedgerow. It is from these pages that some of the mysterious remedies which sustained the horses of our Long Furrow are explained. Our search and enquiry was suddenly illuminated with a dazzling array of information.

Precise details are given in the preparation of each mixture and include:

No. 8 Cough and Cordial Balls for a horse

Opium 1¼ drams   Aniseed Powder 4 ozs   Liquorice 3 ozs
Carraway 4 ozs   Squills 4 ozs   Tincture of Tolv. ½ oz
Mix up in honey into 30 balls.

No. 13 for a horse that is poor and has a loss of appetite.

Angelico 2 ozs   Liver (sic) of Antimony 3 ozs   Lesser Cardanum 2 ozs
Fennugreek 2 ozs   Ellecampane 2 ozs
All in a powder . . . one tablespoonful in the corn, morning and night.

No. 23 After the Strangles.

Give the horse:
Genton 2 drams   Cammomile 2 drams   Ginger 1 dram
Given in a ball.

Other treatments include the use of:

"1 dram of camphor, 1 pint of mint water, tincture of opium, 1 dram of catmint, ½ ounce of ammonia, 3 drams of powdered aniseed, 2 drops oil of asher, 5 drops oil of sadium, 15 drops of oil of penny royal."

But the mixtures and treatments go on. Later we read of:

"the oil of chodium, oil of cummin, white wine vinegar, turpentine, tincture of myrrh, oil of vitriol, aquafortes, sugar of lead, castor oil, oil of thyme, olive oil, origanum, bay berries, grain of paradise, long pepper, oil of carraway, flour of brimstone, and the oils of amber, cloves, sodium of fenugreek, antimony, mercury sublimate, nitre, spanish fly, liquorice powder, hard soap, powdered raisin, oil of juniper, linseed oil, flour of sulphur, sulphate of copper."

Other preparations included:

No. 29 For the grease or any other wound.

Take ½ lb of Hogs lard   ½ lb of Honey   ½ lb of Alum Powdered
The white of 2 eggs
Heat the first three ingredients together, when nearly cold add (sic) the white of egg. Keep stirring until they are cold.

No. 36 Restive Horses

20 drops oil of Rhodium   10 drops oil of Origanum 15 drops of Aniseed
The above oil and ¼ ounce Sunds or Orris (sic) powder and apply it to the nostrils or tongue.

No. 37 Condition Powders.

4 oz Liver of Antimony   4 oz Powdered Nitre   4 oz Sulphur   4 oz Resin
Mix and divide it into 16 powders. Give the powders every other night.

No. 48 Fever Balls for a horse.

1½ to 2 drams of Emetic Tartar   1 ounce of Liquorice Powder
3 drams of Treacle enough to form a ball.

Finally, amongst the notes are detailed instructions on how to "stop blood", "rub the tail" for pin worms, "stings and mosquito bites" and how to "throw a horse" (i.e. to lay it down).

But if these were the preparations for the "calling" agents and curative medicines of the quasi-vet, head horseman and farm foreman, what do we know of the more aggressive potions of animal subterfuge, whose powers we have illustrated within the farm altercations of Victorian England?

On a May evening in 1982, I finally discovered the last piece of the jig-saw of horse mastery that for twelve months I had been searching to locate in the Long Furrow of Bulmer and Gestingthorpe. I was sitting in a farm-worker's cottage in one of the four parishes of which we have written. I was conducting the last but one interview before commencing the final "tidying up" draft of the whole publication. My septuagenarian companion was an erstwhile horseman and lifelong farmworker. He will be known to many of our readers. We were vaguely discussing the authority of the head horse-man, and the furtive concoctions that he manufactured.

Possibly my mind had begun to wander from the conversation. I had reached this point in the enquiry so many times before, only to have my questions deflected by vague generalisations that failed to penetrate to the rock core of fact that I sought. Besides, I had almost finished the book; summer was coming; I wanted to get the project finished and done with. Possibly a note of boredom and disbelief may have entered my voice.

"Well, I'll tell you something else about these old horsemen," my companion asserted forcibly, possibly sensing my indifference.

"Years ago, I should think at about the turn of the century, there was a stallion leader in these parts—he was a man that could do anything with horses—he was one of these that would be seen creeping about long before anyone else was up in the morning, and he had this knowledge, this special knowledge passed down to the eldest son and accumulated over hundreds of years."

I began to listen intently. The tension in the twilight of the beamed cottage became tangible. The farmworker continued:

"But one night this stallion leader, we won't worry about what his name was, one night he got drunk." He paused momentarily, cleared his throat and then revealed:

"and as he lay in the road outside the pub (which still stands) . . . a little wodge of handwritten paper fell out of his pocket. Now these notes were picked up by a passer-by and later they were returned to this stallion leader." He stopped and then, speaking very slowly, continued: "But before they were given back to him, somebody—my mother in fact — made a copy."

Now, stallion leaders were the wiliest, craftiest and most expert of all horsemen. They were the "old darvils" of the whole system. I had spent almost a year looking for such direct evidence of the "inner horse cult" in our Long Furrow. It must be a bit like catching your first fish. One wrong expression or a faulty nuance of voice could have broken the aura of quiet trust and mutual respect.

"Yes," I muttered, half choking in confusion. There was another pause, and then he continued:

"Now, my mother gave that copy to me."

He paused again; for a long moment, and then with great caution, declared:

"But I'm going to let you look at it."

The notes—for they were little more, of this long dead stallion leader, who would have walked down every lane and visited many of the farms within our Long Furrow, amount to just fifteen items. But as such they would be sufficient to set him apart as a man with knowledge separate to all others. Even the old, secretive "head horseman" would have recognised him as a horsekeeper who was further into the esoteric cult of horse mastery, possessing knowledge superior to his own. The notes provide brief descriptions in three or four lines only of the following techniques. Possibly, from the manner in which they are written, they had been dictated down to the stallion leader on a candle-lit table in a cottage corner as they had been similarly entrusted by word of mouth for generations before. The instructions include:

How to manage restive horses.
If you wish to make him look well (to sell at a fair).
If he is a savage entire horse (to quieten him).
If you want to make him savage (to others but not yourself).
If you wish to make him awkward (to others but not yourself).
If your master turns you away (how to "stop" a horse eating).
To stop an entire horse from biting.

Within the highly confidential and discretionary ethos that the older horsemen have impressed on me, I have listed none of the "entire" leader's ingredients. It is out of respect for that lore and that mystique that the individual recipes and mixtures for specific objectives have been withheld. Yet even in reading this list, we can tell something of the stallion leader himself. We know that he could control savage stallions and make amenable horses savage to all others but himself. He could both "call" and "jade" his horses. He could earn guineas for himself or his master by temporarily making an enfeebled horse appear "in prime condition". He would have been feared and respected by under-horseman and farmer alike.

The farmworker who has quietly kept this information has done great service to our understanding of rural life and I am grateful to him, for placing his trust in me.

Yet, it is in thinking of this catalogue of ingedients, of the carefully defined concoctions and the wily, secretive manner in which they were guarded, that the ultimate value of this rural history becomes evident. The stable may be deserted, the meadows replanted with wheat and the old wooden cart lodge with its sagging thatched roof is long forgotten and dismantled. The horseman's cottage may have been condemned and rebuilt, his public house revamped and renamed, his horse brasses abandoned and lost and his gravestone neglected and over grown. But through the stories that are passed down, the ultimate element of his life will live on. Finally, in the gloaming of the dusk and the thickening of night-time we will have enough information to visualise again the going out of the horses, the steady instruction, the furtive shake of the pocket and the lining up by the headland and furrow.

But what of those in our survey who do remember? What are the lasting and indelible memories of the horseman and day ploughman who have been so helpful in recreating this image of the furrow and stable?

For Harry Winch, it was the horse commands of:

Wurdy	right
Cub-i-wuh	left*
Wuh, back	back

and the ability of horsemen George Bunn and Charlie Rowe to control their horses for hours on end with never a need for line or rein. "If George Bunn kept on calling 'wurdy, wurdy'," recalls Harry, "a horse would turn right round". And he tells of "Farmer", a horse of colossal strength that was headstrong and capable of tremendous feats of exertion. For Charlie "Pod" Martin, the foremost recollection was of "Gilbert", a lovely, quiet, gentle old horse that, "could do more to break in a colt than a man ever could" when put together during the colt's first day of ploughing. For Horace Elsie it was "Sharper and Depper", two horses controlled with effortless mastery by horseman Bill Toatley, and of "drilling the first bout with the seed barrel empty to make certain that the mark was dead straight". For Ken Day, then a schoolboy, it was the memory of dogs, crazy for the parrings from the horses' hooves in his grandfather's Waldingfield smithy, whilst when first at work, his lingering memory was the sight of horseman and tractor driver, Jack Mann, "possessing almost supernatural powers of concentration as he ploughed and drilled as straight as a gun barrel across hilly and sideways land."

* Another interesting example of village colloquialisms. In the Belchamps the abbreviated "wuh" was used for left. Similarly, whilst "Pod" Martin was "clagging" his sheep prior to shearing them in Bulmer, in Belchamp St. Pauls, George Chatters was "tagging" them.

149

For some the memories were of ploughing matches. Of Sunday afternoon walks with other horsemen, inspecting the week's work, and of the neat, perfectly matched bouts of the drill. It was an age when the whole farm was a manifestation of an intense and competitive expression of art and perfection.

For other contributors, there were the recollections of the "master horsemen", the "stallion leaders", the "Entires" (stallions) and the knowledgeable itinerant horse dealers like Harry Slender who brought horses to Sudbury from Ireland and Wales. Special moments have lived on; of "breaking in"; of the visits to the blacksmiths, and the journeying to mill or station with brasses shining. It was an age when the horse population between Halstead and Sudbury could be counted in hundreds.

"There were," explains farmer Lawrence Hyde Parker, "between three to four horses per 100 acres. A village like Bulmer or Gestingthorpe would easily have a hundred heavy horses."*

But the horses who performed such a role for three hundred years have departed and gone. The ploughs that they pulled are sold as antiques. Their stables have been converted to other purposes. But beneath the greying cobwebs of dust and crumbling mortar, the red brick walls still bear the scratched initials of the old horsemen. Beside the door and into the woodwork of the jambs, they read like a lingering roll call of a bygone wisdom. Occasionally, when inspecting crops, one picks up a long cast shoe, rusting like the broken crucifix of a lost religion, whilst in the homes of some respondents, their old brasses still hang, polished and bright, that have not been used this last half century. In later chapters we will review the coming of mechanisation and the introduction of tractors. For a few it was a sad departure, yet for most, the young and enthusiastic, it was an exciting, dynamic and interesting innovation.

But as we leave the horse era, let us, in passing, pay a visit to the Smithy, where the horses were shod, the hooves were pared and the banter of village and furrow exchanged.

*   *   *

If the horse cult contains all the mystery of an orthodox religion, based on esoteric doctines and sustained by a gospel of "straightness", then the blacksmith could well be seen as the archdeacon of that creed.

Horace Elsie, who today lives beside the old Smithy in Bulmer Tye, reminisces:

"It takes about an hour to shoe a horse all round, although some people never ever shod their land horses at all. At Jenkins, we would bring them to the smithy after we had finished our acre of ploughing,

* In 1910, at the peak of their population, there were 1,137,000 working horses on British farms.

although it wouldn't matter if you waited a day or two. A blacksmith can weld two old shoes together. Where colts were being shod, a 'twitch' was put on the nose which took 'all the go out of them'. Of course, after the colt was shod for the first time, the horse keeper and the blacksmith would have celebrated with a bit of a drink."

Two and a half miles from Horace Elsie's home on Bulmer Tye, is the village of Gestingthorpe, where we first met Charlie Chatters. Passing the church with its memorial to Scott's Antarctic hero, Captain Oates, one arrives at the forge and smithy of Frank Nice. Here again is a great sense of tradition. His grandfather and father both shod horses in the "travers" and the bricks are crumbled away in the floor where the horses stood. The iron bracket that the legs of an unsettled horse were roped through still hangs on the door beam.

In the smithy itself are the two forges, and the red brick wall is worn away where the hand bellows were once pumped. Besides the anvil, which has remained in the same position for the last hundred years, are the "sparkles" three inches thick on the wall, that accumulate with every ring of the hammer on the hot forge welded metal. The tools of the old profession are still in profusion, many of them made and designed by his grandfather in the long years of the nineteenth century. They include the special beam drill—one of the few remaining in East Anglia and of which we have a diagram, the "hardy", the "swage tools", the tyrebender, the tongs, the mandrel for shaping the big iron rings and the anvil. Beside the forge is a brick cavity where the silver sand (a flux) was once kept and the "slice", (used for raising the coals when the silver sand was sprinkled on) hangs closely beside it. Throughout a morning of thoughtful explanation, a picture evolved of the "shoe-ing", "tyre making", "tyre shrinking", and the laying on and resurfacing of "ducksfoot" cultivator points, the manufacture of "docking spuds" and the skilled craft of forge welding, with its "upsetting", "scarfing the end" and vital hammer hit at the culmination of the process. It was a technique of considerable expertise, for amongst the welds made at Gestingthorpe Smithy, were those of binder knives and these would need to be accurate to the finest of measurements.

The accounts book of Dick Nice (1892-1968) is of great interest and illustrates the variety of work that he undertook.

The charges to bicycle repairer, Percy Downs, for 1926 were: £ s. d.

		£	s.	d.
March 27th	Soldering pail			3.
July 1st	Sharpening punches			6.
August 16th	Soldering and repairing gear case			9.
August 16th	Sharpening shears		1.	0.
November 27th	Soldering oil tin			4.

From 1927 we read the account to haulier and bus proprietor, Harry Rippingale:

March 7th	4 new window clips	2. 0.
March 24th	Making set of irons for steps to lorry	14. 0.
June 7th	New iron frame for spare wheel and bolts	10. 0.
November 27th	Lengthening axle	5. 0.

Similarly, in 1931, he was commissioned by the village cricket club to repair and paint the club' roller, mower and scorboard for which he charged fifteen shillings. For Gestingthorpe Hall, in the same year, he provided a new pipe and cap for the greenhouse stove, soldered kettles and saucepans and sharpened bill hooks and scythes. At the end of the year, the account to Mrs. Oates who scrutinized each item of expenditure in the smithy's special "Gestingthorpe Hall" work book, amounted to £4. 6. 2. (or £4.31)

But in a farming history it is the agricultural work that is of most interest. The bill to smallholder, A. B. (Razor) Finch, indicates the costs of both shoeing and "moving" shoes.

		£ s. d.
April 26th 1926	2 shoes moved	1. 3.
May 6th	1 shoe (new) and 1 moved	1. 10.
June 19th	1 shoe	1. 3.
July 8th	1 shoe moved	8.

The total half yearly charges eventually amounted to £1. 15. 4.

But there was more involved in the blacksmiths life than the shoeing of horses. On June 13th, 1931, he trimmed the feet of Mr. Hart's donkey. For this he charged one shilling. Later in the year for "altering tyre and shoeing wheels" he charged twelve shillings. For a similar amount, he "mended and repaired" three iron hurdles.

A final insight into the diverse skills of the village blacksmith is provided with a synopsis of the 1939 account to Mr. Branwhite:

		£ s. d.
January 3rd	4 shoes turned up	3. 0.
	Frost nails	1. 6.
March 23	Altering tyre and shoeing tumbrel wheel	6. 0.
April 8th	Time; and repairing and mending spokes to tractor wheel, bolts and rivets	10. 6.
May 4th	4 shoes	8. 0.
February 10th	"Laying" 89 Harrow teeth	1. 11. 6.
May 17th	Repairing horse hoe stalk	6.
June 2nd	Mending and repairing mower knife	2. 6.

Certainly the blacksmith's shop of the horse era was a place of warm parochial gregarity, and many older contributors recall the cheery conversations beside the glowing forge as the news of the rain lashed harvest, crooked ploughing or village cricket was passed along.

Douglas Hasler conjures up the atmosphere in the following typewritten note:

"When Dick Nice was blacksmith and farrier, his 'shop' was the focal point of the village. Every Tuesday afternoon, Stanley Randall, the Halstead Gazette reporter, came to see him.
'Anything happened, Dick?' he'd ask.
'So and so died, Randall,' he'd reply.
The blacksmith knew most things that happened in the village."

He continues with an anecdote that is typical of the competitive approach to individual prowess, that was so dominant a chord of village life at the time.

"In those days in the blacksmith's shop, there was a cast iron cone about 30 inches high and weighing approximately 1 cwt (used for making hurdle wheels). Now, Dick Nice could lift it by gripping it at the top, but I never saw any one else who could, until Scantlebury (Cyril's brother), who had taken Rectory Farm, came in the shop one day, and Charlie Downs, who'd bet on anything, said 'Bet you half a crown you can't lift that with one hand, Mr. Philp'. But Scantle just laughed, and picked it up, saying 'Where do you want it?' and took it across to where Charlie sat. By and large, Dick Nice enjoyed company in the smithy but if there was too much horsplay, he'd turn us all out."

But ultimately it was the coming of tractors that spelt the death knell of the village smithy. By the mid nineteen fifties, when Dick Nice retired, work had considerably declined and except as a personal hobby, the doors of the business were closed.

For nearly two decades, Gestingthorpe Blacksmiths shop became a place of bygone memories, half shadows and dusky recollections. Driving past, Dennis Rippingale would comment:

"When I was a lad, I used to bring four horses down here on a wet morning, and Dick Nice would say: 'You people all want to come here at the same time'."

Today Frank Nice has re-opened the smithy of his father and grandfather. He works principally with iron, manufacturing the hearth side fire box and ornate gate-work that is now so much in demand. Whether or not he represents the beginning of a reversal in the trend which has taken so much work and industry away from the villages to the towns is something we shall discuss in our final Chapter.

But with "Harvest", "The Horse Year", "Shepherds" and "Horsemen", we are almost at the end of our investigation into the farming years of the horse era. But not quite. We have ploughed, drilled, milked, shepherded, thistled, rogued, reaped and shocked. We have brought the sheaves back to the farmyard, the stack has been built and thatched. There is only one activity left and that is to stoke up the traction engine, line it up with the drum and call out to the "feeders" and "pitchers".

It is of this; threshing and threshing machines, with their gregarious atmosphere, legends and warm recollections of which we shall write in the following chapter.

TRADITIONAL BEAM DRILL AT GESTINGTHORPE FORGE

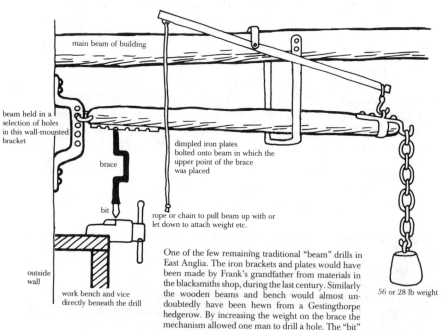

main beam of building

beam held in a selection of holes in this wall-mounted bracket

dimpled iron plates bolted onto beam in which the upper point of the brace was placed

brace

bit

rope or chain to pull beam up with or let down to attach weight etc.

outside wall

work bench and vice directly beneath the drill

One of the few remaining traditional "beam" drills in East Anglia. The iron brackets and plates would have been made by Frank's grandfather from materials in the blacksmiths shop, during the last century. Similarly the wooden beams and bench would almost undoubtedly have been hewn from a Gestingthorpe hedgerow. By increasing the weight on the brace the mechanism allowed one man to drill a hole. The "bit" was often made from an old file or similar hardened material.

56 or 28 lb weight

CHAPTER THIRTEEN

Threshing Contractors and Threshing Machines– A Bulmer Industry

For Bulmer, the central village in our survey, the threshing industry of the early twentieth century has a special significance, with "The Street", possessing three threshing families–the Rowes, Coes and Cornells. Almost all were related and they sustained a friendly rivalry in the dominion of Bulmer threshing.

The geography of this threshing empire extended over a radius of about six miles and included farms in Borley, the Belchamps, Gestingthorpe, Wickham, Henny, Maplestead, Foxearth, Twinstead and Lamarsh. As such, it represented a major village industry. We believe that at its peak there were five machines operating from the village. Several Bulmer men spent the first year or two after leaving school with a threshing tackle; others during the great depression walked behind one, "whenever it moved, for days on end, in the hope that the farmer might take some of us on for a couple of days 'sheening'."

Fortunately, the man who is to guide us through this episode of our Long Furrow had a longer involvement with the threshing business, spending his youth and early manhood as the engine driver of a Bulmer threshing machine. Silver-haired, robust and enthusiastic, Jack Cornell has been particularly helpful in the research of both this chapter and the publication in general. He has threshing and grinding in his blood. Our first reference to a Cornell is in 1520. Jack's more recent ancestors operated the nineteenth century windmill at Belchamp Otten. His father was in threshing partnership with George Rowe, and Jack continued the business after his death in 1936. Today he lives close to the Maplestead "Cock" and we spent several humorous and informative evenings poring over old accounts, diaries and photographs, with the anecdotes that they brought back to mind and which helped to recreate the atmosphere and mechanical background of the threshing machine era.

"Jack. I'm too young to have ever seen a threshing machine working on a local farm. Could you explain what the various pieces of machinery actually did?"

"Well, there was the traction engine, which pulled the equipment from farm to farm and provided the power to run it when it got there; then there was the 'drum' or the actual 'threshing' machine, and according to what you wanted to do with the straw once it was threshed there would be either a baler or an elevator to put it into a stack."

"And that would all be running at the same time?"

"That's right."

"But it must have required a fair number of men to keep the job going: I mean how many people did you need to work a threshing machine?"

"I used to reckon on about ten to keep the 'drum' going and then you'd need a 'couple or three' more to load and convey the sacks to the barn. You see, it was like this, two men (the 'driver' and the 'feeder'), came with the machine. In addition, you'd have one man to take off the threshed corn from the drum; one man would be bagging off the chaff and another would take the chaff to the barn and collect the water for the engine. Then there would be two to three men pitching from the stack onto the threshing machine where the 'feeder' received their sheaves. Finally you'd need another couple of men to build a stack of the loose straw that came off the elevator. On early machines, though, one extra man was also allocated to assist the 'feeder' by cutting the strings or straw binders. After the First World War, 'self feeders' became available eliminating the need for one of those men."

"And could you always get enough men to keep the system running?"

"Oh yes! Of course a lot of smaller farmers wouldn't have had a large enough staff to operate a threshing machine on their own, but the team would soon be made up with independent 'odd-jobbers', thatchers, school-leavers and smallholders."*

Of this enlarged team, it was the engine driver and the feeder (the driver's mate) who were the most skilful. The feeder's job involved standing in a lowered box on top of the drum (or the threshing machine) and

---

* At Gestingthorpe, the Delvyns Farm year book for 1929 details that contractor Frank Marsh was threshing at the farm for four days in the third week of December. In addition to the permanent staff of G. Rippingale, A. Surridge, Stanley Surridge, C. Felton and E. Smith, all of whom are described as being engaged in the operation, we also read that B. Rayner, W. Surridge, H. Gooderham, W. Brown and C. Tomkins were employed for four days whilst Bertie Hasler and A. Finch worked for two days each. Farmworkers' wages were approximately thirty shillings (£1.50) a week. and the "beer for machine men" is itemised as costing eight shillings (40p).

literally feeding in the sheaves. There was a good deal of skill involved in maintaining a regular input, which improved threshing performance, whilst an uneven or lumpy feed might cause the drive belt from the traction engine to fly off. A poor feeder would quickly become unpopular with the driver for creating frustrating and time wasting delays. Worse, when the drum was overloaded, the governors and the engine had to open up to maintain an even drum speed, and despite having a spark arrester, the resultant smoke often contained burning smuts and sparks. As there were usually unthreshed stacks in the vicinity, a bystanding farmer would soon begin to curse that _____ man on the feeder.*

But the feeder had other duties as well. Depending on the direction that the straw was laid as it entered the drum, it would either produce livestock (well-threshed) or thatching (largely undamaged) straw. After the introduction of the binder, the feeder was expected to cut the twine near the knot and hold it in a bundle in one hand, to save the strings, and stop the livestock from eating them.

The driver was the senior man of the operation. He had responsibility for the engine, and for the more complex tasks of manoeuvering the traction engine, drum, elevator, baler or chaff cutter through narrow gateways, up steep hills and around twisting lanes. On some occasions he would have to reverse into a narrow gateway and "put a rope out and winch the drum through". When using the winch, the rear wheels had to be locked up and effectively disengaged from the main drive.

Jack Cornell explains:

"What actually happened is this. When you're driving forward as normal, the hind wheels are locked onto the axle by a big pin with a feather on it, that went through a big old block keyed onto the axle. But to use the winch you had to take that pin out, so your back wheels were free from the drive shaft. Of course, you put a good wooden block down, to stot (chock) the wheels up with, but if you were stood on a steep hill and the engine were to roll over the block–then you'd lost it–there was no means on earth of stopping it. At least, not on our type of engine (Ransome)†. But sometimes, people would forget to put the feather back in the pin after they'd been winching, and there have been ever so many engines smashed up over that. I can remember 'running over the block' at Weston Hall, Foxearth. I was stood up on the roadway and I was

---

* With admirable attention to detail, in Roman Polanski's recent film version of Hardy's "Tess of the Durbervilles", we see Tess as the feeder on a threshing drum which is driven by a "portable engine" (horse drawn) typical of the era of which Hardy was writing. Later, steam engines were designed to move by their own power and were called traction engines, a term with which we are more familiar.

† Showman's and road engines, explained Jack, had a brake on the back wheel.

roping the drum out and the engine came over the block. There was a big old cast iron water cart just in front of me, but I managed to lock round and miss it. When we were putting the pin back, a passer-by exclaimed, 'I thought you were in a damn muddle there, Cornell,' and I replied, 'So would you have been if I'd hit that blessed cart'."

On another occasion he was using "snatch blocks" in the hedge to rope himself in backwards,

"but all the blessed roots broke off, so there was nothing to winch on to . . . then you're in a bloomin' pickle."

For the engine driver and his mate, the tight corners, steep hills and overhung lanes, that, from our motor cars, we now regard as third gear dropdowns, presented instead, a variety of challenges.

"There were," Jack recalls, "some slopes and corners near to Bush, Boake Allen's at Liston that were none to brilliant. But the worst destination of all," he declared, "was up at your place, where I did my first day's work in sole charge of a traction engine. In those days it was a rotten old farm to get to, when you'd got a threshing drum, elevator and chaff cutter all trailed behind one engine and you were going up that twisting lane, and the yard all slopes and jammed up. Well, we inched about for a devil of a long time, getting everything in line and then as soon as we started up, the blessed water cart sprung a leak, so we couldn't get any steam—was I something roilled!"

"Feeder" Tom Rowe, remembers going up the narrow, steep hillock to Butlers Hall, Bulmer.

"We often had to drop our 'anchor' and winch up; the corners weren't too handy either. It's not possible to change gear with a traction engine on a hill, and there were times when we had to let it 'run back' into the hedge bank, or I would have to put blocks or an iron slipper behind the wheels. We used a shunting bar to help us get the elevator and baler round the worst of the corners."

After a moments pause, he continued, with another story from the pre-war era, with its mixed farming and unmetalled roads.

"On one occasion, we were taking the tackle down a narrow lane, near Grove Farm, Henny. A man was driving some cattle behind us, and one of the cows suddenly rushed forward and slipped under the drum. So we spent all day digging off one side of the bank and then we jacked the drum up. The cow got out safely enough but we didn't earn much extra bonus money on that particular day!"

When the traction engine with its three trailed machines, each a cumbersome and lengthy piece of equipment, had finally been manoeuvred along the twisting lanes and through the narrow gateways into a stackyard or field, the fly wheel of the tractor engine had to be lined up with the drive pulley of the drum.

"We had to get it within half an inch, and if your belt did come off, it wanted to fall off on the far side from the engine . . . usually the stacks were built in rows and you had to try to get the 'drum' midway between two stacks, otherwise there'd be some swearing from the 'pitchers' on the stacks, who'd have to fork the sheaves that much further. Of course, there wasn't any concrete on farms in those days and in wet conditions you couldn't always get the engine out of its own rut and you'd have to jack the drum across, or use angle chains and all that palaver–that's when you needed a good mate or 'feeder' with you," explains engine driver Jack Cornell. He continues, "Of course, being as it was contract work, you wanted to do as much as you could in a day, and when you were ready to move, you didn't reckon on any messing about. Even if you were only going from stack to stack, you didn't want anything in the way, so you'd get a bloke to move the water cart and coal cart and have all your fire irons packed up and ready. When you started again, they'd set the coal cart somewhere near and handy and you'd help them get the old horse out of the shafts and then prop the tumbril up on bits of wood– but then you'd have to be careful how you took the coal out, do else you'd go and tip the tumbril up and you'd be in a worser muddle still," he laughs.

Beside a good deal of ingenuity to tackle the practical problems which confronted him in moving the tackle from farm to farm, the engine driver needed to be mechanically alert when operating the engine. Besides the routine task of "oiling up", there was the water level to check, the fire had to be "well over the bottom" and a good driver would try to go all day without the pressure valve blowing. On other days, there would be soot to clean from the smoke box and cinders from the firebox–both jobs requiring a good deal of care, if the engine was standing on inflammable stubble. Occasionally, an engine might run short of water and a fusible lead plug would melt in the boiler, allowing steam to douse the fire. Replacing the lead plug and relighting the fire was one of the driver's most arduous, tedious and dirty jobs.

But apart from supervising the equipment, the threshing contractors required engineering expertise to maintain their engines. Often they would have to improvise replacement units in home workshops until the correct spare part could be ordered, dispatched and collected.

Jack Cornell provides an example of this "home maintenance" when repairing a small crack in the fire box.

"If you got a small crack, you'd drill it, or rather George Rowe did and I'd help. You'd drill a hole at the top of the crack and then tap it and screw in a piece of copper. You'd screw it in tight and then cut the end off. Then you'd drill a small hole through it, so that you drilled out a bit of copper and a bit of the box. You'd continue with this procedure until you got to the end of the crack and then you'd rivet it all up. Of course, it didn't put much strength in the box but it would fill a crack up so that the water wouldn't squirt over your fire in the box."

It was also the engine driver's job to stoke up on a Sunday afternoon. Jack Cornell estimates that it took as much coal to light the boiler as to keep the fire smouldering "with the hat on" over the weekend.

"But the worst thing," he comments, "was that it took an hour and a half to get up steam from a cold engine, so if your fire did go out, you'd have to perhaps bicycle five or six miles and be at work by 5 o'clock Monday morning to get stoked up in time for a 7 o'clock start. Normally, however, the head horseman would 'take the hat off' when he came to work, giving the flame time to build up."

This, itself, in an age before the telephone had arrived, could create problems as on a morning when the driver considered it was too wet to thresh, he might have to bike several miles to put the "hat" back on again. Jack Cornell retells an old and amusing story:

"Father and George Rowe were threshing at Borley, and it was pouring with rain on the Monday morning when they got up, Dad said to George: 'Let's go to the Smithfield Show'. So he had to bike across to Borley to stoke up and put the 'hat back on' and then return to Bulmer to get changed. As they were biking along Ballingdon Street, they saw the train going across the bridge and Father said: 'Hurry up, George, I'll rush on and buy the tickets'. When George got to the railway station, Father had got the tickets and was cracking jokes with the guard to hold up the train."

If the stories he told are as entertaining as those that son Jack tells, it may well have been the single occasion, in the illustrious history of Sudbury railway station, when its commuters were seen to have smiles on their faces. Another incident in John Cornell senior's threshing career, of interest to local historians, was to have the distinction of being the last person to cross the wooden bridge at Ballingdon, with a complete threshing tackle. There is now no trace of the wooden bridge that caused so much speculation when the heavy engines trundled across, and the railway line is all but demolished.

But there was far more involved in threshing than the pleasant and interesting spectacle of steam equipment. The lad who had taken the chaff away and carried the water, "never had a minute to spare . . . it was a tidy day's work". For the men who lifted and loaded the 18 stone sacks of wheat onto the tumbrels and then stacked them inside the barn, it was a strenuous day's labour.

Certainly, for all involved, it was a dusty day's work. Freddie Hunt (and just about everyone else interviewed) describes threshing machines as the "dirtiest things ever invented". Hory Elsie recalls that when positioned in the barn at Upper Houses, "you couldn't see from one side to the other for dust." George "Jute" Chatters remarked that in the thirties, mildew came off some crops like "smoke", whilst Tom Rowe and Frank Billimore confirmed that the longer a stack was left before threshing, the dustier and more rodent infested it became.

For the pitchers who forked the sheaves from the stack to the feeder on the drum, the rats and mice running about in the stack could easily present embarrassing problems. Although the bottom of his trousers were carefully tied to his legs with a piece of string (tied up at the hocks), there are several apocryphal tales of rats getting into a man's trousers. On one occasion it is alleged, "a lot of land girls were watching". Jack Cornell declares: "We used to tickle people's legs with a pieces of straw and they would jump a mile, thinking that a mouse had got in".

But the killing of rats was also part of the general activity of "sheening". A tally of a hundred or more was not unusual in a day's threshing and this heightened the boisterous and social nature of the work.

"You used to get them in their runs, especially at the bottom of a stack," recalls Reg Rippingale (born 1900), of the days when he was still a bachelor and the owner of two live ferrets.

"Well, when I worked at Gestingthorpe Hall, there was a man who would pick them up by their tails, whilst they were still alive. Now, to stop himself getting bitten, he had to keep the rat swinging on its tail in a big circle. Well, one time, a chap went talking to him and he stopped swinging this rat and it doubled back and bit him. He hully hollered there for a minute, I can tell you!"

The girls of the war-time Land Army must also have proved something of a distraction and Jack Cornell remembers that when

"one poor girl was looking knocked up, I went over to the stack to show her how to pitch the sheaves more easily. So I roared the pitchfork in, boastful like, and picked up two sheaves at once, but then the blessed fork snapped and stuck in my thigh—so the laugh was on me!

The relationship between farmer and threshing contractor consisted of a mixture of humorous mistrust and mutual interdependence. Farmers who had to provide the coal would try to use a poorer quality. The tradition prevailed that on departing from a farm, the coal tender was to be completely filled up. Arriving at the next destination, the farmer suspicious and penny conscious, might ask:

"Has all that coal been burnt getting here?"

"Well, it aint flown away" was a typical reply.

Contractors naturally tried to do as much as possible, but the farmers would grumble and feign dissatisfaction with the sample and find un-threshed grains in the discharged straw. At Gestingthorpe Hall, the crews were only allowed to thresh 90 coomb a day. Some farmers were known and remembered as "old darvills", and the threshing proprietors would try to break even by insisting that clover was put through twice "because it was an hourly paid job."

But in reality, the "jiggery pokery" and gamesmanship was based on the knowledge that both threshing contractor and farmer must survive. The account books of Cornell and Rowe reveal that threshing charges were based on a reflection of the price of wheat, and when conditions were starkly unprofitable in the early thirties, a number of farmers were allowed extended credit of several months, even years, until another harvest or improved circumstances enabled them to meet their commitments.*

Meteorological factors left their capricious mark on local economics. In 1912 a hailstorm devastated crops in Gestingthorpe and Yeldham and Cyril Philp's father had to plough under his ruined crop of winter beans.

---

* Threshing contractors, stack thatchers and day work labourers, all had an interest in the improved husbandry that led to good harvests beside our Long Furrow. There was a total philosophy involved. The larger the harvest, the greater amount of work for the entire village community. Today the same principle still applies. But as we shall explain in Chapter Nineteen it is the national, rather than the parochial economy that benefits.

The maxim that, "what is good for the farm is good for the village" may possibly explain the very genuine irritation of older farmworkers who see examples of bad farming and vehemently declare that "so and so should never *be allowed* to farm". Unproductive farming not only provided little scope for generating additional village employment but also challenged the basic creed of the "great campaign" itself.

As an example, the great depression of the nineteen thirties when derelict and abandoned farms were common, are remembered as "hard old times" by farmers, farm-workers and threshing contractors alike.

The effect on some wheat crops was disastrous. News such as this would be almost as serious to the threshing contractor as to the farmer. The drought of 1921 tells a similar story and the Cornell and Rowe account book suggests that harvest had finished by the fourth week of July, for we read that on July 26th, 104 coomb of wheat (11 tons 14 cwt) were threshed at Borley Hall, for Mr. Payne. The threshing machine remained at the farm for the next fortnight, after which it had threshed 356 coomb of wheat, 44 of oats and 151 of barley, providing a total of about 57 tons. This represents an average of 46 coomb a day (4½ to 5½ ton a day). However, on several occasions throughout the books, over 130 coomb of wheat were threshed, and on February 8th, 1920, 144 sacks of oats were separated at Smeetham Hall.

Jack Cornell explained that the objective was to thresh a hundred sacks a day, but including breakdowns, moving, cleaning down from one crop to another and climatic vagaries, the average appears to have been between 50 and 60 coomb. His own personal record, when he accomplished 214 coomb of oats in one memorable day at Brook Hall, Foxearth, is still a source of pride and interest. He comments:

"I had heard of people threshing 100 coomb before dinner, but this was the only occasion in my life when I ever did it; what's more, things were going so well that I was able to do as much again in the afternoon."

Charges for threshing declined as confidence in agriculture deteriorated. The account made out to Mr. Hyde Parker of Smeetham Hall in the drought year of 1921 reads:

		£.	s.	d.
Sept. 21	89 coomb Barley	4.	16.	5.
Sept. 22	5 coomb Barley		5.	5.
Sept. 22	22 coomb Beans	3.	9.	1.
Sept. 23	32 coomb Oats	1.	14.	8.
Sept. 23	¾ day Linseed	3.	7.	6.
Sept. 24	5 hours Clovering	2.	17.	6.
Oct. 10	75 hours Wheat	4.	1.	3.
Oct. 11	6 hours Rakings		6.	6.

In that year, wheat, barley and oats were being threshed for one shilling and a penny per coomb (about 5.4 new pence per 100 kilogram), but by 1926, when the price of wheat had fallen from £19 to £12 a ton, the Smeetham Hall account is based on a charge of only 8d. per sack.

In 1920, repairs and maintainance cost the partnership seventy eight pounds five shillings and four pence. Individual expenses, which are so neatly and elaborately itemised, with the leisurely hand writing of the day, include:

	£.	s.	d.
Paid C. J. N. Row for Insurance	5.	12.	6.
Washers		1.	2.
Tyres	1.	10.	0.
Dixon Scott	2.	0.	0.
Coal for forge		3.	1.
Wood and nails	1.	0.	6.
Whitlock		8.	3.

Some idea of the value of the partnership's threshing equipment can be gleaned from the sale held on the Sudbury Croft, on 27th July, 1939 at 2.30 p.m. The following equipment belonging to Rowe & Cornell was sold:*

	£.	s.	d.
Ransomes 7 h.p. Traction Engine No. 23803	90.	0.	0.
Ransomes Double Dresser No. 54 Threshing Drum	120.	0.	0.
Wards Elevator	25.	0.	0.
Whitlocks 5 Knife Chaff Cutter	25.	0.	0.
Ruston and Proctor Seed Huller No. 21731	75.	0.	0.
7939 Powell Straw Baler (as new)	235.	0.	0.
Sundries	43.	0.	0.

Total   £613. 0. 0.

---

* For the technically minded, it may be appropriate to document some of the equipment operating from Bulmer. John Cornell had a Ransome engine and Marshall drum. Albert Rowe was using a Wallis and Stevenson 6 h.p. engine and a Garrett 7 h.p. engine. In addition, he operated a Clayton drum, medium and light Ransome drums, two Maynard chaff cutters and a Ruston and Proctor seed huller. The equally well known Fowler, Garrett and Burrel engines had also been used from the village, whilst in the early years of the century, an Eddington had seen service.

Jack Cornell calculates that a traction engine used approximately seven hundred-weights of coal a day on threshing work and when they were gradually replaced by tractors, it was found that the latter burnt around 10 gallons of paraffin a day. Historically, we believe that the village's first threshing proprietor was Joseph Coe, who started business somewhere around 1902. Albert Rowe, later to be the largest contractor, commenced operations in 1906. Harry Winch recalls that the Auberies was still using a "portable" steam engine, which was pulled by horses, until the First World War. He also described the improvements that were made to the early threshing drums; these included "avelers", "double dressers" and "self feeders", all of which rapidly became part of the equipment that was being operated from Bulmer Street.

The equipment found its way back to Bulmer and between August 1944 and May 1945 (a threshing year), Jack Cornell established a new personal "record", when he threshed an unsurpassed 17,419 sacks. In addition, the tackle performed 120 hours day work, 75 hours chaff cutting and 165 hours baling behind the drum. Many of the village's residents still recall the engines and drums being given their summer overhaul in the meadows by Bulmer Street. Others will have man-handled those 90lb straw bales, which the balers compressed and of which it was remarked laconically: "they get difficult to pitch a long way above your head if you make them much heavier!"

But the tide of history that has flowed along our furrow knows neither patience nor remorse. The death knell of the threshing industry had been struck in the early nineteen thirties with the first commercial use of combine harvesters in the United Kingdom.

On 26th August, 1947, the Ransome Traction Engine that had served Bulmer men for three decades completed its last day's work. It was replaced by a Ford Major petrol/paraffin tractor. Jack Cornell surmises that the threshing business suffered no decline until 1947, but thereafter it fell slowly and inexorably away.

Albert Rowe's remaining machine was sold in the late fifties and we think that Spencer Coe's last commercial operation was in 1961. As the drum was brushed down for the final time, it signalled the end of an industry that for half a century had been the life blood of Bulmer Street and an integral part of village prosperity.

Today we would be disappointed if the largest of the combines that have replaced the binder, shockers, pitchers, waggon loaders, stack builders, thatchers and threshing machines, could not achieve an output of 10-14 tons an hour. Ironically, it is the same target (100-120 coomb) that Jack Cornell and eight men would have worked hard to have threshed in a ten hour day.

Yet, the principles of separation in a combine harvester are basically the same as the threshing machines that they have replaced. It was not until 1981 that a major development occurred, when the revolutionary, rotary flow combine harvester was released for general distribution in England, pioneered by International McCormick Harvesters, whose binder Emily Hearn had first seen those eighty summers before, by the turning to Upper Houses.

The rise, fluctuations and decline of the threshing industry is a typical phenomenon of the twentieth century. In our next chapter we shall look at the bankruptcies, dereliction and abandoned farms of the great depression. Many aspects of agriculture which have flourished for a few years beside

165

CHAPTER FOURTEEN

The Thirties

"The Agricultural Depression and the Contentious Tithe"

"Land has ceased to be either a profit of a pleasure: it gives one position and prevents one from keeping it up." (Lady Bracknell, 'The Importance of Being Earnest') Oscar Wilde.

"Well, I've never met a poor farmer!" came the cryptic reply as I tried to explain the present chapter of the "Long Furrow". Doubtless the remark is one for which, during the past forty years of prosperity and stable marketing, there is a good deal of evidence. But in this chapter we will review the financial depression of the 1930s whose consequences were so severe in Britain's industrial north and rural east. The repercussions of the recession were felt keenly beside our Long Furrow and the memory of those impoverished times is still of import and influence.

We saw in Chapter Six how the price of wheat had fluctuated so dramatically in the nineteenth century. These fluctuations continued until the Agriculture Act of 1947. As a consequence of the widescale importation of American prairie wheat into England, the nadir in the cycle of prices was reached in 1934. In that year domestic wheat sales averaged £4. 16s. 8d. per ton.

Price of Wheat per Ton

Year	£	s.	d.
1730	8.	1.	8.
1812 (Napoleonic blockade)	28.	0.	0.
1844	11.	2.	8.
1877	13	5.	6.
1896	6.	1.	8.
1913	7.	8.	4.
1917 (World War I)	17.	13.	4.
1922	11.	3.	4.
1934	4.	16.	8.
1939	5.	0.	0.
1941 (World War II)	14.	13.	4.
1949	23.	5.	0.
1960	21.	6.	8.

A pertinent local example of the collapse in the value of wheat can be glimpsed in Bulmer with a quotation from George Rowe's poultry book:

29.3.1929: Purchased 8 cwt wheat from Albert (his brother) £4. 1. 0.
4.10.1932: Purchased 9 cwt wheat from Albert   £2. 1. 3.

This dramatic deterioration in the grain trade was to have a devastating effect on the villages of our Long Furrow. East Anglia, it is generally agreed, was the worst hit region of England. The authoritative "Agrarian History of England and Wales"* declares of the nineteen thirties:

"There were three types of land in the East of England where profits were almost impossible to secure by traditional methods, given the high costs of cultivation by horses and the low prices of grain. In Suffolk, Essex, Huntingdonshire and Cambridgeshire, farms were again falling derelict, as their occupiers' capital drained away under the impact of annual losses. Only farms with exceptionally low costs or exceptionally high yields avoided disastrous losses from 1929 onwards. It was the clay land farms which had the highest costs and the lowest yields. Moreover, the highest proportion of their land was under wheat, the grain whose prices fell the most. Many of the large farms were paying wages in those years from an increase in debt and it was inevitable that farmers should cut the numbers employed."

"Farmworkers numbers fell in England and Wales from 650,000 in 1927 to 511,000 in 1939. But the extension of unemployment insurance in the 1920s to most occupations had left agriculture as the main industry outside the provision; farmworkers who became destitute either found alternative employment, whether in agriculture or outside it, or were supported by the poor law in the parish of their last residence."

Agricultural bankruptcies rose from a mere 44 in 1920 to the peak of 600 in 1932, even so, "many creditors would have gained little from a forced sale and therefore let their debts run on until times improved . . ."

The sum result was that the price of land dropped to a quarter of its wartime value and abandoned farms were advertised for as little as £5 per acre and even then could frequently not find a purchaser. 20,000 acres of land lay derelict and abandoned between Colchester and Haverhill and as late as 1939 the Suffolk National Farmers Union recorded more than 15,000 acres of land in this category.

The Agrarian History of England and Wales continues:

"Tenants were giving up their farms with the owners often unable to re-let . . . in many areas there was no market for arable farms in 1931

* Agrarian History of England and Wales Vol. VIII, 1914-1939, edited by Edith Whetman published by Cambridge University Press.

and 1932. There was no value in land burdened with arrears of rates, tithe redemption payments and perhaps drainage rates."

Clement Atlee, later to be the Prime Minister who was most reponsible for putting British agriculture back onto a sound commercial footing, commented lucidly at the time:

"Conditions in Eastern England are only comparable to those in some areas of abandoned mines or in derelict towns of Northern England."

Bulmer itself, our "target survey village" in the history of our Long Furrow, seems, as in the previous depression of the 1890s, to have suffered the rigours of the thirties less harshly than some of its neighbouring parishes. Goldingham Hall, however, purchased for £8,300 in 1914, was sold in 1935 for £5,000. The decline in agricultural confidence was total. Farmers "drew back into themselves", farming only the most profitable land in the cheapest manner. Buildings went unrepaired, hedges were uncut and agricultural cottages, in a state of complete neglect, were sold for as little as £30 to £50 each. Local estates discreetly reduced and often absolved rents during the worst years, in the belief that "no rent was better than no tennant". There were instances also, where farmworkers, already enduring a frugal existence, had to wait several weeks for their wages during mid summer, until another harvest enabled their employers to pay their back money.

After so many centuries of seedtime and harvest, the "great campaign" of agricultural development was suffering a crippling and bitter reversal. Lawrence Hyde Parker, Bulmer's longest serving farmer, recalls:

"I'd go to three separate markets to try to get 3d. more per quarter" (about 6p a tonne more).

Roughly a third of Smeetham Hall and most of Goldingham went into grass.

"We didn't fence it in ... or put cattle on," he explains. "On Smeetham it just wasn't profitable ... we would have lost even more money ... all we could do was concentrate on the best land and farm it cheaply ... nobody of your generation will ever understand, Ashley," he continues with feeling, "what it was like for anyone to live through the thirties ... there just wasn't any confidence at all ... we were all basically farming on hope."

Undoubtedly those who survived the slump were either the very ruthless, those on very good land, or the established farmers of which there were several in the area who had built up a "capital reserve". Horseman Horace Elsie surmised that to withstand the depression,

> "You either needed some good land or didn't have to pay any rent . . . 5 sack (11½ cwt wheat) an acre was poor for those days . . . but it was also a common enough yield."

Tom Edgeley, whose father was a farm manager for the Bury St. Edmunds firm of estate agents, Lacy Scott, recalls:

> "It was often the biggest farmers with the largest overheads who went under first . . . the smaller farmers were able to get by with the help of their wives and children. I used to help at the auctions and it was pitiful to see these old farmers–people who had been right at the top of the village–watch as all their possessions and furniture were sold up . . . and know that it was all finished. But you could always tell. Once you started to see the horses going thin, then you knew the end was pretty near."

Of those interviewed for the book, at least four had close relatives whose farms went under the hammer during the great depression, when at its most intense, "a quarter of England changed hands in four years."

But as with all depressions, it was not just the prime producers (the farmers) who suffered. Threshing contractor, Jack Cornell, recalls: "

> "It was a terrible time, there just wasn't the corn to thrash. Land simply wasn't being farmed . . . and where it was . . . you often couldn't get paid."

Bills four *years* old were not an uncommon features of the nineteen thirties.

For several unemployed farmworkers the memories are even starker. "Every time the threshing tackle moved, a group of us would follow it to the next farm, in the hope that the farmer would take one or two of us on for a few days 'sheening'," was a not infrequent comment. But as more land went out of production, so too did the demand for casual work decline. The gangs of "thistlers" were seen less often, the "Lord of the Harvest" required a smaller team; the thatcher had fewer stacks to roof; the contractor less coombs to thresh, the blacksmith a diminished number of horses to shoe; and the daymen would be "sent off home together", if the weather was wet or there was no productive work to be done.*

---

* Douglas Hasler, whose father Bertie Hasler was a thatcher at this time writes: "Farming was having a very lean time then, and consequently my father went weeks without work. He had a single barrelled 12 bore shotgun and we lived on wood pigeons and rabbits."

Even the farmworkers' cottages were abandoned, falling into disrepair and neglect. In Bulmer, Charlie "Pod" Martin thatched the roof of Lower Houses Cottage, (where Philip Rowe now lives) and it was used for an egg packing station, whilst "Wheatcroft" on the corner, had the reputation of allowing daylight to pass from one side to the other.

But the greatest legacy of the great depression and one that has left so much bitterness, suspicion and paranoia in the minds of the farmers who survived, is the memory of the land abandoned, the buildings derelict and crumbling, the hedges wild and overgrown, the fields an assortment of thistles, blackthorn bushes and twitch grass. Haulage contractor, Ken Day reports that Hilltop Farm, Bulmer, was "like a wilderness, with hedges thirty feet high and thirty feet wide." Jack Cornell recalls 100 acres of Hungary Hall, Pebmarsh, being offered for sale at £300. Lifelong farworker George "Jute" Chatters recalls the abandoned farms of the badly affected "heavy land" village of Belchamp Otten: "Bevingdon went wild; the Lodge went wild; the Fowes went wild and Gridleys, in front of the "Windmill", that went wild for a while . . . and some of the others what were farmed weren't very sharp . . ."

Bevingdon Manor itself was once offered for sale (but not sold) at £2.10s. per acre. At the Fowes, the house was abandoned and never reoccupied after 1926. By 1940, remembers Jute, "shrubs were growing through the barn roof, the buildings were smothered over, the hedges so colossal that small meadows infested with rabbits became woods in their own right."

In neighbouring Belchamp Walter a sign advertised, "This property to let for two shillings and sixpence an acre." Such advertisements were frequently no more than a preliminary to obtaining a tenant, who might pay no rent at all, until conditions improved.

But there has been a price to pay for the negligence of government policy during the nineteen thirties. For just as the great depression has left an indelibly bitter scar on the mentality of the Jarrow marcher and his generation of industrial England, so too, a complex of fear and ruthlessness developed in the farmers of East Anglia. The excessive removal of hedgerow and woodland which occured in some villages, during the fifties and sixties, can in part, be traced back to the memories of those times.

But for our final recollections of the great depression and the "tithe war" which ensued, let us turn to the oldest farmer in the survey of our Furrow. Youthful, bright eyed and inventive, he had just completed his seventieth harvest and still enjoys combining out the forty acres of dried peas which are grown on his Castle Hedingham farm. Born in 1899 and now eighty three years old, Cyril Philp declares:

"Rum do-ing that time of day!"

"But how severe was the depression?" I ask.

"In all the Eastern counties it was bad—the heavier the land, the worse it was. There were farms abandoned—one farmer at Hundon hadn't been able to pay his tithe and they told him that the bailiffs would be coming with a court order in the morning. The farmer said 'All right mate, let 'em come. I shan't be seeing 'em', and he picked up his few things and he walked out and left it to 'em. That land went unfarmed until the beginning of the war. There was elm stubbs out in the middle of the fields a foot thick."

"Another farm over at Finchingfield was in arrears for tithe and Mr. Kelk, the auctioneer for Balls & Balls would have taken £4 an acre for it if he could have got it. But if a farm was in arrears for tithe the purchaser had to pay it off as well. No, no—there wasn't anybody much interested in buying land in those days. Well, that farm was abandoned and nothing done to it for three years."

"It was a case of survival; if you made two ha'pence for a penny, you were darned lucky. A lot of land went back to being farmed with only a dog and a stick!

"The Fowes, up at Belchamp, that was abandoned as near as don't matter. The man who had it, just put a couple of strands of barbed wire around the boundary and he used to put his dry cows and young stock up there, and turn them in and shut the gate and that was that. Cor! bushes, hedges there, mountains high! Rabbits—swarms of them! The farmer had a little steam tackle of his own and bloomin' great elm bushes grew up through the wheels—he had to cut them down before he could move the engine. That was more or less wilderness. Oh yes! several years like that."

He pauses and then comments philosophically: "No, there was nothing done whatsoever. It was a case of 'you don't spend anything because you'd got nothing *to* spend! And there was nothing to come back anyway. No, that was poor do-ing that time of day."

For farmers, farmworkers and rural craftsmen alike, the thirties are re-membered as "hard old times". And as Cyril Philp implies, it was also the decade during which the long festering sore of tithe payments came to a head.

We already have seen the evidence of "Tithe" (or the "one tenth" which a farmer had to pay to the clergy) beside our Long Furrow of Bulmer and Gestingthorpe. The Overhall Court roll of 1528 lists "Nicholas Clerk, William Clerk his son, John Chamberlain, William Spurgeon, William Stronge and John Parker as tithing men". Later, we read in "Bulmer: Then and Now", of a dispute in 1768 between the Rector of Wickham St. Pauls and farmers Brewster and Ruffle. The rector "had been of the law and knew very well how to introduce prolixity and expense into the ensuing law suit". The rector insisted–against local custom–that after cutting a field, the shocks should be left standing until he had collected every tenth shock for himself.

We do not know who won the Wickham case. Basil Slaughter suggests that as in many such situations the chief beneficiaries were the lawyers. But tithe continued to be levied "in kind" until the 1840s. Tithe assessment maps were then produced and the "due" subsequently paid in money. During the First World War, tithe was calculated as a proportion of the price of cereal crops–a direct reflection of farm profitability. In 1925, the assessments were "stabilised" but by the early thirties, following the crash in grain prices, a considerable imbalance had developed. Continued payment of this anachronistic levy began to arouse intense disquiet amongst an already unprofitable agricultural community. The resentment was particularly strong amongst the growing number of self-made, nonconformist, small farmers, who were effectively supporting a denomina-whose religious services they did not attend. In fairness, it should be said, that some clergymen were particularly sympathetic and understanding, and would tactfully enquire of farmers, "How much can you spare toward the tithe this year?" But other rectors behaved with equally great ineptitude and insensitivity at a time of severe international and parochial depression.

One Suffolk farmer suggested in 1932, that under the prevailing circumstances, a compromise might be attained by which he paid a proportion of his tithe. But the parson, a Rector Hazelwood, and a man of considerable private means, announced from the seat of his brand new Armstrong Siddeley car, that, "he would have all his tithe–or nothing." The farmer stormed in reply, "Then you'll darned well have nothing."

As grain prices plummetted to their nadir in 1932 it became impossible for many farmers to continue payment. In retaliation, the Church Commissioners instructed bailiffs to levy distress (i.e. seize animals and implements) from selected farmers who were in arrears. Three villages, Elmsett in mid-Suffolk, Stoke by Clare and Gestingthorpe became notable for the fracas which ensued, when bailiffs, surrounded by hostile crowds, attempted, but failed, to either auction or seize the implements of the defaulting farmers.

In the financially precarious May of 1932, the farmers of Elmsett, near Hadleigh, Suffolk, reacted with ebullient rural vigour to the intended sequestration of Mr. Charlie Westren's stock and implements at Elmsett Hall. A herd of cattle to be distrained, "mysteriously" wandered away during the night. Immediately the hauliers lorries arrived at the farm to seize the equipment, a group of men enthusiastically commenced hacking at the trees along the single entrance route. In the ensuing protest, it was the sight of saw and sound of axe, which alerted the bailiffs and hauliers to the fact that retreat was essential. After their departure, three excited ladies rang the bells of Elmsett church as a "symbol of victory". Half a century later, a memorial of the "Elmsett Tithe War" still stand opposite the Church Tower.

At Stoke by Clare, the Church Commissioners, with what can only be described as blatant naivety, attempted to auction the seized equipment of a farm which was in arrears. But solidarity prevailed amongst the militant tendency of the farmers ranks. Each "lot" was dispensed for a pittance. Legendary examples include: "a shilling for a cart, one and sixpence for a binder, ninepence for a tumbrel." The equipment was then returned to the rightful owner.

The resistance to the payment of tithe provides one of the most colourful episodes in the history of our Long Furrow. In May 1933 an attempt was made to "levy distress", on the goods and chattles of Mrs. Marjorie Gardiner at Delvyns Farm, Gestingthorpe.

As in previous "engagements", the bailiffs and auctioneers were bedevilled by a mixture of genuine bitterness in combination with high spirited, resourceful and practical obstructionism.

The report of the "Gestingthorpe Tithe Case" which was heard in the High Court, is recorded in the Halstead and Colne Valley Gazette of July 28th 1933, whilst the Daily Mirror carried the story on July 26th under the headline:

ANGRY SCENE AT WIDOWS FARM
Court Story of Barn Drama and throwing of eggs.
Rector loses his case.

It was explained by the Mirror's legal reporter that £48 (one year's tithe) was owed. "It was a time of depression and the tithe question" argued Counsel, "had become very acute. There were 1000 distress warrants in Suffolk and Essex. The levies of tithe, which had been stabilised in 1925 were quite impossible to pay: so far from it being one tenth, it is in some cases 70%" claimed Counsel.

The court heard that it was impossible to hold an auction to raise money for the tithe payment, as no farmers would bid—out of sympathy for the farmer, Mrs. Gardiner. Consequently, two tumbrels, two waggons, a reaper, two ladders, a shredder, a binder and two geldings were advertised by tender. Mr. L. J. James, a Swansea acutioneer, had placed a bid of £60 which was accepted.

On May 22nd, Mr. Rose (bailiff acting for the church), Mr. James and Mr. Gibson (his solicitor) visited Delvyns Farm to inspect the goods for which Mr. James had tendered.

What the Welsh auctioneer did not realise, was that the "seizure" was "technically incorrect" and as such illegal. Mrs. Gardiner had been advised of this by her solicitor, whose opinion was subsequently upheld by the High Court, as described in the Daily Mirror. As such her relatives and fellow farmers felt justified in resisting the movement of the "illegally distrained" equipment.

Consequently, when Mr. Rose (the bailiff), Mr. James and Mr. Gibson arrived at Delvyns Farm, things were not quite as they had expected to find them. The story is continued by farmer and steam enthusiast, Cyril Philp. At the High Court he was one of eight who had sworn affidavits read in support of Mrs. Gardiner. Later, he was amongst the 36 farmers who appeared at Hedingham and then Chelmsford Assize Court, charged with unlawful assembly. Describing the measures taken to prevent the removal of the "illegally seized" farm equipment, he explains:

"The bailiffs had put the waggons and tumbrels and a binder in the barn and locked the doors until they could be collected."

"But my brother, Charlie and Arthur Gardiner and one or two others, they took the wheels off the waggons and the carts—anything that had got wheels on, they took off, and took them all down to a little wood at the back of Delvyns."

"Then to complicated things a little more, they pulled Frank Marsh's baler right in front of the doors. He did all the threshing there, that time of day—and I believe he took the wheels home to Wickham on the excuse he was going to do something to them."

"So when the bailiffs came to collect these things, they could just get into the barn, but they couldn't get anything out, nor could they shunt the baler about very far without it having any wheels."

"What happened when the bailiffs arrived with the Welsh auctioneer who had purchased the goods?"

"Well, the bush telegraph soon notified the various people round-about—I should think there must have been 100-150 or more got there, all to enjoy the frolic. The news soon got about. Even if the bailiff had got something to shift these things, there was enough of us there to see that nothing would get stolen away. Well then it got that we kept the bailiffs more or less prisoner in the barn—they would have been there now if the police hadn't come and rescued them. Of course, whilst they were in there, we gave those Johnnies a few home truths. We told 'em, we didn't think it a 'much-er'—them coming such a distance to collect things which weren't theirs."

"There was no mutiny—nobody getting hurt or anything like that—but they were our prisoners and we were technically guilty of obstructing the forces of the law. Toward the end of the day, the police had to exert their power and release these men. Then they collared-hold of those of us who were close to and eventually we had to appear at Hedingham Court and then Chelmsford Assizes accused of unlawful assembly."

The Halstead and Colne Valley Gazette devoted almost the entire back page to the proceedings of Hedingham Police Court held on August 3rd 1933.* The headline declared:

SEQUEL TO GESTINGTHORPE TITHE DISTRAINT
CHARGES OF "UNLAWFUL ASSEMBLY"
ALL DAY SITTING OF COURT

The article commences:

"Great interest was manifested over a wide area, in the proceedings which took place at Hedingham Police Court yesterday, when 36 farmers and others, were charged with "unlawful assembly", at the execution of a tithe distraint at Delvyns Farm, Gestingthorpe.

The scene in the Court Room was an unprecedented one. The large dock, with its door at the rear leading to the cells, was totally inadequate to accommodate the defendants, and arrangements had to be made to provide seating accommodation for them in part of the Court on the public side of the dock. This considerably limited the space available for the general public. The facilities in the Court for the Press were also severly taxed, as, in addition to the usual reporters, there were also present representatives from the Press Association, Central News and several of the big "daily" newspapers.

Before the proceedings commenced, the scene outside the Court was a very animated one, and the Press photographers, of which there were many, were very active, "snapping" the various personalities in the case as the opportunity offered."

The case opened and Mr. Melford Stevenson, acting for the farmers, pointed out that during harvest "absence from their farms was a matter of hardship".

The justices then refused his somewhat impractical suggestion for 36 separate trials, but agreed to adjourn until after harvest before the next sitting. Proceedings commenced and the bailiff who was attempting to

---

* Reported in the edition of August the fourth.

"seize" the implements gave his evidence but soon found himself in difficulty. He explained that he visited the farm on the 18th and 20th May.

Mr. Pollock: "Why did you go there?"

Witness: "I was trying to remember. I have my notes."

Mr. Pollock: "Did you make the notes at the time?"

(Witness took typewritten notes from his pocket).

Mr. Melford Stevenson (sharply): "Did you have a typewriter with you?"

Witness: "No."

Mr. Pollock: "Then you must not read them."

The bailiff continued his verbal evidence and was followed by Mr. Gibson, the Braintree lawyer who was acting for the Swansea auctioneer. He described events at the barn and an amusing exchange on the subject of bad language followed. The Gazette continues:

"At that time there were probably 100 to 150 people outside the barn. The witness entered the barn at the request of the bailiff. Mr. James (the Swansea auctioneer) was with him and a crowd of 60 or 70 people 'practically swept into the barn'. The attitude of the people in the barn was very hostile and very filthy language was used. One of the phrases was "dirty Welsh ....". When asked for more of the language, the witness then asked to be allowed to write it down and handed it to the Bench.

Mr. Melford Stevenson: "One of the words is spelt wrong."

Witness: "Evidently Mr. Stevenson is more familiar with them than I am."

Witness added that the bad language was used by only a small section of the crowd. Some of the crowd said, "You dirty '...............' to come here to take away a poor widow's goods."

Mr. Gibson then claimed that, "he received a rotten egg at the back of the neck and that he saw Mr. James receive another; more chaff was scattered on his head, (later a farmer explained that this had been done with great thoughtfulness to prevent yolk running down his neck). Mr. Gibson then expounded the theory "that a hive of bees might be unloosed on them". But Mr. Stevenson, for the farmers, quickly interjected:

"How were the bees to differentiate between you and the tithpayers?"

Witness: "I understood they were threatening to lock us in the barn with the bees . . . but I may have been wrong."

Throughout the case, an air of humour appears to have permeated the proceedings. The Chairman of the Magistrates confessed to being, "in the very unhappy position of having to consider cases against our friends and neighbours." Within the structured society of pre-war England, some at least would have schooled, shot and hunted together in more prosperous times. The Hedingham magistrate concluded by admitting the defendants to bail of £5 and committing them to trail at the next Assizes.

In the context of the somewhat jocular replies and comments at Hedingham Police Court and Chelmsford Assizes, it would be easy to forget that the farmers in question were witnessing a catastrophic depression in cereal agriculture. We must remember that it *was* 1933; grain prices had halved; land was being abandoned. The seizure was "illegal". Mrs. Gardiner *was* a widow and if her farming career had been terminated, Delvyns Farm may well have lain derelict and its farm staff become unemployed until the Second World War.

The Assizes Court at Chelmsford was held in early November and received full coverage from the Halstead & Colne Valley Gazette in the editions of November 3rd and 10th. The defendants who were able to quote the ruling of the High Court, that the seizure had been technically illegal, now attempted to demonstrate that they had not constituted an "unlawful assembly". But why then, it had to be established, were the individual farmers in the barn with Mr. James, Mr. Rose and Mr. Gibson?

The farmers individually provided their explanations:

CHARLIE GARDINER declared with the flamboyant cheerfulness for which he will always be remembered: "Being her brother and an *Englishman,* I went to watch over her interests."

But other defendants were more evasive producing what can only be described as a series of amusing schoolboy-headmaster replies.

SAMUEL LAWRENCE said he went to the farm because he heard there was going to be something going on. He went to do nothing and did nothing.

Prosecution: "How far had you come to do nothing?"

Witness: "I do not know; I hadn't been there before."

ALFRED HALLS stated he was offered a ride and accepted, but did not know where he was going.

ARTHUR DREW explained, that "he took Mr. Buck's motor car out for the purpose of making a trial run, after repairing it, and requiring "ballast" they had picked up Halls."

THOMAS AMBROSE deposed that "he had instructions to send a binder from the farm that he managed if Mrs. Gardiner's was seized."

DAVID PARTRIDGE was bicycling past.

GEOFFREY RUFFLE claimed he went to Gestingthorpe to see his blacksmith.

CYRIL PHILP said he went to Delvyns Farm to inspect some pigs.

BASIL PAYNE replied that having heard rumours that Welsh miners were coming, he went to the farm. He entered the barn when the luncheon was on. He was playing cards in the barn."

By now the Prosecution was becoming intrigued by the beer and sandwiches which farmers had found in the barn. Surely, it was implied, the availability of lunch confirmed the contrivance of the assembly. The exchanges with SIDNEY RUFFLE were particularly humorous:

"He had gone to Delvyns Farm to look for his brother Frank Ruffle. He went into the barn to get some bread and cheese. Whilst he was there, an egg was thrown and the crowd sang "Taffy was a Welshman".

Prosecution: "Why should you be supplied with a free lunch?"

Ruffle: "I don't know. It was there and I was hungry and glad to take it."

Prosecution: "Was it a surprise?"

Ruffle: "A pleasant surprise."

Prosecution: "Who supplied it?"

Ruffle: "I don't know."

Prosecution: "Have you ever been supplied with a *free* lunch in that barn on any previous occasion?"

Ruffle: "No."

Prosecution: "Does it occur to you that someone wanted you to stay there?"

Ruffle: "No."

Two farmers subsequently came forward and explained that they were responsible for the beer and sandwiches. With this, the prosecution changed tactics and attempted to discern who was responsible for wiring up the barn door and keeping it shut. But attempts at examination proved so inconclusive that Mr. John Flowers, K.C., acting for the plaintiffs expostulated in frustration:

"Everyone in the barn seems to have had his back to the door or else was playing cards and witnessed nothing!"

Finally, after the defendants had been questioned, 29 were acquitted and Mr. Gilbert Beyfus, K.C.,* summed up in defence of the remaining seven:

"If the persons concerned honestly believed that an illegal distraint was to be made upon implements of husbandry, which might lead to the farm becoming derelict, they would be justified in passive resistance and what they did was no danger to the public peace. Indeed, the bedrock of the issue, was the question of the illegal distraint."

The jury, with the case for the prosecution and defence completed and the judge's remarks concluded, were asked for their decision. The sat for 59 minutes and a verdict of "guilty of unlawful assembly" was passed on the

* Not a typing error! K.C. is, of course, King's Counsel.

remaining seven defendants, who were bound over to keep the peace for two years.*

Forty nine years after the "illegal seizure" by the Church Commissioners of the Delvyns Farm implements, Cyril Philp is still able to conjure up the atmosphere of the Assize Court proceedings, with a few warm-hearted remarks. He concludes, with a farmer's natural indifference for his advocate's eloquence and verbosity:

> "We had a lot of moral support . . . the blooming place was right full of people . . ."
> "Mr. Justice Horridge was the judge—our legal representative Mr. Steed, got some K.C. or one of his old mates to speak for us. I don't think he charged very much, it was a nice little exercise for him to defend us at the Assize Court and all the rest of it. Of course, he pitched a right good old tale—he'd have talked there for an hour or more about nothing! Any rate, come to the finish, Justice Horridge was very serious and all the rest of it, and said he couldn't overlook our disregard of the law."

The acrimony which many farmers, (and some farmworkers who also saw their livelihoods at risk), felt towards the Church Commissioners during intensely depressed circumstances, succeeded through the Tithe Payer's Association to initiate a reform of the whole vexatious and contentious question.

Tithe was given a fixed duration. It was due to expire in 1996. Upon the sale of a farm, a purchaser could redeem it in a single payment. When Goldingham Hall, Bulmer, was advertised for sale in 1972, the 394 acres carried the not insignificant redeemable liability of £508. The annual tithe paid on the 460 acres of Cyril Philp's Kirby Hall was £145. At Hill Farm, Gestingthorpe, the 220 acres were assessed at £84.24 a year. But tithe was not only assessed on the large landowners and farmers. Horseman Bert Surridge paid one shilling and fivepence on the half acre of his garden next to the Gestingthorpe "Pheasant" and when he "redeemed it" during the Second World War, it cost him £3—or the equivalent of two weeks wages.

But the story of tithe will not linger on until 1996. In the early seventies it was found to be costing more to collect than the revenue repaid.

---

* One interesting aspect of the Tithe War, was the presence in many troubled villages of small groups of Oswald Moseley's "blackshirts". One independent Gestingthorpe observer comments: "They seemed to turn up, wherever there was the chance to be involved in a bit of tension from which they could get some publicity. I don't think that the half dozen or so who camped at Delvyns had been invited by the farmers or the Tithe Payers Association, but there was a general feeling that the farmers were wrong for not sending them packing—straight off back to London again."

On an evening in the frustratingly wet autumn of 1976, unable to be drilling or lifting sugar beet, as the torrents of rain streamed down the drain pipes and flooded off the gutters, I sat down to some office work and on Lloyds Bank cheque number 478012 signed our last £82.24 payment of tithe. Man had been on the moon for seven years; Concorde was airborne and flying. For just a few seconds I thought back to the stories I had heard of the incorrigible Marjorie Gardiner and of her defiant stand at Delvyns Farm.

After a thousand years of tithe paying, the last vestige of a feudal custom had finally ended. Appropriately, in the same year, another aspect of the same, lingering, medieval influence, which had stretched into the twentieth century of the British farmworker was also abolished. It was the tied cottage. And if not completely abolished, at least modified to a level that Victorian landlords would have found difficult to recognise.

Before we take our leave of the Gestingthorpe "Tithe War" however, let us pay a visit to Stanley Surridge (born 1909) who was a horseman at Delvyns during the seizure and who latterly became farm foreman. The relationship between the farmers and the local rector is of particular interest and Stanley (who overheard the date of the intended seizure and warned Mrs. Gardiner) emphasises:

"I must stress," he says, "that there was no personal animosity between the majority of the farmers and the rector. In fact," he continues, "I'd go as far as saying that Reverend Greening was one of the best clergymen we've ever had in this parish; he was particularly popular with the working people."

"In this village the agitation was against the payment of tithes, not against the individual clergyman. I can clearly remember, when the hearing was over, that Reverend Greening walked across and shook hands with the farmers. He was respected for that, and they called him a good loser."

Throughout the story of our Long Furrow, we have witnessed periodic outbursts of civilian tension in our villages—the peasants revolt, the outbreaks of disorder in Halstead, the era of rickburning and machinery smashing, the farmworkers' strike an Belchamp Walter and the "tithe war" in Gestingthorpe. Each in isolation tells an interesting story, but taken together, they weave a richer colour into the tapestry of British history.

With Hitler's invasion of Czechoslovakia in March 1939, and the increased prospect of a U-boat blockade, Government statisticians at last awoke to the looming food crisis facing an embattled island with a run-

* Douglas Hasler in a separate article endorses and embellishes this view.

down agriculture importing 70% of its nutritional needs.* The alarm bells were ringing. "Back to the land" became a propaganda slogan.

At last our Long Furrow, so neglected and abused, was to be revitalised. A desperate vigour was unleashed. The old campaign was back in action! The fires of progress were kindled anew. Tractors, bulldozers and crawlers became involved in a frantic endeavour to reclaim the derelict countryside. Basic slag and chalk were subsidised.*

Hedge removal was encouraged. The farming of Britain's forgotten countryside was given a military priority. We are ready at last, for the second agricultural revolution.

---

* As late as 1938, in his Kettering Speech, Prime Minister Neville Chamberlain declared, with what can only be decribed as patent myopia, that:
"Britain would not be starved in the event of war; there is no need to encourage the greater output of food at home."

CHAPTER FIFTEEN

Traditional Rotations and Tractorisation

The Second Agricultural Revolution–A village study

With the outbreak of hostilities on September 3rd, 1939, agricultural survival became a matter of the highest priority. Suddenly those farmers who had survived the slump and who had been part of the boisterous resistance in the Tithe dispute at Delvyns farm, were called upon to plough up the abandoned acres. The beacon of agricultural improvement that had faded like an old gutted candle was fuelled again with positive objectives. County War Agricultural Committees were established to stimulate the ploughing up of neglected farms and unproductive grassland. To provide a variety of diet, these "War Ags", supervised the statutory growing of potatoes and sugar beet.

The Land Army became evident in the area. Jack Cornell declares: "The first thing I used to say to the land girls who helped us was, 'HACK THOSE BLESSED FINGER NAILS OFF!'" Of course, some girls were just as capable as men in feeding the drum or taking the chaff off, but usually it required double the girls for "stacking" or "pitching". But between August 1944 and May 1945 (a threshing year) he achieved a record 17,419 sacks, with their assistance.

Later in the war, captured German and Italian prisoners were allocated to assist in manual activities such as lifting sugar beet, picking potatoes, mucking out cattle yards and hoeing root crops on local farms. "Toffee" Everton Halls was a popular administrator of the prisoners, and there are several colourful stories of his tirades against Hitler and Mussolini, being angrily interrupted, to his considerable surprise, by the occasional English speaking prisoner, fluently taking issue with him, in the most vitriolic of terms!

But before we leave the background of war time for the specifics of farming, let us glimpse for one moment into the days of Dad's Army and the Bulmer Village Home Guard, as they trained one evening on a field at the rear of the Sudan Poultry Farm. Jack Cornell takes up the story:

"Yes, we were all there lined up in our uniforms and I've got to admit that we didn't always take it terribly seriously. Anyway, we were a bit bored of being hollered at and parading around and I'd begun to 'lark about' with an old mate of mine, Cyril 'Cheddar' Pope. Well, the sergeant soon put a stop to this and sent Cheddar off, to march up and down the drive to Gogum Hall and every time he got to a telegraph pole, he had to come to attention and salute it. So off he went and made a start. Of course, being as saluting telegraph poles is what you'd call a proper helpful way of winning a war, I stood there watching him and trying to keep a straight face. Well, suddenly the sergeant bawls out, 'Private Cornell!' 'Yes Sarge', I replied. Of course, you know what he told me to do, don't you. so there we were, Cyril Pope and me, both marching in opposite directions, saluting telegraph poles. Huh! Saluting blessed telegraph poles! That was a tidy way to spend an evening, I can tell you!"

With this brief memory of the Home Guard, let us look more closely at the developments within agriculture itself. With the eventual cessation of hostilities and a return to peacetime conditions, the NAAS (National Agricultural Advisory Service) was established to continue the work of the county "War Ags" and encourage farmers to pursue higher standards of husbandry. Most important of all was the 1947 Agriculture Act which placed marketing on a stable basis and ensured a guaranteed minimum return for agricultural produce. It is entirely due to this policy, that cereal agriculture has prospered and its productivity increased.

*   *   *

Development of tractors had begun in the United States of America in 1889. By 1906, Case, Fordson, John Deere and International Harvester had produced models and the British made Ivel was exhibited at the Royal Show of 1903. We have a photograph of Bulmer threshing contractor, Albert Rowe, driving an Ivel tractor in 1915. We think that it was owned by Frank Marsh of Wickham St. Pauls. Irrespective of the tractor's ownership, the photograph heralds the departure from steam, horse or bullock ploughing to the tractor-ised concepts with which we are now so familiar.

But the widescale commercial adoption of tractors on English farms, did not occur until World War I, when the British government placed an order for 6,000 Fordsons, which were imported from America. Farmer, Cyril Philp of Castle Hedingham, who has proved such a fund of knowledge in the research of early mechanisation and steam cultivation takes up the story.

"These tractors started to come into the country about 1917. The first one we had was in July 1918–that was a Fordson from the first batch."

"Did it have a number, or a class type?"

"Good Lord, no! You didn't want to distinguish it–there simply wasn't any other model that time of day . . . it was the only one they had made! We had the second tractor delivered to Whitlocks at Yeldham who sold them."

"What would it have been rated at–30 horse power?"

"No, no! It would have developed about 20-25 horse power. It was a four cylinder job and it would manage two furrows."

The subsequent tractorisation in Bulmer was with surplus Army equipment sold after the Versailles peace of 1919. Harry Winch who had served with the Machine Gun Corps during the Battle of the Somme, drove a petrol/paraffin Clayton Caterpillar for Mr.J.Stennet of Armsey Farm in 1921. Typically it was ex-government stock and was only partially suitable for land work as the tracks wore out too quickly. When used for ploughing, a second man was required to sit on the plough to steer it and lift it out at the headlands. At about the same time he drove a Sanderson iron wheeled tractor and recalls:

"The Sanderson was a more powerful tractor–but it was much larger, in fact built like a small traction engine. We used it for ploughing or driving a threshing drum. It might have pulled three furrows on kind land, but we only had a two furrow plough."*

Jim Stennet, was obviously a progressive farmer in the mould of Robert Andrews who had farmed the same land beside Ballingdon Hall, 150 years before. Besides owning a steam tackle (2 traction engines complete with mole drainer, 6 furrow plough and cultivator), Harry also had experience of driving Fordson, International, Austin and Overtime tractors. Many, such as the early Titan, Mogul, John Deere and Overtime were two cylinder models. All were driven by engines which were warmed on petrol and then "turned over" to paraffin.

"You needed to be a monkey to drive the Overtime, the turnover mechanism was so difficult to get at," he comments.

* Cyril Philp confirms that to pull 3 furrows, the Sanderson required kind land. "Miss Oates had one at Gestingthorpe Hall and it wasn't very satisfactory behind the wood on heavy land with 3 furrows," he recalls.

Yet the rapid adoption of tractors by Jim Stennet at Armsey Farm, was not typical of the Long Furrow which we are tracing. There were several reasons for caution. An obvious criticism of tractors was that, "you can't breed from them." Horses may have cost 40-60 guineas each, but they *were* self perpetuating. Doubtless resistance by older horsemen also played its part and there are local instances, where an old horseman was told to mark out the stetches for a contractor's tractor . . . "but you can be darned certain he made sure they didn't match up!"

An indication of the gradual acceptance of tractors can be seen in the 1931 Cambridge University Economic Survey of Agriculture in the Eastern Counties which quotes the percentate of farms equipped with one tractor or more in that year:

20-50 acres	3%
50-100 acres	10%
100-150 acres	23%
150-300 acres	47%
300-500 acres	64%
Over 500 acres	78%

Newspapers of the era carry advertisements by contractors for ploughing, cultivating and binding.

Jack Cornell describes Spencer Coe's contracting operation, which also involved pulling binders with a tractor—at one time the most tiring of jobs for the horses.

"By the early thirties he had Lance Dixey, Bert Townsend and his brother Lawrence, out tractor ploughing and pulling a binder at harvest time. These tractor drawn binders needed a man on them in anything but ideal conditions, and should have had a sheaf carrier so you didn't run over them on the corners. But our old Albion binder didn't have a sheaf carrier and if you were looking about for a moment, or waving at one of your pals and you ran over a sheaf—and the farmer saw you—well, there'd be hell to pay."

"Spencer Coe had Fordsons mainly; on the blue ones the air intake was through the steering wheel. Then they brought out the yellow Fordsons. You could have a 'red' spot model or 'green' spot depending on the gearing ratio that you wanted."

Most of our horsemen cum tractor drivers have similar memories of the first tractors, which are little less than affectionate. They seem, in fact, to have revelled in the prestige of driving the new equipment. In passing, it should be said, that they were all still fairly young during the phase of transition. Had they been born in 1870, instead of 1900, their reactions to the depletion of the stable and the extension of the tractor shed, may well have been different.

Frank Billimore, who worked at Hengrave (for another member of the Stennet family for whom Harry Winch had worked in Bulmer), provides some recollections of tractor driving in the nineteen thirties.

"The first tractor I drove was a Ruston. it was shaped like an International. Then I had an Oliver which was sold by Mann of Saxham and was very good on light land. We had Fordsons of course, and I also used a Lanz Bulldog for a while. The Lanz Bulldog was a very powerful and well made tractor, I'll say that. You had to heat a bulb up with a blow-lamp afore you tried to start it. Then to turn it over, you took the steering wheel out and put it into the crankshaft. But being as it was a single cylinder, two stroke engine, it might start with the engine running in reverse. Because it was a single cylinder engine it shook about like bill-io when the tractor was stationary and if you tried to adjust the plough with the tractor running—Good Lord, it would almost shake the plough to bits first."

"Was it very noisy?"

"Noise! I should think it was. They reckoned you could hear it five miles away."

"Did you ever have any bad luck with tractors backfiring or anything?"

"No, I was lucky with that one, although several of my mates broke their wrists from one thing or another. But I jolly nearly lost a tractor altogether once, and that frightened the life out of me."

"How did that come about?"

"Oh! I was going from one field to another and I had to cross the Melford to Bury railway line. Of course they don't use it anymore, but that time of day it was quite busy. Well, I only had an early type Fordson with iron spade lug wheels on. Anyway somehow or other, the spade lugs got caught together in the rails . . . then the tractor stalled and conked out. Next thing I heard was the whistle blow as the train left Long Melford. There I was, stuck on the railway line! Was I worried! I knew it was no good trying to start the old girl on petrol when it was hot. So I swung it over on the paraffin and I was in luck, because it caught on—so I leapt back onto the seat and by jumping the clutch managed to bump it out of the tracks and into the gateway. I was just off the line when the train went by–phew, worried! I should think I was! For a moment I thought it had me beat. You know I shall never forget the sight of that fireman shaking his fist at me as he went by–but it was the nearest one as ever I had."

About a mile from Frank Billimore's home near the Cock & Blackbirds in Bulmer Street is the "other half" of the village known as "Bulmer Tye". It was here at the old smithy and surrounded by the tools of that ancient trade, that Horace Elsie, horseman, tractor driver and latterly colleague of Frank Billimore, recalls the early Fordsons that he drove.

"The first Fordson that I used, ran on a coil rather than a magneto. Of course, the paraffin made them terribly smelly when you weren't in hard work. The clutches weren't very bright either; you had to hold them down with a bracket overnight and when you were in work, you wanted to start thinking about de-clutching about 20 yards from the headland! On the other hand, though, they were simple old tractors to work on, in an engineering sense, I'll give them that. It wasn't long before I had either learnt or figured out how to do most major repairs and overhauls."

"Did they make much difference over horses though?"

"Oh yes. Once the 'guvnor' got a tractor on Clapps Farm, we could break the land up and plough that bit deeper . . . it almost doubled yields on its own."

"I've heard that you could get off and walk behind these old tractors and they would steer themselves and the wheel wouldn't come out of the furrow. Is that right?"

"Yes, it is. 'Chance time,' if there's been a hard patch on a field, I've jumped off and rode on the plough to help hold it in. But you must have lugs on the back wheels and iron on the fronts. Rubber front wheels are no good, they just ride straight out of the furrow."

One horseman, who climbed the ladder to become a farmer at Acton and who remembered this, "walking beside a tractor", is Tom Edgeley, who worked at Belchamp Walter in the early thirties.

"Yes," he recalls with amusement, at his retirement bungalow in Long Melford, "it was a bitterly cold day and I jumped off and walked beside the tractor to get warm; well, at one point, the tractor began to spin and I pushed my foot between the spokes to help it get some grip–but oh, golly! then I slipped and couldn't get my foot out! So there I was, going along the field towards the brook with my leg going round and round with the wheel. Of course with each revolution that brook came a little bit closer. I thought, 'you've got to turn it this way and then the other way and it will come out'. I was lucky and it did, but we went several yards before it came!"

"But you know," he continued, "it wasn't at all unusual to get off an iron wheeled tractor and I have seen two men hedging at either end of a field, just turning the tractor round, pulling the rope, setting it in the furrow, jumping off and going back hedging again!"

Eventually the iron wheels were replaced by rubber tyres. During the Second World War, crawlers for ploughing and bulldozers for land reclamation became more common. Some of the Caterpillar, Allis Chalmers and International crawlers from that era, are still successfully employed on the fields of our Long Furrow and may be seen after harvest, with mole drainer or subsoiler behind them.

In the early nineteen fifties, Ken Day was contract ploughing with a Fowler FD3 and the demand was such that the Cansell Brothers were able to start their successful contracting operation from Bulmer at the same time.

But the most important advance in tractor engineering for 20 years was released in 1946, when Harry Ferguson's "hydraulic" system of lifting implements, which revolutionised the tractor's capabilities, was incorporated onto a tractor sold by the Standard Motor Company of Coventry.

Today, Charlie Winch operates the controls of a 295 horse powered Ford Steiger FW30 encapsulated with tinted glass, air conditioning, radio and stereo outfit, that at the time of purchase was one of Britain's twelve most powerful tractors. The mechanisation of Bulmer's furrow has come a long way since his father, Harry Winch, had first tractor ploughed, numbed with cold, windswept and deafened with a 25 h.p. engine across the same fields of Armsey and the Auberies, now sixty one autumns before.

Whilst tractorisation occurred slowly but relentlessly during the twenties and thirties, the introduction of the combine harvester did not commence until 1928, when they were introduced from America, where elementary models had been developed since the late nineteenth century. By 1938 there were still "less than a dozen combines in Suffolk and in 1942 only 32". Indeed very few combines were used in a truly "commercial" sense until the middle thirties and in 1936 the sight of a combine harvester working in a Suffolk wheat field was a sufficiently spectacular sight to become news headlines in the Daily Express.

The photograph beneath the caption shows a Case tanker combine, pulled by a Lanz Bulldog tractor. The tractor driver in the photograph is Harold Cooper, now part of our Long Furrow of Bulmer and Gestingthorpe, and he explains:

"My father, brother John and I first saw the combine when the Suffolk Show was held at Stowmarket. When we bought it, the price was £550 and an American, Oscar Linguist stayed with us during the first harvest, to help assemble the machine and show us how it worked. The cutter bar had a twelve foot width and my brother John stood beside the platform with a wheel, to raise or lower the cutter bar (table) as necessary. The overall width was 25 feet, so we soon had to open up a few gateways to gain access around the farm."

"How much could you cut a day?"

"Between 15-20 acres, although we once did 27. But the crops only "ran" about ten or fifteen hundredweight an acre. So you can't really compare output with today's combines."

"Did it create a lot of resentment?"

I think it might have done, initially, although the land we were working had all gone derelict, so we weren't really making anyone unemployed. Not surprisingly, when we first had the combine it created a tremendous lot of interest. On the first day, after it appeared in the 'Express', over 200 people came and looked at it. After that there would often be 20-30 people passing by who would stop and take a 'look-see'."

One early local purchaser of a combine harvester was Mr. Wilfred Williams of School Farm, Little Maplestead. Hubert Meeking who worked for him at the time, recalls that it was a "trailed" Massey Harris with an eight foot cutter bar. The combine arrived in 1942 in a number of packing crates. Again, one man came to assemble the machine and explain how to use it.

At about the same time, an improved model—the Massey Harris 21— was marketed. This was a purely self propelled machine and far more manoeuvrable than earlier models. Tom Nott of Pebmarsh had an early "21", combining four hundred acres in the first season.

The impact of combine harvesters was colossal. In one stroke the usefulness of the binder and threshing machine were placed in jeopardy and jobs such as shocking, pitching, stack building and thatching of which we have learnt were instantly imperilled. Yet there was no dramatic switch to combines. During the war they were in short supply and sold on "allocation only". Similarly, Jack Cornell reckons that the threshing machine business was fully buoyant until 1947, but thereafter gradually declined over the following fifteen years. "Of course, we put round all manner of tales that combines made a ghastly muddle," he laughs in retrospect.

* * *

Yet amongst the excitement of the new machinery, we should not forget the fields of our Long Furrow, which were ploughed by the improved tractors and whose crops were harvested by the new combines. To fully appreciate the improvements in husbandry that occurred between the mid thirties and the mid fifties we will investigate Smeetham Hall, Bulmer, in some detail. The farm provides an excellent example of the rotation, stock numbers and labour force typical of the nineteen thirties. In its gradual integration of tractors, combines, sprays and fertilisers it is totally representative of the area.

Four fields in the late nineteen thirties indicate the variety of cropping sustained in our Long Furrow at the time.

Field Name	Year 1933	1934	1935	1936	1937	1938
Thistley	Peas	Wheat	Fallow	Wheat	Oats	Trefoil
Claypits	Trefoil	Wheat	Oats	Fallow	Wheat	Barley
Further Brook Field	Barley	Fallow	Wheat	Barley	Red Clover	Wheat
Broom Hill	Oats	Mustard	Barley	Red Clover	Wheat	White Turnips

During these years, the fields of Smeetham Hall were tilled by eighteen working horses, the farm was supporting cattle, pigs and poultry and the rotation which also included: beans, sugar beet, linseed, buckwheat, turnip seed, potatoes, kale and tares, was carefully constucted to allow soil recuperation and weed control through fallows, spring crops and leguminous nitrogen fixing "breaks". With great courtesy, churchwarden and farmer Lawrence Hyde Parker, spent a beautiful summer's morning, amongst the spreading trees and wide lawns of Smeetham Hall garden as he described the traditional system of mixed farming to a latter day "cerealist". His own farming career had started in 1933 and he explains:

"Everything had a purpose . . . nothing was wasted from a farm in those days . . . all the arable by-products were integrated and utilised. For example, the pea rice (haulm) and clover stuver made stock feed. All the wheat, barley and oat straw was used for bedding and feeding. Mangolds, turnips and swedes were grown on lighter soils for livestock. If the beet tops were grazed by sheep there was the extra advantage of manure being provided directly on the field. In any event the livestock provided a tremendous quantity of farmyard manure."

It is this feature of each crop providing multiple benefits to the total farm enterprise that is so different from the "single gross margins" that a farmer expects from his fields of the Long Furrow in 1983. Lawrence Hyde Parker takes one example, red clover, and elaborates on its multiple benefits:

"The hay provided feed for the horses and because it was cut in mid June all the wild oats were removed prior to seeding. Later on, of course, there was the clover seed to sell and finally, the crop is an excellent nitrogen fixing 'entry' for winter wheat."

"I believe that the choice of crop and its date of drilling played an important part in controlling weeds."

"Yes. Tares, mustard and kale were good 'cleaning crops'–because they smothered everything. In those days, one had to be cautious about growing two crops of winter corn in succession, because the weed problem could so easily get out of hand. To assist weed control the drilling of spring crops was often delayed to allow grass and broad-leaved weeds to 'chit' first. Linseed was valuable in this respect because it wasn't sown until early May, which allowed extra time for 'working the land'. Turnip seed offered the other alternative of being harvested in late June and this facilitated a 'summer fallow'."

"So fallowing was still an integral part of the rotation?"

"Very much so. This used to frustrate me as a young man, but my father would say: 'Look what a good opportunity it is to get on top of your twitch and weed problems, to stagger your work load and incorporate atmospheric nitrogen'. A fallow provided a wonderful preparation for winter wheat and improved soil structure. In prosperous times, for example, it provided a good opportunity to call in the 'steamers' for mole draining and deep cultivation."

Other nitrogen fixing crops were peas, beans, trefoil and clover. A rough guide to pre-war cropping at Smeetham was to fallow a field every eight years and muck it every fourth year. But a portent of the great changes that were coming to farming were already being manifest at Smeetham Hall.

"By 1939, we had a couple of tractors—old type Fordsons, iron wheeled, petrol/paraffin engines, noisy throughout and bitterly cold to drive in winter. But—and this is the great thing to note—unlike the horses, the tractor didn't get tired and they didn't have to rest after 8 hours' work. Moreover, the move to tractors released land which had previously been horse meadows, or grown root crops for horse feed, and these fields could then be utilised for arable production.

"Just before the war, things began to improve and I started using fertiliser again. Before the introduction of the combine drill (in 1941), I mixed up the fertiliser and seed corn together and sowed it out, using the big cups of a Smyth drill."

During the Second World War, Lawrence Hyde Parker left Smeetham and volunteered for the RAF, where he flew Hurricanes with 208 Squadron in the Western Desert.

After his return home in 1945, he was able to watch his yields grow as new varieties were introduced. The Smeetham Hall field book, illustrates how varieties of wheat such as Rivet, Little Joss, Squareheads Masters and Yeoman were gradually replaced by the first fields of Capelle wheat (1955) and the introduction of Proctor and Pioneer Barleys. Together with the introduction of selective weedkillers in 1948, cereal yields increased from a pre-war average of below one ton an acre to something approaching two tons by the mid nineteen fifties. Within twenty years, the combined work of plant breeder, herbicide chemist, fertiliser scientist, tractor designer, progressive farmer and adaptable farmworker had succeeded in doubling yields. Stimulated by the neccessities of war time, the limitation on yields which had existed for two hundred years had finally been overcome.

As a consequence of these developments, the need for rotation has diminished. Today, Smeetham Hall grows beans, sugar beet, wheat and barley. But at Boxworth Experimental Husbandry Farm, near Cambridge, Sykes Field has grown wheat continuously for thirty three years without adverse effects. Similarly, in the Broadbaulk experiments at Rothampstead research station, individual plots have grown uninterrupted wheat crops since 1844. That rotations remain today, is more a means of spreading the farmers financial risk and the logistics of his work load than out of any strong necessity to "rest the land". There are still important weed control, soil structure and occassional disease benefits to be gained by varying ones crops, but increasingly, a larger acreage of North East Essex is being devoted to continuous cereals, more specifically continuous wheat.

By the early 1950s, Smeetham Hall had purchased its own combine and the last of the 18 horses was being phased out. In 1955 the farm carried 120 cattle, was selling up to 1400 pigs a year and running a poultry enterprise.

The fifties themselves, when almost every farm still carried a stock enterprise and grew a variety of crops, was to be the last decade of the traditional East Anglian "mixed" farm. For Lawrence Hyde Parker, and countless other farmers of the thirties, who had come through the slump "on hope alone", things were "finally beginning to come right."

Meanwhile, John Reid, who farmed in our Long Furrow at Jenkins during the fifties, was running the village's last flock of sheep. Often these would be grazed on the rye grass and early wheat of his neighbours. Frank Billimore recalls:

"It was a system that worked well for both parties. John Reid got the grazing and the farmer got free muck and the sheep tended to reduce the wild oats population,"

Despite successfully growing a wide range of crops including: carrots, parsnips, potatoes and peas, it is the sheep and the shepherding for which John Reid will be remembered in the area. Ultimately it was to sheep that he turned, when he emigrated in 1962 with his wife, 2 daughters and 5 sons, to the undeveloped homestead on Hawkes Bay, New Zealand. He still farms there today and a descendant occasionally returns to view once more the undulating countryside of Bulmer and Gestingthorpe and the sandy variable soils of Jenkins Farm.

Today, Jenkins grows: wheat, barley, oilseed rape and dried peas, and like Goldingham Hall, Armsey, Kitchens, Griggs and Hilltop Farms, the stockyards, stables, cowsheds and sheep folds are empty and quiet. At night time the sound of breathing animals and the champing of straw is replaced by a haunting silence, that is only broken by the solitary rat that scampers over the rusted hinges of a long shut door.

It is of interest that Bulmer did not overnight transform itself from a village growing 20 crops and carrying 7 types of livestock to a parish growing five crops with 20 bullocks, 2 pig herds and a turkey house. Rather, it took 40 years. On each farm the pace varied because the circumstances of labour availability, soil type and capitalisation were different. But the conclusion must be, that the decisions affecting Bulmer's cropping, have been made more by the twentieth century itself–the plant breeders, polititians, engineers and consumers–than by the land-users themselves. The farmers, as we shall show in Chapter Eighteen have only responded and adapted to the prevailing economic wind. From where the wind blows next we cannot predict. Doubtless, flexibility of farm management will be as necessary in the future as it has been in the past.

One acreage to rise and decline rapidly during the Second Agricultural Revolution beside our Long Furrow has been fruit. At one point in the mid-fifties, Bulmer had 150 acres (5½% of the total parochial land) in orchards. This was principally at Butlers Hall, which grew 130 acres and itself is not far from the Romano-British farmstead village at Hill Farm, Gestingthorpe. Here our agricultural predecessors would have tended apple trees, fruit bushes and vines in the centuries of Hadrian and Constantine.

Inevitably the thought of orchard work presents an image that is both rosy, romantic and healthy. But despite the long tradition of the orchard, our contemporary fruit growers have some serious commercial misgivings.

Fruit grower, Peter Minter, whose nearest 25 acre orchard is beside the ancient kilns and rich hedgerows of the Brickyard, which he also runs, explained:

"As labour conditions have changed and international competition increased, so too has the type of apple tree that we are growing been modified."

"Today, we need low trees that can be picked without ladders. The objective of these new trees is to raise a 'hedge of fruit' involving 3-600 trees an acre producing 500-1000 bushels of apples."

"But since we entered the Common Market we have found that our competitors (the French) have the benefits of extra government assistance to facilitate their replanting schemes. No one minds fair competition," he says, "but what we're up against is lop-sided interference."

In the last decade, both the fruit farm at Gestingthorpe and the Butlers Hall Orchards have been grubbed out. The economic winds are not always favourable and today Bulmer has only 40 acres of fruit and fruit nursery remaining.

Two other enterprises which increased on many farms during the twentieth century were poultry and pigs. Both have represented an integral part of our furrow from the earliest of times and at Doomsday we read that Overhall, Gestingthorpe, had "wood for 60 swine" whilst at Goldingham Hall, Bulmer there were 66 . . .

"The highest number of sow that I had," explains Peter Minter, "was 30, from which I sold about 500 weaners a year. At the time it represented an almost full time job for one man."

At neighbouring Butlers Hall, sow numbers were increased to 200 during the fifties and sixties and at the same time Smeetham Hall was selling 1,400 pigs per year. Similarly, Hilltop Farm, Bulmer, had a herd, and most other local farmers kept sows in their yards. But Lawrence Hyde Parker, Harold Cooper, Arthur Day and Peter Minter have all sold their last sows.

"You either had to borrow a lot of money and get into it in a big way or you decided to specialise in an alternative line. It was simply a case of capitalisation," explains the latter.*

As we move through the late twentieth century, the mass of commercial and political pressure upon agriculture is towards increased specialisation, with a concentration on one or two most profitable lines. It is a trend that most of the older farmers who were interviewed disliked and mistrused.

Whilst intensification, and high capital cost buildings are required for all forms of livestock rearing in contemporary agriculture, there is no clearer example of the colossal changes of the past half century than the poultry industry.

Poultry became popular in the twenties and thirties with field scale "free range" production of eggs. The Auberies kept large numbers of both chickens (and rabbits) on this basis. So too did Goldingham Hall and we remember that during the depression, "Pod" Martin had converted a farmworker's cottage into a packing station.

Local bellringer, Tom Bird, who now works at the Brickyards, was poultry man at Wickham Hall during the nineteen forties and kindly spent a morning, explaining the system of outdoor laying hens, which were so common a sight on the fields of our furrow at the time.

"How long would you keep the hens?"

"About eighteen months to two years."

"And what was involved in looking after them?"

"Well, every morning wet mash was taken around with a horse and cart and in the afternoon they had wheat and maize. Of course, we had to collect all the eggs up and we had a hut in the middle of the field where we did the packing".

"How many hens could one man look after?"

On a free range system, I used to reckon on looking after about 1500. Mind you, they'd be scattered about over about fifteen acres. Of course, you didn't get the eggs then as you do now. Take the hard winter of 1947,

---

* Today, Butlers Hall carries 120 pedigree sows along the lines of the intensive breeding and fattening operations that has replaced others.

our hens were out on an 'open range' and we sometimes had to break the ice six times a day on the water butts to let them drink. When it was very cold we used to heat the huts with paraffin stoves, but those chickens didn't look very happy hobbling about on one foot in that weather. I'd say that the 'deep litter' way of keeping them is altogether more sensible. The chickens are warmer and it is easier to feed them and collect the eggs."

Half a mile from where Tom Bird had been poultryman on the fields of Wickham Hall in the forties, Peter Minter embarked on one such deep litter* venture at Hole Farm in the mid fifties.

"I had 5000 chickens and for a while I did very well," he comments.

So too did many other farmers and smallholders. But all too rapidly, the battery type, "egg efficient", temperature controlled, unit began to predominate. Whereas Tom Bird could look after 1500 birds on 15 acres in the forties, Peter Minter required 5000 to make a commercial proposition in the fifties. In 1982, turkey farmer and businessman, Danny Rowe, estimates that one man must now be able to look after 30,000 layers to be profitable. There are now no commercial chickens in Bulmer.

In this chapter then, we have traced the developments of local agriculture from the horse age to the era of selective weedkillers and giant tractors. We have watched yield of wheat double and seen similar developments with fruit, pigs and poultry.

Today, the village of Bulmer grows only five arable crops and its agriculture continues on a logistical tightrope. A shortage of any one input could result in devastating yield losses. We shall discuss the possible consequences of these trends in our final chapter.

But the new machinery and more productive agriculture has demanded more than the installation of diesel tanks and workshops. To facilitate the intensification of cereal farming and allow the big new equipment of tractor and combine to work efficiently, existing hedge boundaries were rearranged and field sizes increased.

But what, the reader might ask, has been the effect of these changes upon the flora and fauna of the woodland and coppice that has dwelt beside our Long Furrow these past milleniums?

It is this we shall investigate next.

* Not to be confused with battery chickens. Battery hens are kept in a close confined space but "deep litter" birds have complete mobility in an indoor, straw floored, environment.

PART THREE

Hedges, Woodlands, Flowers and Fauna

CHAPTER SIXTEEN

Ancient Woodlands, Hedgerows, Whistles and Withe Making

"The Furrow and the Coppice"

Save elm, ash and crabtree for cart and for plough
Save step for a stile, of the crotch of a bough
Save hazel for forks, save sallow for rake
Save hulver and thorn, thereof flail to make.

Tusser, 16th century

Throughout this book we have stressed the interdependent roles of mankind and nature. We could have called it "The Furrow and the Coppice". For beside the Long Furrow across these many centuries has dwelt the woodland and hedgerow, the spinney and the pollard. Tusser's poetic advice and the comments of hurdle makers, wheelwrights and thatchers embellishes this relationship. But the age old clearing of woodland and the domination by man of his countryside, has also been a continual theme. Initially by browsing and burning and latterly with axe and horse, the destruction of our ancient wildwood has been an integral part of our rural history.

Yet there is a prevalent belief at this time, that it is only in the twentieth century that the English landscape has suffered a major reduction in its woodland size. Throughout this book, particularly in Chapters 1, 4 and 5, we have attempted to modify this contention.

In "Trees and Woodlands in the British Landscape", Oliver Rackham testifies to the "colossal exertion of energy expended by our predecessors in clearing woodland". He also suggests that by 1200 A.D., the English landscape had taken on something of the appearance that it has today. Later we read Arthur Young's observation of 1805, that "the country around . . . Gestingthorpe and Bulmer is very much improved . . . in hollow draining and in throwing together many little enclosures crowded together with pollards."

In this chapter we shall examine Bulmer in detail, and use our "target village" as an example of the general trend toward woodland clearance within the area of our Long Furrow.

From a collection of early maps and perambulation records, tithe assessment and ordnance survey sheets, we are able to review the decline in Bulmer's woodland.

1775	At least	300	acres woodland
1808		263	acres woodland
1848		244	acres woodland
1981	approx	200	acres woodland

Yet these figures are slightly deceptive. For although the total acreage of woodland appears to have dropped by only 30% in the past 230 years, the reduction of ancient woodland–the most ecologically valuable, is in the order of 70%. Approximately half of the village's 200 acres of contemporary woodland is fairly recent plantation. Simultaneously there has been a considerable, but necessary, reduction in hedgerow mileage.

It is the lingering remnants of ancient hedgerow and woodland that are of most ecological importance. In Chapter One, Colin Ranson of the Nature Conservancy Council, described them as "reservoirs of wildlife that cannot be recreated".

"The older the hedge or wood is," he explains, "the more ecologically valuable it becomes, supporting an inherited abundance of plant, insect and bird life, whose inter-relating habitats, have been established over several milleniums. During that time they have constructed a micro environment of their own that is virtually impossible to recreate. These areas can only be compared in their importance to the decreasing acreages of unploughed pasture and moorland in which are preserved a wealth of rare flowers, grasses, symbiotic insects and birds."

"Could you remind us how to identify ancient hedgerow or woodland?"

"Yes. There will be a tremendous variety of both trees and shrubs– at least 20 species are commonly found in most ancient woods of five acres or more; these ancient woods, may well be on parish boundaries and bordered by a deep ditch. Moreover the existence of small leafed lime, oxlip, wood anemone, dogs mercury and to a lesser extent, bluebells, indicate that woodland may be ancient."

CHANGES IN WOODLAND SINCE 1755

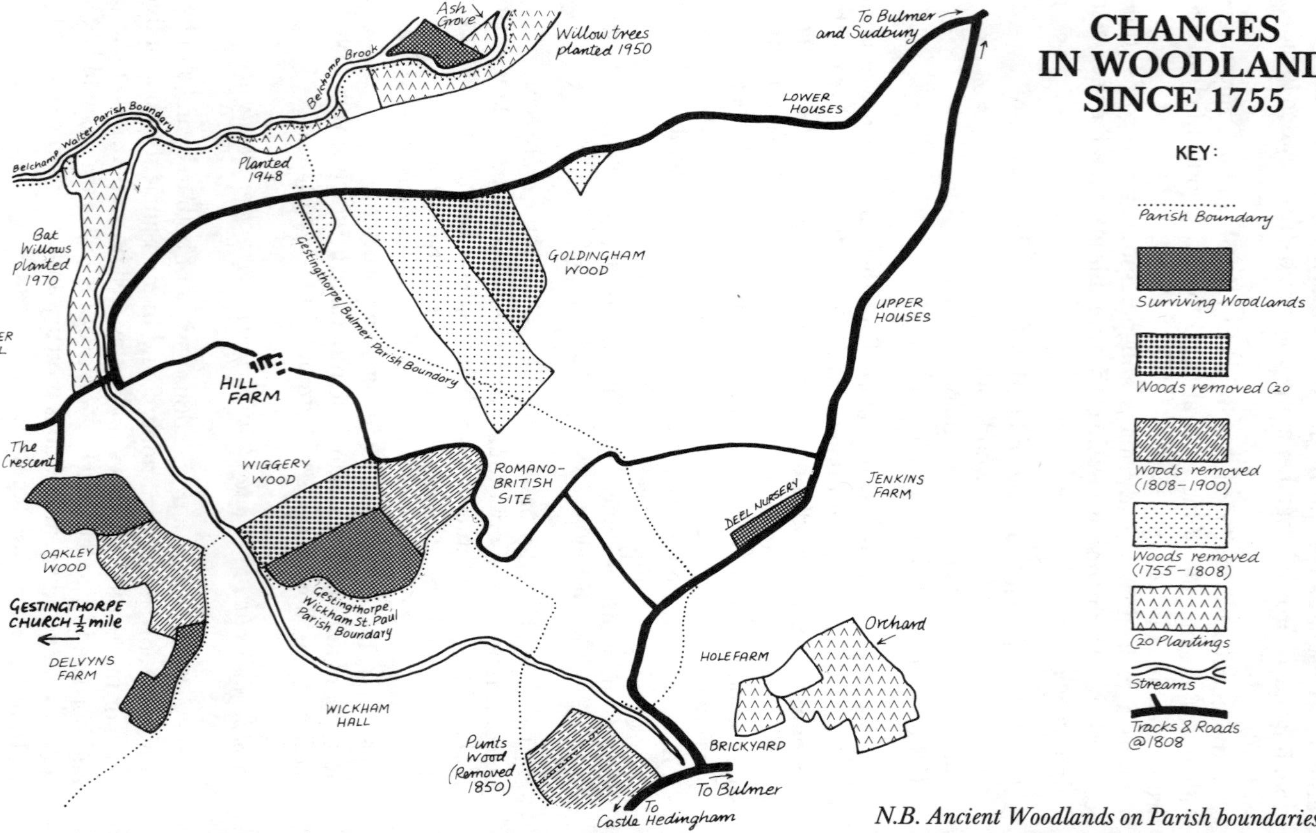
KEY:
Parish Boundary
Surviving Woodlands
Woods removed C20
Woods removed (1808–1900)
Woods removed (1755–1808)
C20 Plantings
Streams
Tracks & Roads @1808
To Bulmer and Sudbury
Ash Grove
Willow trees planted 1950
Belchamp Brook
Belchamp Walter Parish Boundary
Planted 1948
LOWER HOUSES
Bat Willows planted 1970
GOLDINGHAM WOOD
Gestingthorpe/Bulmer Parish Boundary
UPPER HOUSES
NETHER HALL
HILL FARM
The Crescent
WIGGERY WOOD
ROMANO-BRITISH SITE
JENKINS FARM
DEEL NURSERY
OAKLEY WOOD
GESTINGTHORPE CHURCH ½ mile
Gestingthorpe, Wickham St. Paul Parish Boundary
Orchard
HOLEFARM
DELVYNS FARM
WICKHAM HALL
Punts Wood (Removed 1850)
BRICKYARD
To Bulmer
To Castle Hedingham

N.B. Ancient Woodlands on Parish boundaries.

"I believe that there's some sort of theory by which one can begin to estimate the age of a hedge. How does one go about it?"

"By actually counting the number of species within it. As a general guide it is reckoned that for every tree and shrub species found within a 30 yard stretch one can assume a hundred years of existence. If over ten species are identified the hedge will almost certainly be pre-Norman Conquest in origin and possibly the perimeter of an erstwhile area of ancient woodland."

Once one has had an afternoon in the company of Colin Ranson and begun to identify tree, shrub and flower species–the names and characteristics of which were inculcated in our forefathers' mentality in many miles of companionable walking to church, work or homestead, the procedure of hedge and wood dating becomes both easy and fascinating. The discovery of ancient hedgerow or woodland is especially exciting.

The enormous variety of living creatures and plants, humming, throbbing and striving together, with a frantic lust for life must surely be superior to fleeting pleasures of the glamourously advertised African game park. After a bad deal on the grain trade, a tiring day's spraying or a maddening harvest thunderstorm, the quiet hedgerow search can be especially relaxing and rewarding.

Several factors have influenced the reasoning behind the creation of the recent plantations in Bulmer. Some woodland such as that on Long Smallbridge field is simply pasture that "went behind" in the great depression of the 1930's and was subsequently never reclaimed. Charlie Chatters was "amazed" to see the tangled mass of blackthorn, elder, ash and sycamore when for sixty years his memory had been of a green meadow.

Similarly, beside Long Smallbridge is the 22 acre willow tree plantation established by Stanley Nott of Goldingham Hall. They are a good example of how external forces have influenced land use in the village. When tractors replaced the horses which had previously grazed the flood meadows*, the farmer had a choice of either utilising the grass for bullocks, (semi profitable and complicating an arable system) or utilising the land in a different manner. Stanley Nott elected to grow willow trees to be sold for cricket bats.

Almost a mile to the east of the Goldingham willow plantation is Bulmer's largest estate and most pleasantly appointed house–the Auberies. It was in the Auberies' grounds that Thomas Gainsborough painted the famous portrait of its eighteenth century occupants, Mr. and Mrs. Robert Andrews.

---

* 2,000,000 acres of grass and arable were required to feed working horses in 1939: (Farming and Wildlife by Professor Mallanby: published Collins, 1982).

Peter Burke who took responsibility for administering the 1200 acre Auberies estate in 1951 has since planted almost 100 acres of woodland. He declares "I want to live in the countryside; and I want to enjoy it. I don't want to look out across a prairie".

At the time he represented an almost unique blend of profitable progressive farmer and landscape conservationist. "When I took over," he continues, "several fields were too small for modern agriculture. When these hedges were removed, we would find other fields of one or two acres which would still be too small if every hedge was bulldozed. It was these that we planted up". Today he is able to give clear and valuable avice on woodland establishment.

"Initial advice was to plant on a five foot square, but with the single exception of Christmas trees," he continues, "it is better to plant on a ten foot square. At five to six feet you get too many brambles and can't do the job mechanically; you must be able to tractor clear them."

Of the 132 acres of woodland on the Auberies estate, the 100 acres planted in the past 30 years are principally softwoods—Larch, Norway Spruce and Scots Pine. "The softwoods," explains Peter Burke, "look nice, grow quicker, and are better suited to the poorer land." But he is keenly conscious of the intrinsic, ecological value of natural hardwoods. "On the better land, especially where we planted over old hedges, the traditional trees such as elm, holly, ash and especially oak, will all come anyway." But he has also been to some lengths to induce a variety of species into his woodlands and each winter a few days are spent in planting dogwoods, broom, snowberry and coppice hazel in the bottoms.

Terminating the interview he concluded with a rapt comment that could well be adopted as the maxim for any farmer or landowner: "The objective," he surmises, "must be to leave (the farm) in better condition than you found it."

Today one only has to drive through the lanes of Bulmer or up Ballingdon Hill, to admire the result of 30 years vigorous estate management, and what can only be described as almost two square miles of landscape gardening.

At Pelham Hall, Twinstead, Kenneth Nott reflects the views of Colin Ranson of the Nature Conservancy Council. "Many woods are now in an unholy mess—woodland management actually does mean management, it isn't just a passive thing" he declares. During his lifetime he remembers both Butlers and Gentrys Woods being clear felled and recalls that there was a renewed interest in firewood during the nineteen thirties and Second World War.*

---

* Previously this trade had been substantially reduced by the coming of the railways and the introduction of cheap coal to the countryside. As early as 1800, Arthur Young laments:

"Forty years ago farmers burnt little else than wood. But at present a large proportion burn a considerable quantity of coal."

COPPICING
Timber cut down to stub height
will then grow again.

POLLARDING
On a tod tree, livestock cannot
eat the young branches.

If continuously managed in this way, pollarded trees or coppiced stubs
can live for many hundreds of years.

Most of the old countrymen in our survey have particular associations with the wood from the hedges and spinneys that they coppiced.

Ernest Lott (born 1899) recalls that faggots were sold from Butlers Wood to both the maltings and bakery in Long Melford. Horseman Horace Elsie explains that the waggon held 50 faggots and that the journey required two horses.

On the estate where he first worked, north of Bury St. Edmunds, Frank Billimore was involved in coppicing 10 acres each winter of a 100 acre wood, (i.e. a 10 year "managed" cycle). If perpetually managed in this way, there is no reason why the "stools" or stubs cannot become immortal. Ash, he remembers, was used for hurdles, nut (hazel) for faggots, and whitethorn for "burning at the big house". Kenneth Nott recalled that one use of birch, was for clogs, whilst another, says Ben Perkins, is for the besoms (or bushes) of a "witch's" broom. Walnut, is fashioned into furniture and gun stocks. Hornbeam—an exceptionally hard wood was traditionally utilized in the manufacture of flails, ox yokes, mallets and mill gears, whilst the wooden chopping block that is used in the present day butchers shop was probably made from the same tree. Pod Martin, who remembers the hornbeam in the now reclaimed field of Goldingham Wood, had used the timber for stock railings and suggested that the wood could be burnt when almost green. Poplar has been found in the shell of an older Bulmer cottage whilst black poplar, now extremely rare —was almost splinter proof and ideal for the floor boards of carts. Peter Burke, believes that the Scots Pine from the Auberies plantations will eventually make pit props or window frames. The larch that he has planted is rot proof and is especially useful for boat building and the floors of cattle trucks. Wheelwright Hazell Chinnery (born 1892) enthused about larch as a "strong, resilient, pliable wood . . . used for making the shafts of dog carts.

Cecil Smith, whose father was a blacksmith at Felsham in mid-Suffolk, recalls that in the making of cart wheels wych elm was used for the hubs, ash for the felloes and oak for the spokes. The latter provides a wood with a multplicity of applications from fencing posts to timber building frames; of more local interest, however, was the collection of oak bark for tannin.*

Within the old rurality, every species of wood had its own particular use and individual foible. The lingering hedges, that we see as a blurred amalgam of trees and bushes from the passing car, were repositories of many separate characteristics to the men of our Long Furrow over the many seasons of past centuries.

For our erstwhile thatcher the hedgerow and coppice was the source of his hazel springels and broaches: for the horseman it was the site of his well placed snare: for the itinerant gypsy it offered a few days peg making: to the old man it provided kindling for his fire, pea sticks for his garden, walking sticks for his perambulations and herbal cures for his ailments. For the youngster the hedgerow was a "toy shop" of bird nesting, home made whistles and catapult manufacture. To his parents who "picked the hedge fruits as they came into season" it supplied the nuts, jams, preserves and wines that were an essential variation to a meagre diet. To some, the straggling hedgerows represented an additional source of income from the sale of firewood, oak bark, acorns, rabbits and goldfinches.

For all our former parishioners, be they farmers or hurdlemakers, wheelwrights or builders, the ancient woodlands of the village were the single source of their timber needs in the centuries before widescale transportation had developed. During the middle ages, for example, it was the hedgerow teasels that were used for "teasing" or carding the wool, whilst woollen costumes were dyed with the essence from local flowers. But even the advent of technology in the twentieth century, has not completely destroyed this symbiotic relationship. Douglas Hasler whose father "thatcher" Bertie Hasler had cut his "bundles of nut hazel springels from Oakley Wood", recalls how, "about 1929, we had our first wireless set which was one of the first in the village. So father took me down to Oakley Wood and cut an ash pole down for the aerial." (A wireless needed an aerial in those days.) "He lifted the thick end of the pole on his shoulders and I put the small end on mine. But I was only a boy then and couldn't manage, so he

---

* Earlier this century, Philip Rowe senior had sold oak bark to a tanners yard at Bures. Here it was soaked in water to extract the tannin which was subsequently deposited into pits with the leather hides.

sent me home for the wheelbarrow that he'd made, and I wheeled the big end with the barrow and he took the small end and we got home like that".

Other contributors provide additional recollections: Emily Hearn, born in 1890, citing an old custom, remembered that, "father had a fence (hedge) off one of the farmers every year ... he liked whitethorn best as it burned well and gave off more heat." It was with this wood that the family baked its bread as described in Chapter Eight. "Jute" Chatters, recalls that holly was ideal for the manufacture of walking sticks. Reg Rippingale, described the sale from Wiggery Wood of faggots at sixpence each. Bert Surridge demonstrated how to make the "withe" or band which was used to tie up the bundle. "Old" Philip Rowe, who quartered brambles for "binders" had also made a "frail basket" from bull rushes. The frail basket recalls son Tom, was used to take the hot dinner out to the fields at harvest time. Threshing contractor Jack Cornell, insisted that dogwood, or "gartridge", provided the best twigs for the manufacture of brick sparrow traps, "because it is one of the few strong woods that provides an equal and double crotching–necessary to trip the mechanism", Farmer, Harold Cooper, immediately declared that dogwood had been ideal when he was a child for making arrows, "because the double crotching prevents the wood splitting when you put the feather in". Like many other country lads of his generation, he had made "whistles from ash and pop guns out of alder" from which the pith is so easily removed. Philip Rowe, described the manufacture of whistles, from both horse chestnut and wild oat stalks. Bob Raymond suggested that the best whistles could only be made in the springtime when the sap was rising: we have illustrated the process of pop gun and whistle manufacture at the end of this chapter.

Other shrubs and trees provided food and extra income. Whilst Philip Rowe senior was involved in any of his numerous crafts, his children were earning a shilling a bushel for picking up acorns. Similarly for his wife and countless other women of her generation, it was the sloes, bullace, blackberries, hazel nuts, walnuts and crab apples that provided an interesting and nutritious source of variety to the rural diet.

But there were other medicinal properties, poisons and superstitions within our ageing hedgerow. As we saw in Chapter Twelve, the root of bryony was one of several plants discreetly used by our old horsemen, when caring for their animals. Similarly, shepherd Charlie Martin, had induced a sick ewe to eat, by offering it a sprig of young ivy, when it was recovering from Black Gargett. But the treatments were not limited to the animal world. At Wickham St. Pauls, farmworker Cecil Smith recalls that "feverfew (chrysanthemum parthenium) was good for migrane", whilst wife Hilda reports that "my father's generation placed silver weed (potentilla anserina) in their boots to make their feet feel more comfortable when they had a long way to walk . . . the plant always grew right up to the edge of the road". Appropriately silver weed is known in the area by the colloquialism of "foots-ease".

Similarly some flowers ending in "wort" were traditionally considered to have curative and herbal values, e.g. St. John's Wort (prescribed to stop bleeding) figwort (believed to be an antidote to piles) and woundwort (leaves were used to dress wounds). By comparison, the berries of cuckoo pint (lords and ladies), common in Bulmer hedgerows, are poisonous to children. So too are hemlock, black and white bryony, lily of the valley, deadly nightshade, holly and ragwort. But possibly the most common irritant to our bodies is blackthorn. The sharp needles can quickly inflame the skin and swell joints, especially if pricked in frosty weather. One Bulmer resident of the nineteenth century, David Rowe, grandfather to so many of the contributors to this book, had to have a finger removed because of this toxin. Possibly this is why it is considered to be bad luck to bring blackthorn in to the house. Ill fortune is also reputed to follow the burning of elder on the domestic hearth. But in the authors experience it only provides an anaemic flame, and the belief may well be a subliminal warning to avoid the misplaced labour of cutting it down.* Finally of bat willow, we have found—since the first crop was taken to provide the golden wands of English youth—that although it cracks, snaps and violently spits if once split or quartered, it will be as docile and quiet as any other wood, if simply left to burn in circular or log shaped lengths.

But before we leave this Chapter on the uses of the plants of our hedge-rows and gardens, let us spend a rainsoaked, grey, November Saturday morning, amongst the dusty, half lit, shelves of the Essex Archaeological

---

* An old motto corroborates this hypothesis and advises, "if you can burn elder you can burn the devil".

Top left: Cowlsip.

Top right: Midway between a cowslip and a primrose, these oxlips are some of the last to be found in Gestingthorpe or Bulmer.

COUNT THE COWSLIP COMPETITION!

"In an age before television, radio or motor cars," recalls Dennis Rippingale, "you had to walk everywhere and it was a natural talking point if you saw a bird or a flower that was slightly exceptional"

The cowslip (or "paigle") shown has 27 heads, competitors who provide entries of cowslips with more than 35 heads will be given a free copy of the next publication.

Below: The size of coppice stools—something else that would make a good competition to look out for! The hazel from this stub, has provided thatching springels, pea sticks, withes and firewood for at least 300 years and possibly longer.

Alastair Tuffill–Photography

Cecil and Hilda Smith.

Bee orchid–photographed locally.

Silver Weed–"Footsease"

Society's library, beside Colchester Castle in Hollytrees House. It is here, amongst the fading manuscripts and rare leather bound books, that we discover "The Kings Evil" by John Morley Esq., apothecary of Halstead. The first edition of this work was printed in 1776. The library contains the twenty second edition published in 1824. In garrulous style, the author declares that his work, "is published for the good of mankind. Particularly the common people". It consists of an essay on, "the nature and cure of Scrophulous Diseases commonly called the Kings Evil". For this malignant complaint he prescribes "the herb Vervain and its root". He continues by describing his success with this medium declaring that, "many of my patients are quiet cured, others greatly relieved. Limbs condemned to amputation are preserved, and some turned out of hospitals as incurables are cured . . ." He insists, "all I have related is strict truth, nor do I take any money for my advice . . .". He implores readers and sufferers not to be disheartened by the simplicity of his principle recommendation, which is for a, "fresh common purple vervain root about three or four inches long and about the size of a patients little finger. Let the buyer take heed. Cut all the fibres off smooth but as little of the rind as possible. The root is to be worn at the pit of the stomach and tied with a yard of white satin ribbon, half an inch wide and around the neck of men and women of ordinary stature . . . but no other coloured ribbon must be used because the dye maybe prejudicial . . ."

Morley then provides sixty case histories of patients, whom he has successfully treated with this and similar herbal cures. Several have local connections. We read in Case One of Philip Winterford, a journeyman barber of Halstead; in Case Four of Elizabeth Reynolds, wife of Joseph Reynolds, farmer of Halstead and in Case Six, of Deborah Alston, wife of Thomas Alston of Henny, Essex. Simultaneously, he prescribes "elder ointment . . . which is made in the spring by boiling the young leaves in mutton suet," whilst he is also administering "a cataplasm of groundsel; 20 millipedes bruised in whey, egg liquor and ointments of hemlock, antimony, black plaister and sorrell."

During this Chapter we have examined the decline in the total area and uses of woodland within our Long Furrow. Recently, as a consequence of escalating fuel prices, a trend has developed towards installing wood burning stoves for domestic heating. Possibly, indeed hopefully, as a consequence of this movement the coppice and the pollard may be given a new lease of life and rotational woodland management may again become a positive commercial feature of our Long Furrow. Contemporaneously a growing enthusiasm is developing for traditional and herbal therapies. Before we investigate the ecological transformations which have occurred within our villages in the past centuries, let us conclude this chapter with two of John Morley's case histories from the decades of Arthur Young and Robert Andrews in the late 18th century. Both have local connections and the first is a name which persistently recurs throughout our villages.

Case XV

"Elizabeth Golden, wife of John Golden of Water Belchamp (sic) in Essex, husbandman, had a most violent hot salt humour in her left leg, which broke almost into numberless Water Bladders; itched much and was greatly inflamed and the flesh hardened; and the inside of her thigh on the same side began to be affected in a like manner. I advised her to drink half a pint of tea made with the Common Red Dock Root, sliced thin, morning and night or boiled in cheese whey, then to wash her leg and thigh all over, with an infusion of Green Hemlock leaves, and to annoint the same with Elder ointment; in 3 months she came to me almost well, but complained of a coldness at her stomach, for which I ordered a gentle purge of jalop, with a little grated ginger once a week. About 2 months after she came to thank me, being quite free of her complaints.   *Note:* No root prescribed as I thought it (the ailment) more scorbutic than scrophulous."

In another case, Morley describes his treatment of Esther Maxham of Foxearth aged twenty seven. He utilised a Vervain Root and records that she visited him four months after.

Case XXXVII

"Some scrophulous ulcers developed within side the right hand, near the roots of the two smaller fingers and several near the joints, on the backs of the same fingers: the sinews in the palm of the hand were hard and contracted, the corners of the mouth scabby. She had (was prescribed) a Vervain root and took gentle Physic to keep her body open. The hand was poulticed with white nettles, mallows, fat and fine oatmeal and was quite well in two months and she now has no other scrophulous complaint about her."

Two centuries later the elder leaves, groundsel, hemlock, sorrell, red dock, white nettles and mallows are still to be found amongst the hedge-banks and lanes where Dr. Morley administered them. I have been unable, however, to locate the herb Vervain in Gestingthorpe or Bulmer.

HORSE CHESTNUT OR ASH WHISTLE

To be made in spring or early summer whilst the sap is rising.

cut notch here

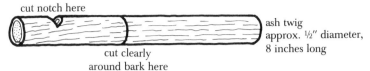

ash twig
approx. ½″ diameter,
8 inches long

cut clearly
around bark here

Revolve the wood whilst tapping the bark
and eventually by twisting, the bark will come free off the body

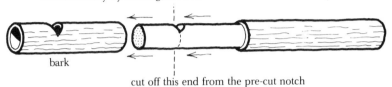

bark

cut off this end from the pre-cut notch

now cut a small
sliver from top

of small end

place this in the end of the hollow bark

Now press the bark back over the main stem blowing as you push. There may only be one place at which the whistle will blow effectively. It was suggested that horse chestnut was the most suitable tree for whistle making.

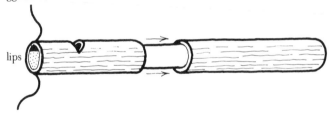

lips

WILD OAT WHISTLE

Take a wild oat or wheat straw and cut off at a node. This forms a natural barrier and is the end of the whistle. The reed is formed simply by slicing a pen knife toward the node on one side of the stalk. A few holes can be cut into the hollow stem. The other node, will be cut off.

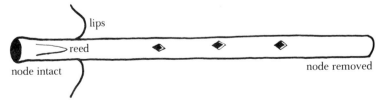

lips

reed

node intact

node removed

Jack Cornell neatly summed up the pleasures and pursuits of rural life for a Bulmer lad born in 1919 (the pre-television and motor car era) with the following remark:

"That time of day, if you were a boy and you could get yourself a penknife it was like having a prize possession; you could really begin to do things then and a whole range of opportunities opened out to you."

"There was two lovely horse chestnut trees outside the church when I was a choirboy. One Sunday I went in thinking about a nice piece I'd spied, just ideal for a whistle. When the service was over, I rushed off and was half way up this tree to cut a bit down. Then the squire came out of church. He hully hollered at me! I wasn't too popular for a little while after that."

POP GUN MANUFACTURE

1. Cut a piece of elderberry wood approximately eight inches long and one inch in diameter. Extract the soft pith with a narrow screw driver or a six inch nail, until you are left with a hollow tube.

2. Cut another piece of wood (not elderberry) about two inches longer and allowing about two inches for the handle, trim the remainder down to act as the plunger.

Make a pellet from moist newspaper and push up the "barrel" until it reaches the end or the plunger will go no further. Then place another pellet at the entrance and give the plunger a short jerk. Anything happen? If not, you have either shaved too much–or not enough off the plunger. For "quick fire action", the mechanism works better with the aid of soapy water.

*   *   *

As we were putting the pop gun away, John Llewellin came into the yard and for a few moments thought I'd taken complete leave of my senses. Before he arrived, we found that pellets of "The Times" would travel a distance of 66 feet. We made a few modifications and tried a few slugs from the pages of "The Sun". Performance improved, and in still conditions we reached the 100 feet objective. We think, that possibly the paper from "The Sun", may have–er–a better–body in it?

CHAPTER SEVENTEEN

Wild Flowers and Nesting Birds
An Ecological Survey

The advent of mechanisation and the consequent demise of the working horse and free range livestock enterprises of pigs, poultry and sheep, has resulted locally in an almost total abandonment of rotational leys, and ecologically rich, permanent meadow ground or rough grazing. Although we have no precise figures, it can be assumed that somewhere between 250-600 acres (10-20%) of the parish would have been grazed in 1900. Today this acreage is minmal. Alongside these transformations a new, intensive non-rotational, cereal agriculture has developed, sustained by the imported fertilisers and chemicals which have enabled its yields to double since 1940.

But what are the repercussions of these innovations upon the ecological balance of the locality? What price has the natural flora and fauna of our Long Furrow had to pay for these dramatic and inspiring agricultural achievements?

To definitively answer these questions would have involved conducting an ecological survey at regular intervals in the past century. Obviously this has not happened. However, a surprising amount of information can still be pieced together by applying a local historians approach to the task of writing a "natural" history of the "target" area. Frequently, for example, when researching chapters for the "horse era", I would stumble inadvertently across information for the wildlife survey, when a source was illustrating an unrelated agricultural story. For example, "we were hoeing sugar beet one day and that was suff'en hot and I hung my jacket up on an old bit of gartridge . . ."

Equally the pursuit of semi-related subjects supplied several useful openings. The recollection that: "mother always used to make homemade wines and we children would go and help her pick in the hedges", would provoke the question, "where would you go? Where were the best bushes?"

As in any investigation, the direct question often proved to be an unrewarding stratagem. This is not because the interviewee is deliberately attempting to withhold information, but a more languid, circuitous approach, gives an older person's memory more time to adjust. The direct statement: "Do you remember any wild orchids in your youth?" might result in an uncertain and hesitant "No, I don't think so", but the same question constructed around familiar cornerstones, such as, "I was talking about orchids to old .... last night, he lives down in .... now, and he said that years ago when he was a boy, there used to be a meadow full of them up by ....", might well stimulate an enthusiastic, indeed competitive, "Yes, and there were some behind the house here as well!" Later, a policy of enquiring into the local names of wild flowers, provoking memories of adverse climatic conditions and discussing the game bird and rabbit ferreting syndromes of rural life, all provided additional information in our search to discover the breadth of our local ecological heritage.

Yet irrespective of the rhetorical ploys adopted the most provident evenings of all, were spent interviewing not one, but rather two, older people together. With just the occasional prompting the vivid memories of their childhood days were brought back to mind, not by my questioning but rather through the energy and interchange of each others thoughts.

In many respects this portion of our enquiry, far from being completed, is is reality only partially started. What I have tried to demonstrate—and hope will be continued by other people—is the process by which one can quite quickly begin to gain an impression of the former flora and fauna of an area, identify the changes which have occured, establish which plants, meadows or hedgerows—if any—are of especial value and by monitoring the slow rejuvenation of our depleted environment, stimulate the voluntary enthusiasm which can assist the process of its preservation. Within this ethos, it is knowing what to look for and being able to recognise what one has found, that is of paramount importance. Identifying and then coming to appreciate for example, that the small clump of oxlips on the bank in the corner of .... field, is possibly the last site in Bulmer where they are still growing, when forty years previously they were a common flower, provides an additional inducement and purpose to the whole project. Later we will learn how to make the identifications.

Let us, however, commence our enquiry into the dissipation of wildlife species, with a telephone call to farmer Kenneth Nott of Pelham Hall, Twinstead, who declares that, "As a boy you couldn't hear yourself speak in a wood, there was so much natural activity." He provides some general observations that have since stimulated many further questions and interviews.

"Frogs have almost completely disappeared, rooks, bats and owls have become scarce and there are very few badgers left."

Indeed it must surely be the decline of the frog population, (colloquially known as "jakeys") that is so devastatingly evident, in the ponds and streams beside the Long Furrow of Bulmer and Gestingthorpe today. Thatcher, hurdlemaker and brickmaker Philip Rowe, used to "pick frogs up in clusters" when digging brick earth amongst the damp pools of Bulmer Brickyard. Reg Rippingale recalls an old farmworker putting a "jakey" in his shirt front to keep himself cool when mowing grass on Brook Field, Gestingthorpe. Horseman and tractor driver Frank Billimore, had to dismount from his bicycle when riding past the pond, on his way to work at Goldingham Hall, because, "the frogs were so thick on the ground". Today, the single remaining sanctuary of frogs in the entire parish is amongst the carefully supervised lake of the Auberies. But it is not simply frogs alone, whose population has been decimated. Other aquatic species have completely disappeared. Several older respondents recall eels, roach and pike swimming as far upstream as Gestingthorpe, in the meandering and flood prone valley of the pre-war Belchamp Brook. As a boy, Reg Rippingale had gone fishing for the pike and the roach, whilst "old" Philip Rowe devised a means of snaring the eels, which were quite common in the pools of Belchamp Mill and the swampy "horse mash" (marsh) of Goldingham Hall. Otters too, which have now vanished, inhabited the same stream and Jack Cornell recalls that the otter hounds were hunting the brook during the nineteen forties. But if the demise of the local otter, frog and fish population, with its implication of broken food chains, is an evident consequence of twentieth century developments, what has been happening to our less obvious flora and fauna?

Seventy five years after she last walked around the chalk pit of Goldingham Hall as a parlour maid, Emily Hearn asked excitedly whether "maiden hair grass still grows there?" It doesn't. Nor do the harebells that once graced the Deal nursery beside which her invalid father carried his postmans letters to Wisborough Hill. Of the five favourite flowers of Mabel Chatters—ladies hair, king cups, milkmaids, cowslips and pigs feet—it is only king cups and cowslips that remain in any profusion. Farmworker "Jute" Chatters recalled the fields of Fowes Field being so severely infested with "crows onions" that the harvested wheat was rejected by millers because of the resultant "taint". Today "crows onions" are a locally rare plant. Hilda Smith, a keen amateur botanist, confirms the loss of sheepsbit (like scabious), milkwort and Jack-go-to-bed-at-noon. Corn marigold, which husband Cecil remembered by its local name of "Boodels", grew in abundance near Butlers Hall; it is now but rarely seen. Jack Sultzberger identified oxlips in Belchamp Walter in the early fifties; they have since disappeared.

Numerous other contributors bemoan the loss of the oxlip from the diminished meadows of their youths. In fact, the oxlip is enmeshed in confusion with out oldest octogenarian contibutors referring to them as "cowslips". The cowslip itself has the very general and common sobriquet of "paigle" The latter is pronounced peg-el and a not infrequent expression is "as yellow as a paigle".) Undoubtedly both species have suffered numerically in the past half century, but the oxlip—always the rarer has declined almost to local oblivion.

I found my first oxlip—of which the older respondents had spoken so excitedly, on a Friday evening in April 1982. Ironically I was spraying MCPA, when I saw the similar, but distinctly different, oxlip features amongst some cowslips on a chalky embankment. In my excitement I jumped off the tractor, and had almost reached the spot when I remembered that my wellington boots were also drenched in chemical . . . later I hauled wild flower artist Benjamin Perkins from the companionship of the Otten "Red Lion" to confirm the identification. Suitably tanked up, and well after closing time, we stumbled about with a flashlight until he pronounced the verdict to be good. I think it is the last place in Gestingthorpe or Bulmer where they are still growing.

Yet far from proving confusing, the differences in nomenclature between oxlips, cowslips and paigles, only stimulated a deeper investigation into other alternative names for wild flowers. Farmworkers daughter, Hilda Smith of Wickham St. Pauls, has made the study of wild flowers her special hobby for the past seventy years and she provides the following list:

Flower	Nickname	Flower	Nickname
Pink Campion	Plum Pudding	Cinquefoil	Creeping Jenny
Speedwell	Birds Eye	Meadow Sweet	Queen of the Meado
Groundsel	Simpson	Vipers Bugloss	Our Lords Flannel
Silver Weed	Footsease	Valerian	Pretty Betsy
Hogweed	Cowmumble	Stitchwort	Shirt Buttons*
Sunspurge	Milkweed	Teasel	Sweeps Brush
Ladies Smock	Headaches	Laurel	Wood Laurel
Burdock	Gypsy Rhubarb	Snake Head	Dead Mans Bell
Archangel	Yellow Nettle	Heartsease	Garden Gate

But amongst Hilda Smith's keen botanic interests is a special fascination for wild orchids. She recalls that the early purple orchid grew in the now reclaimed Wiggery and Goldingham Wood whilst the Summer or Marsh

---

* Nick Pluck, gamekeeper of Wickham St. Pauls adds that "shirt buttons are called 'poppetts' when they develop a seed pod; whilst an alternative name for lords and ladies or cuckoo pint is hot poker".

orchid was an erstwhile Twinstead flower. Each year she pays at least one visit to a nearby sanctuary where the early purple orchid still grows, and where in smaller isolated areas that most spellbinding and startlingly disguised wild flower of all, the Bee orchid may still be seen. The photograph of the Bee orchid that we have included was taken entirely as the result of Hilda Smith's keen and enthusiastic encouragement. In our target area of Bulmer and Gestingthorpe the early purple orchid is still seen, although the Bee orchid, which once grew "in profusion near Hilltop Farm" is now only seen in two occasional and tenuous locations.

Yet the most exciting of all of the discoveries of the botanic past of our Long Furrow must surely concern the military orchid. This plant, believed for many years to be extinct, is now preserved on just two sites in the British Isles, to which photographers and natural historians make dedicated pilgrimages when it flowers in early summer.

Two centuries ago it was growing "near Belchamp Walter parish, on a little hillock, in the corner of a ploughed field adjoining the way leading from Goldingham Hall by the lime kiln towards Gestingthorpe". At that time it was obseved by the botanist Dale* who identified Man orchid in the same area. The source for this information was Ruth Steed, who "almost screamed with amazement" as she stood in Sudbury's Kestrel book shop, browsing around for a birthday present, when she found on the opening pages of Richard Mabey's book "The Flowering of Britain"†, the botanical details of her childhood homestead.

But if the miltary orchid, tottering on the verge of extinction has long since disappeared from the villages of our Long Furrow, the Pyramid orchid was identified as recently as the nineteen thirties. Tom Rowe explains:

"During the depression of the thirties when everything went behind, I went tractor mowing with Harry Cansell, on some of those farms that had been put down to grass and which were being farmed 'on the cheap'. One man drove the tractor and the other sharpened the knives. We were cutting on Reeves Farm in Belchamp Otten, when I came across this flower that I'd never seen before. When I got home that night, I looked it up in the book and it was definitely a pyramid orchid. But that was the only one, and I've never seen another one since then."

---

* Dale was an apothecary at Braintree and later a physician in Bocking. He lived from 1659-1739 and is remembered for his study of the distribution and localities in which he found various wild flowers. We wonder whether he first saw the military orchid when visiting a sick patient or simply out on a botanical foray.

† "The Flowering of Britain" by Richard Mabey and Tony Evans published 1980 by Hutchinson. Additional material from "The County Flora of Essex" by Stanley T. Jermyn.

Another particularly keen observer of the changes in the flora and fauna beside our Long Furrow is one time estate manager and now wild flower artist, Benjamin Perkins of Liston and Maplestead. During the 25 years he has lived in the area, he has maintained a detailed record of the variations in wildlife behaviour and the fluctuations in its population. He reports;

"Cuckoos, swallows, nuthatches, rooks, spotted fly catchers and nightingales are definitely rarer. The snakes whose population varies considerably (in one year farmworker Cecil Smith saw 'hundreds' at Wickham Hall) are however declining* and the red squirrel has disappeared. Its place has been taken by the grey squirrel whilst reed buntings, magpies and kestrels also seem to be increasing."

The reference to kestrels, magpies and grey squirrels, reminds us too, of the influence and variation within the population of game birds in the area. In Colchester Natural History Museum, we read that the Red Legged Partridge arrived in England about 1770 whilst gamekeeping exterminated the last polecat in Essex around 1850. At around the same time the final pinemartins in the county were killed whilst buzzards and ravens both ceased to breed in Essex during the nineteenth century.

More recently Reg Rippingale recalls seeing "up to 50 magpies beside Wiggery Wood in the nineteen twenties" whilst his gamekeeper father-in-law Albert (Ben) Abbot† could raise forty to fifty brace of partridge every weekend of the shooting season when he was "keeping" on Wickham Hall between the wars. Thirty years later, the decline in the partridge population could almost be compared to the decimation of frogs. Recently, numbers have recovered slightly, and agricultural pesticides—at one time thought to be a contibutory factor to their decline (by destroying their food chain)—are becoming more sensitive to the birds needs. Farmer, business man and game enthusiast Ian Swift, of St. Mary Hall Farm, Belchamp Walter, provides some statistics to illustrate the trend.

Season	Partridges Shot	Pheasants Shot
1955/56	72	15
1963/64	11	256
1967/68	Nil	110
1974/75	1	197
1977/78	46	209
1981/82	11	210

* We believe that numbers may now be slowly increasing.

† As a final comment on rural nicknames, Albert Abbots daughter now Elizabeth Rippingale point out, "Almost everyone called father, Walter, although a few people nicknamed him Ben. We didn't know his real name was Albert until he died and we looked at the birth certificate. Today, great grandson Nick Pluck continues the families interest in country life and is currently employed as gamekeeper over nearly 3000 acres of land including Byham Hall, Maplestead and Spoons Hall, Pebmarsh.

It can be seen that pheasant numbers have considerably increased since World War II. This is a consequence of increased "keeper" rearing and keener farmer interest. Simultaneously the partridge population has suffered a major decline. Numbers recovered considerably in the late seventies but since then they have stabilized at a somewhat lower level. Within this, the "English" partridge has declined in favour of the Red Legged partridge.

But from game shooting with its close understanding of wildlife predators such as foxes, stoats, weasels, jays, magpies and carrion crows it is time that we looked instead at the smaller nesting birds of hedgerow and garden.

Ornithology has been a lifetime's interest to two of our oldest contributors, both of them born and bred in our Long Furrow at Bulmer. Wheelwright and carpenter Hazell Chinnery (born 1892) shares the interest with Philip Rowe (born 1900). In a fascinating conversation at the latter's cottage amongst the snow clad fields of a Christmas Eve, they provided the ornithological observations of two lifetimes.

"There used to be thousands of goldfinches by the brickyard in the twenties," recalls Philip. "They settle on a different bush each night and they used to be caught and sold to bird fanciers. They are very attracted to dandelions and meadow thistles."

"Did you ever see a golden crested wren?" asks Hazell Chinnery. "They are the smallest British bird; they build a little nest with a roof over the top with two holes, one for the head and one for the tail. There used to be some nests on the corner by the crossroads on the cedar trees."

"Like the long tailed wren" explains Philip, "they go in one way and out the other because there's not enough room for them to turn round. Then there's the 'titerene', or what you'd call the ordinary wren.

"But what other birds have declined over the years?"

"You see far fewer green woodpeckers now. You see but very few thrushes* and mistle thrushes," exclaims Hazell. His remarks are corroborated by Philip Rowe and Hazell continues, "and there used to be little hay chats . . . they'd build in nettles and on sheeps parsley. Hay chats they called them. Then there was the reed warbler and the ring ousel."

"What's a ring ousel?" I ask at the clock ticks on towards midnight and Christmas Day, in the quiet, snow covered cottage as the two men, whose limbs have known so much work and exertion, sit beside the fire, their minds as enquiring and active as a youthful enthusiast's.

---

* In corroborating this remark, George "Jute" Chatters of Belchamp St. Paul refers to thrushes as "mavis".

"Well, it's like a blackbird but it's got a white collar. There always used to be some down Smeetham Hall Lane," says Philip, who continues, "I tell you what interested me . . . was greenfinches. I did a lot of work one year near a flock of sheep and these greenfinches built their nest out of nothing but wool."

It is at this point that Hazell Chinnery surmises the whole conversation and mutters, "There's so many birds practically extinct now, somehow" He remembers the "butcher bird . . . and the redstart. They used to like to build in old tombstones–they'd search around and then they'ud find a little crevice and go in there and build."

"But what was a butcher bird?"

Philip Rowe replied, "The first I remember of them butcher birds was when my dad used to keep bees . . . and there was a pair of these butcher birds used to come and get his bees . . . and then they'd hang the bees up on the hedge near the nests . . . that's why they were called butcher birds, because the dead insects looked like meat in a butcher's shop. He had to get someone to come and shoot them at the finish they took so many,"

"But what did they look like?" asks wife Mary.
"About mid sized between a blackbird and a green finch."
"And what colour?" she continues.
"Something like a bullfinch but the colour is not so pronounced."

"Another bird you don't often see now," interjects Hazell, "is the whitethroat; it's a very delicate bird. Most of the plumage is pale grey with a little white underneath it. They come in April, they're summer visitors."

"Migratory birds," interposes Philip, "But there used to be several about here years ago."

"They used to get on my rows of peas," confirms Hazell, who lists four types of wagtails and the flycatchers "which used to dart about across meadows". Then there were the water-rails and the land-rails, which made a "peculiar row a bit like a partridge".

Finally, there was the memory of "a very little old owl, that came over here during the First World War . . . reckoned to be to frightened of the noise," says Hazell, who served with the Essex regiment until being taken prisoner in 1917.*

"They're the smallest owl that there is," corroborates Philip Rowe who remembers that, "they used to nest in tree stumps or rabbit holes and would often be seen on telephone poles or wires."

* Colchester Natural History Museum claims that isolated small owls were first recorded in Essex in 1865. Their numbers, however, only increased gradually from 1899 and corroborating Hazell's remarks concludes that they were, "encountered frequently by 1919".

"Of course we didn't have the distractions that your generation have," continued Hazell. "Birds and cricket were my interests." And with cricket we embarked on another conversation with memories of Hobbs, Hutton, Bradman and Bailey.

This then was Christmas Eve, with two men whose total formal education could not have exceeded seven years but whose self education had continued for a lifetime. I walked home across the glistening snow and the frosted furrows, inspired anew, to continue the search into the changing ornithology of our Long Furrow.

This presented some difficulties. Philip Rowe and Hazell Chinnery had provided me with a fascinating insight into the local bird population of the First World War and nineteen twenties. More recently Benjamin Perkins and others had lent me their diaries of contemporary observations. How though, was I going to fill in the intermediary years of the nineteen forties, from which point we would have the final record of our parochial bird population, in the last decade, before the pattern of agriculture had so changed.

For a few weeks I discussed the problem with almost everyone that I met. Finally, I was rewarded in early spring, when, after interviewing Cyril Philp, I called in at the "Pheasant" and neighbouring farmer's son Tony Minter, enquired how the project of the Long Furrow was developing. I recounted my predicament and rather to my surprise, he quickly reported that his father, more widely renown for his enthusiasm as a wing forward on the rugby pitch had conducted just such a survey in his boyhood.

"As a lad, my great hobby was collecting birds eggs," explained Peter, Minter (born 1933), on the Monday afternoon of the Spring Bank Holiday, as he uncovered the labelled and cotton wool encased display box of his childhood ambitions.

"Of course, bird nesting is now illegal, but at the time it was the sort of competitive pastime that almost all country boys went in for. Possibly I was slightly keener than most, because I also made a map and stuck identification flags into it, so that I could monitor the distribution of different birds. To find the nests in hedges, you have to crawl right under the bottom and then look up, and you can see them through the dark canopy of branches and leaves."

But of the forty six different birds eggs that Peter collected, it is the kestrels egg of which he is particularly proud.

"Yes, this kestrel always built a nest right at the end of one of the oak trees around the three cornered marsh. I can remember looking at it wistfully for the first three years, but it wasn't until the fourth summer that I could finally muster the courage to climb that far out on a swaying branch to get one of its eggs."

Appropriately Peter Minter's own sons Tony, (born 1957) and David "Tige" (born 1962), have sustained their fathers interest in natural history and have provided a similar list of the nesting and migratory birds that visited the brickyard and orchards of Hole Farm in 1982. When taken in conjunction with the recollections of Philip Rowe who worked in the brickyard during the nineteen twenties, we are able at last to construct a faint and skeletal framework of continuity in the search into the wildlife of the lingering coppices of Bulmer and Gestingthorpe. It is from these memories, the recorded details of his own schoolboy hobby and the observation list of his sons, that Peter Minter is now able to objectively summarise the fluctuations within the local bird population of Hole Farm, Bulmer over the past sixty years.

I asked first about the Butcher birds and goldfinches of which Philp Rowe had such vivid memories: Peter Minter remembers: "There was the occasional butcher bird in the vicinity during my youth, although there are now none at all. The numbers of goldfinches," he says, "have declined" and he considers that there are also less yellow hammers, owls, nightingales, whitethroats, woodpeckers, garden warblers and jackdaws. The latter have been reduced, he believe, as a consequence of the removal of the "tod" trees in which they live. Several species have completely disappeared. These include the meadow pippet, butcher bird, hawfinch (last seen 1950) and sparrow hawks (1979). Interestingly, however, the number of species identified by both father and sons has not varied. Peter estimates that in 1945 there was a total of 51 species nesting at Hole Farm and son David listed a similar number in 1981.* In addition the farm and orchard is also visited by approximately 23 migratory birds. By comparing the note books of two generations we can deduce that redpolls, twites, linnets, siskins and collared doves are the new arrivals to Hole Farm, whilst the family observes that the numbers of black caps have increased. Yet it would be misleading, indeed erroneous, for conservationists to take to much comfort from these statistics.

As Peter Minter is keen to point out:

"Although we still have a wide range of species, the actual number of almost all birds within a species, have declined dramatically. With a few exceptions, most species which I remember seeing in flocks of 20 or 30 are now reduced to two or three pairs only."

* Details of the ecological survey are included in Appendix A.

Equally pertinent in our appraisal of ecological trends in the area is the wealth of undisturbed and varied habitat to be found at Hole Farm. By sustaining his boyhood ornithological interest into the commercial world of adulthood, Peter Minter has preserved in the orchards and hedgerows of Hole Farm, an ecological wealth and diversity that is generally unrepresentative of the larger acreage fields and farms that surround him. On the more typically intensive arable farms of the area, bird counts and comparative surveys of species numbers conducted in 1942 and 1982 might well have shown a reduction in species numbers by 30-50%. At Hill Farm, for example, we have only 45 species,* of which a high proportion would have been identified in either Wiggery Wood or amongst the untrammelled willow tree plantations beside the Belchamp brook.

But if in the past decade we have witnessed the decimation of the frog population, the apparent disappearance of eels, roach, pike, otters, red squirrels, butcher birds, hawfinches, harebells, and the reduction of numerous bird flocks and wild flower sites, what, the reader might well now ask, is there still left to be seen growing in the lingering hedgerows, woods and coppices of Bulmer and Gestingthorpe? How many of Hilda Smith's wild flowers and Jack Cornell's gartridge bushes are still to be found amongst the lanes, the waterbanks and spinneys beside the pleated earth of our Long Furrow?

The definitive answer to this question is unavailable. But over the 700 acres of Hill Farm, Gestingthorpe–a fairly typical East Anglian holding, we still have the following:

127 species of wild flowers
45 species of birds
16 species of mammals
15 species of mushrooms
1 species of snake
9 species of butterflies

Initially the list seem quite impressive. But how many more species would have been included if the survey had been conducted in 1900 instead of 1980? 200 flowers and 90 birds? Moreover, in direct congruity to the bird population at Hole Farm, Bulmer, a great many of the wild flower identifications on Hill Farm, Gestingthorpe are now of "single site" finds only; the last remaining plants that are found tenuously growing in the corner of a field. Eighty years previously they would have been seen in profusion and abundance when the same field was a horse meadow or pasture.

* Identified by Gordon Steed during six month's harvest and autumn work in 1980.

Ironically, and with what can only be described as kindergarten naivety, when I started the survey in May 1979 I imagined that it would take "a couple of Saturdays". What dwells particularly in mind, is the frustrating tedium of the first identifications.* Other farmers attempting a similar project may well find that the first hurdle of "learning how to do it", is much the most difficult. However, once a few flowers have been identified and one is familiar with basic botanical descriptions, it suddenly becomes much easier†. Moreover, it is only quite recently that neighbouring farmer's son, Tony Minter, and myself have realised that we were embarked on similar projects. That we are is a possible indication to the drift of pursuits and interests in the countryside.

Meanwhile the complexities and fluctuations of nature continue. The combines of recent harvest have been surrounded by house martins, and at night the cab windows are covered with a mass of flies and insects. Sometimes, after cultivating a field, one will walk across it and be astonished at the speed at which the gossamer field cobwebs have been re-established.

The growths of the hedges between March and August in the persistently wet summer of 1981 was a staggering 1 inch in 3 days, and the hedge that had been so totally thrashed back in March stood an amazing 4 feet tall by September.

But for a final comment on the continuing coppice and the importance of conservation, let us return briefly to Hole Farm, where Peter Minter declares:

"Basically we're all trying to relearn the lore and lost language of our natural heritage. But what *particularly* frightens me" he continues, "is that so many of our bird and flower sightings are of single nesting pairs or solitary plants, verging perilously close to local disappearance when years ago the same species were so numerous... Because I've been able to monitor this decline it has compelled a real urgency and importance to the way we approach our peripheral farming activities. Everything," he exclaims, "is part of an intricate food chain and it is so easy and

---

* If Ron Allen of the Soil Survey had not suddenly turned up, to identify some dogs mercury, after I had spent an increasingly irritated half hour searching through the guide books, it is quite possible that the whole interest may well have been still born. The dogs mercury which Ron identified became the first entry into the photographic album that I subsequently made of the wild flowers on the farm.

† A particularly good book in paperback is by Roger Phillips, "Wild Flowers of Britain" published by Pan. The series also includes works on Trees and Mushrooms. The "Concise British Flora in Colour" by W. Keeble Martin is often recommended but is more complex and expensive. Collins produced a useful and comprehensive series of Field Guides. The author has found that children's books in the "Spotter" series by Usbourne Publications have proved extremely helpful at the outset of an interest. They are free of complicated jargon, and fit conveniently into a jacket pocket. The "AA Guide to the British Countryside" provides excellent background material to rural life and contains interesting information on traditional toxic or medicinal properties of flowers and shrubs.

The late Sid Rowe, writhing thatching springels.

Black Poplar.

Below:
Fastest pop gun in the East—that's Patrick Hasler whose great grandfather, Bertie, thatched the stacks for local farmers at harvest time.

Colin Ranson believes that there are less than a thousand Black Poplars left in England. This one, photographed at Eystons Smyths Farm, had produced typical Black Poplar burrs or blisters on the trunk. The Barton family have been especially sensitive to the needs of conservation in their farming practice.

Below:
Paul Elsdon, whose grandfather was a horseman at Parkgate Farm, demonstrates how to play an Ash whistle.

Alastair Tuffill–Photography

Alastair Tuffill–Photography

Alastair Tuffill–Photography

tempting within the concept of 'tidy farming' to unnecessarily destroy those food chains without contibuting a single additional penny to net farm income" (e.g. repeated mowing of lane verges, ditchbanks in the summer and repetitive rather than routine hedge cutting).

At Hole Farm, Peter, Tony and "Tige" Minter are applying their philosophy by cutting hedges at different heights (to avoid denying a bird its total territorial domain in any one year), preserving small corners of marshy ground, leaving grassy lane banks and appreciating the value of farmyard and trackside thistles (a food source for butterflies and goldfinches) whilst maintaining the occasional dead elm for the grubs which consume the bark and are subsequently eaten by woodpeckers.

"I think," says Peter reviewing the past forty years, "that we have come throught the worst phase of ecological depletion which was during the mid nineteen sixties. I believe that numbers are very slowly increasing, but for a very, very long while to come, we have got to consciously keep making this effort."

Possibly in fifty or even sixty years time, sons Tony and David will make another nesting bird survey; if they do, it will provide Hole Farm with an ornithological record that covers over one hundred and twenty years of time span. For anyone else who may be around at the time, it should make interesting reading.

WITHE MAKING

"Wally Cook of Maplestead", recalls Jack Cornell, "had the reputation of being able to make a 'withe' quicker than you could take a piece of string from your pocket." Jack demonstrates how it's done:

1. *After twisting the stick to tension it, a loop is made at one end, which is held together by twisting back and under.*
2. *Putting the withe round the bundle.*
3. *Pulling together.*
4. *Knotting it up, by bending the free end back and into the faggots.*

Reg Rippingale recalls the faggots being sole from Wiggery Wood at 6d. each.
(We have used peas sticks for illustrative purposes.)

Below: Tony and David "Tige" Minter, identifying another wild flower for the ecological survey.
(Chapter 17). In the background are the pits from which brick earth is dug. Both London Clay and the "Reading beds" are in close proximity and explain the manufacture of bricks at Hole Farm, for several hundred years.

It is elder brother Tony, who provides the final summary of the family's philosophy:

"Interference by man," he says, "has resulted in the entire ecological spectrum, with its complex food chains, breeding habitats and symbiotic relationships reaching a point where the scales are so precariously balanced that man must now keep himself involved, to ensure that both he and the wildlife survive. In the past we have misused and mis-handled our superior means of control. In the future we must use our abilities with more thought and sensitivity."

This then is the continuing coppice. It has dwelt quietly and without attention beside the activity of our Long Furrow throughout these many chapters. But as we close this chapter, let us remind ourselves that wild flowers have served an additional purpose in all walks of life and across all centuries that is greater than botany, history or domestic economy itself. Let us leave this account by glimpsing into the spring of 1928 when Hilda Rowe was walking through Twinstead meadows with bachelor Cecil Smith. As they strolled they came across a small area of cowslips. A few were picked by Cecil and presented to Hilda. Returning home, father Harry Rowe remonstrated that enough should have been left to allow the colony of cowslips to survive.

53 years and half a century of married life later, Hilda and Cecil Smith returned to the same meadow: the cowslips they report are still there, in the same field and occupy the same amount of land as before.

PART FOUR

The Green Revolution:
The Furrow and the Future

CHAPTER EIGHTEEN

The Third Agricultural Revolution

Trials Work and Sprayers

In reviewing the "third" agricultural revolution, we will commence our journey at Jenkins Farm, by the Sudbury-Halstead road. We have visited Jenkins several times before. In previous Chapters, Ernest Lott had cut faggots and Horace Elsie had delivered them to Melford Bakery. Earlier, "old" Philip Rowe had been "Lord of the Harvest", Sid Rowe had thatched the stacks, Bill Toatley had "ploughed all day without line", Bill Arbon had shepherded the flock and Gertie Coe had watched her mother prepare the food for the harvest "horkey".

But if Arthur Young had visited Bulmer in 1970, instead of 1805, he would undoubtedly have been fascinated and intrigued by Richard Dawson, who farmed Jenkins at the time.

It was during the early seventies that he pioneered a revoutionary technique of seeding, now known as "direct drilling". By using hydraulically pressurised coulters, these drills avoided the need for any preparatory ploughing, cultivating or discing.

"We started direct drilling in the late sixties," he explains. "Not in the piecemeal way that it had previously been tried, but as part of a total farm system."

Although still investigating direct drilling on the heavier soils of Pebmarsh, where he farms today, he found that at Bulmer "the crops deteriorated after two or three years . . . the lighter land tends to run together," (by which he refers to the "cohesive properties" described by Young in 1800 and colloquialised as "cappy" or "lashy old land").

But Richard Dawson's enquiring mind, had already begun to investigate other limitations on cereal yields. Nutrient deficiency, poor drainage and ineffective weed control were already understood, but routine fungicide applications to control debilitating attacks of mildew, septoria, ryncho-sporium and rusts were still in their infancy. The increasing availability of products to control these diseases and the degree of attention and personal supervision which farmers such as Richard Dawson gave to their crops, heralded a new era in cereal farming which was rapidly adopted across the wheat and barley fields of Eastern England.

I have described this event as a "revolution", because in the course of a few exciting years during the mid seventies, cereal yields were increased by around 50%.

To fully appreciate how far we have travelled let us recap on the levels previously obtained. There are suggestions that crops yielded around 6 cwt per acre in the thirteenth century. From Robert Andrews and Arthur Young, we know that the Auberies was averaging around 16 cwt of wheat an acre and 19 cwt of barley in the decade 1773-1783. This level of production was not substantially increased until the introduction of artificial fertilisers, tractor mechanisation, chemical weedkillers and improved varieties (e.g. Capelle, Pioneer and Spratt Archer) gradually raised yields from a ton an acre in the late thirties to between 35-40 cwt in the mid sixties. At the close of that decade a new wheat, Joss Cambier, improved on yields of Capelle, and in 1972, Maris Huntsman was released from the National Plant Breeding Institute. This variety which was bred by John Bingham, leader of the wheat department at the PBI's research headquarters at Maris Lane, Cambridge, provided the first evidence of field scale three ton an acre wheat crops. In 1976, a semi-dwarf wheat, Maris Hobbit, became available and field averages in excess of 70 cwt became commonplace.

Despite thse achievements, the impetus toward higher yields has continued. In 1982, local ADAS officer, John Llewellin organised five replicated trials on that part of Goldingham Wood field that had been Ancient Woodland until 1775. On the same land that Jack Cornell had once threshed with his Ransomes engine, shepherd George Barrel had folded his flock and horseman Bill Humm had ploughed his "acre a day", so too, an investigation took place into winter wheat and barley sowing dates, nitrogen fertiliser rates, herbicide techniques and comparisons between "growth regulators" whose effect is to reduce and strengthen the stem of the cereal crop. These trials were supervised by Agronomists Ken Hubbard and John Martindale, Plant Pathologist David Yarham, Soil Scientist John Archer, Entomologist Mary Short and Virologist Steve Hill, who operate from the regional ADAS headquarters at Brooklands Avenue, Cambridge, whose offices are the nerve centre of East Anglian agriculture. The Green Revolution with its dramatically increased cereal yields is not something that is restricted to the Punjabis of Central Asia or the Mexicans of the Yucatan peninsular. It has happened here. Across the undulating fields of Bulmer and Gestingthorpe; amongst the Long Furrows of Belchamp Walter and Foxearth; Beside the hedgerows and woodlands of Pebmarsh and Wickham St. Pauls.

Within this new, contrived, yield conscious cereal agriculture, the farm sprayer or fertiliser applicator has become the most utilised and important piece of farm machinery today. Here, as in everything, considerable changes have occurred. As a boy, Charlie Chatters spread guano (an early fertilizer) by hand and remembers that:

"Train loads of sprats came to Sudbury Station, from where they were taken away by horse and cart and then spread on the fields by hand."

Cecil Smith, warm hearted and cheerful, recalled the first elementary sprayers at work during the nineteen forties at Wickham Hall:

"We reckoned on spraying about 8 acres a day with a tumbrel pulled by a horse with a water butt inside. An 8 nozzle boom was attached to the rear and this was pressurised by a hand pump. The system required three men,"he explains. "One to steer the horse, one to pump and one to get the water (with a bucket from a nearby pond), and mix it up with the chemical on the headland."

Forty years later, with an armoury of fungicides, pesticides and weed-killers at our disposal, designed to maximise the photosynthesising potential of every plant, the farm sprayer has developed an importance not dissimilar to a Spitfire aircraft in World War II. Expressed simply, it is on perpetual alert: it may cover 200 acres a day.

But what of the Long Furrow itself? What transformations have occurred to the fields and the rotations of our furrow in the past decades. For the motorist or walker, passing through the lanes and roadways of north east Essex, the most obvious consequence of these agro-technological achievements will be seen in the fields themselves.

The estate acreages for the Auberies over the past sixteen years provide a typical representation of agricultural trends in the area. The acreages are expressed in percentages to fully appreciate the trends.

Winter wheat	27.9	30.8	56.5	59.0
Spring barley	43.1	34.2	6.7	3.9
Winter barley	12.2	14.1	27.0	24.6
Sugar beet	7.7	6.7	2.87	–
Beans	5.5	14.2	7.2	–
Clover	3.6	–	–	–
Oilseed Rape	–	–	–	12.5

From these figures, we see that in 1966, "only" 40% of the farm was down to winter cereals. On a winters walk up Ballingdon Hill, one would have seen plenty of brown, furrowed, ploughed fields. The acreage of winter sown crops was limited by the weed problems which would develop in excessive "runs" of autumn seeding. Moreover, at the time there was only a small differential in yield between winter and spring sown cereals. In 1966, Spring Barley was the largest acreage. Beans and Clover provided nitrogen and with sugar beet (possibly at its financial zenith) account for the farms break crops. Minor changes had occurred by 1970. At this point 44.9% was autumn sown. Clover as on many other farms, had been finally abandoned. But by 1979, entry into the Common Market, with its favoured status for wheat and rape; chemical advances in weed control and the development of wheats which were far out-yielding barley had dramatically altered the situation. The acreage of beans, spring barley and sugar beet have noticeably declined. Equally, it was becoming increasingly apparent that the hilly, sticky, variable soils of the area were not ideal for mechanised beet growing.

The estate figures for 1982 reflect a very general trend; rape has become the sole break crop and wheat amounts to 59% of the total farm acreage, of which 96% was autumn sown. It is evident that flexibility of management is a major requirement of contemporary farming.

The effect of this remarkable increase in farm productivity has resulted in a spate of road laying, land drainage and, most visibly, barn building, which is quite unparalleled in any previous century. Within the past decade each of Bulmer's arable farmers have erected new barns and extended grain stores. This is an achievement that has been previously accomplished at only isolated moments in the past millenium.

Yet farmers are not without their misgivings. Bulmer's longest serving farmer, Lawrence Hyde Parker, of Smeetham Hall, commented philosophically on national trends:

"Everything is becoming too specialised. There's too much concentration on single farming systems in favoured areas. You know, I don't believe there's a single dairy cow now, in Bulmer, Gestingthorpe, Wickham St. Pauls or the Belchamps. What's worse, we've become totally dependant on imported diesel, fertilisers and sprays to sustain these high yields."

When he started farming in 1933, Smeetham Hall was self-contained, self supporting and totally self replenishing.

The dangers of this new dependence by Britain's farmers on goods almost totally imported to their villages from outside, will be discussed in the following chapter.

Yet even contemporary arable farming has its lingering elements of poetry. It is sensed on autumn evenings, with the call of peewits across burnt stubble. It is of watching murky land drains in the first deluge of winter. At harvest time it is of the bright ears of wheat packing into the combine cutter bar as the ancient red tiles of Belchamp Walter Church glow warmly in the sunshine. Later in the year, it comes with the jangling of harrows as the drill discs slice through the crumbling soil. And at night-time it is of father, bringing out the bowser and pumping the tractor full of diesel, beneath a cloud blown moon, as we hurry on to finish off the autumn seeding before the breaking of the equinoctial gales.

At this point, we must turn to Bulmer's other non-arable farmers and review their operations. Both Mike Tracy and the Cansell brothers have now become specialists in pig breeding and production, although they also grow cereals as well. By comparison, Danny Rowe and Ken Leech are exclusive specialists and in the pattern of the late twentieth century have started their enterprises on that basis.

It is entirely appropriate that our penultimate chapter should include an interview with Danny Rowe, a descendant of that extended Rowe family, who have played such a full role in the history of our Long Furrow. Today, with wife Susan, he lives at the "Sudan Turkey Farm", close to Upper Houses, where his great grandfather had dwelt 100 years before.

"Similarly to wheat," he explains, "new breeds of poultry have been developed to suit the changing conditions and expectations of the twentieth century. Moreover," he quips, "we're dealing with at least one comparatively recent introduction to European farming. Turkeys," he points out," did not arrive in England until the Seventeeth Century when they were imported from Mexico."*

He continues by describing the history of intensive poultry keeping in the area.

"Commercial poultry keeping started around Bulmer in the nineteen thirties. In those days 1,000 lay hens might employ 1 or 2 people. To survive today, a one man egg producer needs 30,000 layers or to be able to turnover 120,000 broilers a year."

His own business started in 1961, with a deep litter chicken house, but he gravitated towards turkeys; since then his business has expanded rapidly and he has now become prominent amongst national turkey producers.

"Today," he remarks, "the whole turkey business is controlled by 10 large producers who are totally influenced by political decisions."

* Daniel Defoe observes in 1725 that great droves of turkeys and geese were driven through Bulmer, on the way to London.

Although Danny Rowe is now involved with the larger Wishbone Turkey organisation in neighbouring Middleton, the poultry houses in Bulmer still provide a turnover of 20,000 birds a year. Listening to the rapid, computer like facts, figures, statistics and comments he provides on marginal premiums, political decisions of Brussels, currency repercussions on feedstuffs and the intense business pressure behind output, one feels that poultry keeping has moved a long way from the war time image of a bonny land girl, dreaming of a far away soldier, as she skipped round the straw stacks, putting eggs into a wicker basket, like the lass on the Ovaltine advert. Turkeys–a late addition to our Long Furrow–are now definitely part of the third agricultural revolution.

The other "specialist" who is using Bulmer's acres today, is Ken Leech, whose nurseries are not far from the Sudbury-Halstead road and "The Fox" public house.

With a lifetimes experience in the fruit nursery business, he arrived in Bulmer in 1970 and started planting apple stocks in the half acre of his garden, in Park Lane. Today, he has developed that half acre garden to a twenty acre holding, wher he grows certified stocks of apples, plums and pears, that will later be sold as transplants to commercial orchard owners. Enquiring into the operation of commercial propagation made a refreshing interlude in the otherwise heavily cereal orientated research of this book.

Grown in rows 3 feet apart, the stocks are planted by hand with a dibber at one foot intervals in March and April. Propagation takes place in August, when the stocks have budded, to the desired variety. That bud should blossom the following Spring and it will be sold six months later, completing what is effectively a two year cycle.

During this cycle he keeps a close watch for antagonists, such as scab, mildew, red spider, aphids and caterpillar, which are controlled with pesticides, and fungicides, similar to those in use on neighbouring arable fields. In addition, the stocks are encouraged with foliar feeds, basal fertiliser and horse manure. Of the land he farms, 80% is producing apple stocks, of which the familiar varieties of Cox, Bramley, Discovery and Ida Red are to be found.

Just as "dwarfing" of cereals has played an important role in increasing wheat yields, so too is dwarfing of apple trees essential for contemporary commercial picking. This is manipulated in the selection of the root stock.

Ken Leech's achievement is the greater when one recalls that his business started during an era of widescale local grubbing (e.g. Butlers Hall and Gestingthorpe fruit farm), combined with a general lack of orchard confidence upon entry into the Common Market. With justifiable pride, he reports that from Bulmer's 20 acres, he now supplies 80% of the commercial fruit growers in East Anglia. Bulmer, it seems has also joined the export business, for he also trades commercially to Greece and in smaller quantities to Holland, Belgium, East Germany and Hungary. In 1980 he scored a notable success in supplying the Queen's Sandringham estate.

By intense specialisation, in one field, a high degree of supervision and alert marketing flexibility, Ken Leech has shown, like stockmen Mike Tracy, Danny Rowe and the Cansell brothers, that there are still openings to be found in the increasingly large scale agriculture of the late twentieth century.

But despite these individual success stories, there has still been an unremitting "drift from the land", of both farmer and farmworker. During the past half century, horsemen, threshers, stack builders and hurdle makers have joined the ranks of obsolete professions.

Bulmer farmworkers 1878 154*
Bulmer farmworkers 1978 17*

Farmers' numbers have declined less rapidly but reflect a similar trend:
Bulmer farmers 1808 21 (including 6 part time)
Bulmer farmers 1981 12 (including 4 part time)

Yet the old adage of "what is good for the farm is good for the village" has not been totally invalidated. Agriculture still remains one of Britain's biggest industries. On the basis of farm expenditure in 1981-82, one man is employed in farming, or the agricultural service industries, for every 20.8 to 30.2 acres of Bulmer's farmed land.† Yet of Bulmer's 70 to 105 contemporary "farmworkers" only 22 (including 8 of the farmers), actually live in (or have probably even heard of!) the village itself.

Today, the traditional lad with the muck tumbrel has been replaced by the fertiliser chemist, the gang of "thistlers" by the herbicide scientist, whilst the "Lord of the Harvest" is transformed to the oil rig foreman, the iron foundryman and the combine designer.

But the thread of continuity between the 300 farmworkers of Bulmer and Gestingthorpe in 1871, and their great grandchildren of 1982 has not been completely broken. Paul Mann, Roger Hunt and Philip Jeggo have followed their forefathers onto the fields of our Long Furrow. Several of the farmworker's sons have selected the agricultural service and manufactur-

---

* "Bulmer: Then and Now".

† The calculation depends upon yields and prices. The financial output of wheat or barley is between £250-£400 an acre (governed by the quality of land and the aptitude with which it is farmed). Depending on each individual farmers philosophy between 60-100% of this return is being channelled back into the industry (as variable, fixed or investment costs) and this money ultimately sustains jobs. In 1981, the average industrial wage in England was £6,240 per annum.

ing industries for their careers. The Massey Ferguson combines of the area are maintained by Bob Allen whose father is a farm foreman at Halstead; the Hydrocut hedgecutter that trims Bulmer's hedges was designed by David Mansfield, whose father spent a lifetime at Hall Farm, Gestingthorpe; the big grain-waggons that cart the wheat to Colchester dock are driven by Tom and Ken Elsdon whose father was a horseman at Park Farm; and the yellow Doe's service van that brings out the machinery spare parts is run by Eric Rippingale whose ancestors stretch back for over 300 harvests, whilst the cheerful smile that greets you with the cultivator points in "Pan Anglia" is that of Peter Hickford whose father recently retired after a lifetime's land work in Little Yeldham. But even here the lines do not end. When retired horseman and tractor driver Frank Billimore does, "a few days cultivating" after harvest, the injectors in the tractor that he drives will have been distributed from the stores of C.A.V. by son Mervyn while the spray that is applied on the next door field may well have been analysed by research scientist, Trevor Billimore, his elder son.

CHAPTER NINETEEN

Bulmer, British and Global Agriculture: Balancing the Equations

"The last of the few"

With the intensive cereal growing of Richard Dawson, the powerful tracttors of the Auberies Estates, the turkey business of Danny Rowe and the fruit production of Ken Leech, we may seem to have come a long way from our first neolithic farmer tilling his hut side plot of wheat. We have travelled from the iron plough of the Celts to the computer age combine of the nineteen eighties.

As we look to the future, we can discern four elemental factors with an interest in agriculture and land use.

1. A projected increase in the world's population by approximately 50% within the next 20 years.
2. A growing demand for "naturally produced" foodstuffs and an increased awareness of ecologically orientated outdoor recreations.
3. A requirement upon national governments to provide fulfilling employment and satisfaction of lifestyle in a work deprived, micro-chip efficient twenty first century.
4. A growing urgency to ensure the survival of British agriculture and the distribution of its produce and inputs in the event of military disruption or logistical shortage.

Is it possible that these four disparate threads can co-exist as a synthesis for the new agriculture of the twenty first century?

We will briefly discuss these projections and reflect upon the repercussions they may have upon Bulmer and Gestingthorpe.

In our review of the nineteenth and twentieth centuries we have observed the importance of the 1947 Agriculture Act as a foundation to the stable marketing of the past 35 years. Additionally the statute instigated the creation of the National Agricultural Advisory Service (now ADAS) and established a system of grant aiding farmers who were prepared to increase the productivity of their holdings. Since that date we have witnessed a dramatic increase in yields from our Long Furrow.

Bulmer's food production (including livestock–mathematically expressed in the uniform equivalent of food grains) has increased threefold.

1940   1800 tons of food grains
1982   5500 tons of food grains

Farm cropping and stocking has been revolutionised. In 1940 the village carried at least 5 types of livestock and was growing 10-20 different crops. A good deal of this acreage and diversity of land use went simply to feed and sustain the horses.

Yet the 5500 tons of food grains produced in the 1982 harvest were dependant on approximately 15-20,000 gallons of diesel, 1900 gallons of spray concentrate and 1000 tons of fertiliser being imported into the parish. This is a national trend with national consequences. The long term effect of these comparatively new inputs to farming and twentieth century life in general are still unknown. As one farmworker quipped bluntly:

". . . it took 'em 400 years to find out that fag smoke was bad for you".

Yet the high dependence on materials imported into both Britain, the village and individual farms provides a greater warning. In the event of war, or internecine disputes, our agriculture would need to be vigorously supplied and its raw materials would require considerable protection to guarantee its continued high performance production.

Whether the government should revise its policy of the past 35 years, which has encouraged specialised, high input farming is something we shall discuss later. Farmer, Lawrence Hyde Parker comments pertinently:

"I know what I'd like in the event of another war–and that's to be able to grow a field of diesel!"

Let us, however, reflect upon the results of the 1947 Agriculture Act. Great Britain, which was 30% self-sufficient in 1938, now grows 60% of its nutritional needs. Yields from all aspects of farming have considerably increased. In 1946, the average dairy cow produced 4000 pints of milk a year. By 1980, yields had risen to 8500 pints per cow. Similarly the production of eggs has increased from 120 eggs per bird per year in 1946 to 248 in 1980. Nationally (as opposed to locally) wheat yields have improved from 15.2 cwt per acre in 1900 to 47.2 cwt in 1980.

These achievements have been the result of a unique political experiment. State protectionism and advice has been harnessed to the individuality of farmers who have utilised the equipment and products of commercial companies. In an age of industrial stagnation, it is possibly an experiment that should be conducted more often. In 1982, British manufacturing industry is in an almost identical position to the British agriculture of the nineteen thirties. But the three way combination has served a wider role than to simply increase food production. Through the price support and grant aid mechanisms, agriculture has been used as a prime source to pump (or reflate) the national economy.

But there are some sobering consequences of this relationship. The farmer has become in Danny Rowe's words, "little more than a self employed civil servant". Like it or not, most of us are unable to farm very differently from the manner in which we do. We are controlled fairly strictly by a combination of governmental price fixing, multi-national pressures and financial obligations (e.g. rents, capital taxation and service charges).

But what of the future?

Land, as we have shown, is passing into fewer hands—institutions, pension funds, and international companies are now large purchasers. Proposals have been suggested by various pressure groups to limit this trend towards isolated, unapproachable, city based ownership. Unless arrested, the inevitable drift of the twenty first century will be toward mega farms of tens of thousands of acres in size. These unit will be computer organised and robot run.

In the short term, existing farmers, including the author, will use whatever means possible to protract their tenure, by enlarging their holdings with whatever opportunism is necessary.

But we are all keenly concious of the ultimate effect of these trends. Tommy Hogsbjerg of Belchamp Walter, declared at a recent farmers' meeting:

"Unless the government imposes controls to limit the size of holdings, rural life as we know it, will die in this country within the next twenty years. There is more involved here than economics and finance. There's a question of humanity as well."

Whether such legislation will come into force in the United Kingdom, as it has in some European countries, we cannot tell. Sadly, at the time of writing, it seems unlikely.

In the absence of such limitations it would seem especially important to encourage the distribution of some land into smaller acreaged holdings (e.g. 10, 20 or 40 acres)

Minor changes to the law of stamp duty, the assessments for captital taxation and a statute decreeing that 10% of any sale is to be sold in separate units would facilitate this trend. Doubtless there would be numerous and contrived abuses by existing landowners, but these should not obscure the objective.

There are several reasons for maintaining and stimulating this "bottom rung of the farming ladder".

1. The smaller unit provides an opportunity for the expression of individuality in a "work starved" twenty first century.
2. A diversity of land use will result. This may be manifest in organic farming, market gardening or recreational facilities such as pastures for horse grazing, the preservation of rare breeds, wildlife reserves, outdoor museums and "adventure" parks, all of which, will provide purposeful and rewarding openings in the forthcoming century.
3. By increasing the number of occupiers, a greater variety of agricultural practice *may* develop. With government encouragement to sustain such holdings, this diversity might partially reduce our fears of military disruption to the logistical supply lines that are now so much a feature of our highly fabricated farming systems.

We are still faced with an ever growing global population. Although the wheat from our Long Furrow may never feed the extra 250 million Indians who will be born by the close of the century, it would be fair to assume that any other existing global surpluses would soon be absorbed. Similarly, we may well find that the unnecessary "luxury" foods to which we are accustomed will become unavailable, as the countries which grow them convert their sugar, tobacco, cocoa and coffee estates into land producing the more basic essentials of a third world diet, such as maize, rice wheat and protein pulse crops.

Despite the pessimistic global background it is fair to say, that in general terms, our own 1947 Agriculture Act has succeeded in its objectives. But in a wider context than that of national food production, the overall strategy that the Act laid down, may well have run its course. In this, and other chapters, we have written of the loss of ancient woodland and ecologically valuable species; we have dicussed our contemporary agricultural systems and explained their dependance on manufactured inputs. We have touched on energy and logistics and hinted that here may be a long term wisdom in increasing the country's acreage of commercial woodland; finally we have reitterated the need to revitalise village and community life within the context of the twenty first century.

Whether it is better to grow the maximum amount of food, from the minimum amount of land–by whatever means, so that a greater national acreage can be released for other purposes is the nub of what is ultimately a most complex question.

Maybe, thirty five years after the formation of the 1947 Act, it is time to rethink and revise the concepts upon which the Act was founded, and upon which agriculture has since flourished. We must begin to take account of the needs and requirements of rural life, and national food supplies for the year 2000 and beyond.

In the meantime, the vital task of the trials work—which alone can make our other ideals attainable, goes on. Possibly, given time, plant breeders will develop new varieties that will not require the high level of inputs that are so essential to contemporary cereals.*

Today, these botanists and scientists have become the "back room boys", the "Barnes Wallis's" of what is becoming a global race against both population growth and pollution. The time factor is critical. This year as a contribution to the general enquiry into wheat growing, we drilled part of Cort Field Gestingthorpe on August 24th. It is the earliest, I think, that wheat has ever been commercially sown in the United Kingdom. In the final analysis, it may not increase yields any further; but it will teach us *something* and the reservoir of knowledge will be further expanded. The ADAS trials programme continues on a more professional and scientific basis. The plots for the 1983 harvest have been laid down on Overidges Field—just a few yards from where Arthur Rippingales horse disappeared in 1922. (See Chapter One). Being able to assist and co-operate in this work with government officers, such as Welshman, John Llewellin and Kerela born, South Indian, Dr. Vaidy, iw one of the most satisfying and fulfilling phases of a farmer's career.

---

* As an example, the development of very stiff strawed 'semi dwarf' wheats has already eliminated the need for straw shortening chemicals (e.g. C.C.C.) on those varieties. Similarly, projected varieties or possibly 'blends' of varieties *may* further reduce the need for artificial inputs.

CHAPTER TWENTY

The Long Furrow

A few minutes before midnight on the evening of Saturday, 28th August, I
lowered the cutter bar of the Massey 755 combine, and swept through the
last bout of winter beans that loomed out between the headlights. A mass of
insects crawled across the cab glass and a single partridge blustered out
from the thick twisted stalks. Gradually the crop became lighter in density.
I was cutting an ever narrower triangle. Then it happened. The cutter bar
was clear. I swung the combine through a figure of eight, the spotlamps
arcing out across the stiff stubble and threshed swarths. The field stretched
out expansive, vast and utterly empty. It had happened again. Harvest was
over! The land had responded once more, the cycle had come to fruition.

All the tensions, irritations and explosive altercations of harvest were
suddenly forgotten. The reaping was over; the garnering complete.

I brought the 10 ton metallic mass to a halt, slowed down the threshing
gear and brought the 170 horse power engine to idle. One by one, a battery
of lights, digital readouts, loss monitors and warning signals were turned
off. The engine idled for the requisite "cool off" and I thought of
another man who had cut winter beans. Oliver Pearson, who in 1900 had
earned 5 shilling as a boy of thirteen with a "rip" in his hand. I pressed down
the last button and pulled up the stop control as the Perkins AT6.354.4
shuddered to a fade out. Happily humming a few bars from "Chariots of
Fire", I opened the cab door, and breathing the sweet midnight air, stood
by the rail and gazed out. Out, across the bright, moonlit fields of Bulmer
and Gestingthorpe, across to the darker form of Upper Houses, the lurking
shapes of the Deal Nursery and the tree breezed Belchamp Valley where
the mist buffs roll up from the willows. And then further, further in the
distance where the last lights of the Belchamps, Wickham and Sudbury
ring round in a wide circle, that itself has been a circumference for all that is
contained within this book.

There, within those villages and upon the land encompassed by these flickering distant lights, harvest was reaching its climax. Could it be, I wondered, that for three milleniums, other men, broad of back and wide of arm, had felt these same sensations? When, with sweating shoulders they had pitched the final sheaf, and with bended knee, had scythed the fields last swath?

A resonant black cloud, scraggly like a moth eaten garment, eclipsed the moon, encompassing its radiance in luminous, silvery, yellow-blue shrouds. As it passed, I heard their voices and saw their faces as they slipped quietly down the corridors of time. Here; where the "Lord of the Harvest", Arthur Finch had passed up the flaggon of beer, as the oak bough was placed upon the final waggon. There, further in the distance, beside the gaunt, dead elms and weatherboarded barns, Philip Rowe had thatched the corn stacks that waited for the steam and whistle of Cornell's threshing crew.

Here too, amongst these ancient manors, horseman Bill Toatley had ploughed all day without line, shepherd George Barrell had folded his flock, and ploughman Horace Elsie had sat down in the glades of the Deal Nursery and eaten his dinner beside a fire as the horses had fed beside. him. Amongst these pastures Charlie Chatters had moved trefoil in the moonlit hours and later in the day, beneath a burning sun, had passed the gang of "thistlers" with their weeding hooks in hand. Months later, in the cruellest blast of winter, wrapped up in sacks against the sleet grey gale, had trudged Bob Daniells and Freddie Ratcliffe, "pulling" sugar beet, their fingers numbed and blue.

Across these fields Harry Winch had driven Stennets "Lloyd George" tractor and Jack Mann lithely trod the rutted track on his epic walk to Ipswich. Here, along moss grown, muddied lanes, had passed drover Charles Jeggo, shepherd Charlie "Pod" Martin, blacksmith Dick Nice, wheelwright Hazell Chinnery, thatcher Bertie Hasler, horseman Ernie Lott, threshers Marsh and Cook, "Stallion Jack", Emily Hearn, Gertie Coe, and beyond them generation after generation of their forebears.

It was from those coppiced woods and overhanging hedges that nuts, crab apples, and sloes were gathered up; thatching springels writhed, whistles fashioned, hurdles made and faggots hewn and with-ied up. From stubbles such as these, had industrious mothers gleaned and scampering children, absent from their schooling gathered acorns. Here too, amongst the harvest "fourses" had the sweetheart flashed her bright eyed smile; between the banter and the passing of the flagon had they "shod the colt" and cursed the other for his crooked scything.

Beneath us, still, old land drains testify to those who dug and ditched, who worked in bitter gales, with throbbing nerves, and aching limbs and in some solitary respite told worn tales of Waterloo and Sevastopol. It is these who have gone before that we follow; those of flail and hoe, with sinews knarled and weather seasoned bodies, who lie, unrecorded, in the hollows of our medieval history. But still they pass us by; trudging endlessly, anonomously, through the hollows of our own parochial past. The manorial labourer, the pagan Saxon, the villa farming Roman and the ancient Celt; all these; all these who have harvested and reaped before; and who amongst the oaks of ancient woodland called out in chants to their own field gods and spirits, whose names may yet be borne upon the gusts of leaf strew autumn gales. Finally, in some primeval, neolithic dusk, the murky movement of a human hand is dimly seen at work upon the ragged plot. And in that twilight instant of mankind's history itself, we see in one last glimpse the trinity of man and soul and soil in communion for the first time, on the land we still work now.

I walked back; alone, across the grey, moonlit midnight stubble, to the sleeping farmhouse and the flask of hot chocolate that waits on the kitchen table. Within nine hours, this ethereal moment would be forgotten, and I would depair of anyone who could think in such cranky and amorphous terms. Once again we would be frantically cursing and swearing, as we hooked on the cultivators for the autumn seed beds and stubble burning firebreaks. Within nine days the same ruthless impatience would have instigated the first fields of autumn seeding to begin. Within nine weeks, the entire district would be nascent green again, with the next year's harvest planted and emerged.

It has come from behind; over many centuries, creeds, dynasties and epochs of time; it has been always in a state of flux and is ever evolving. We have called it the "Long Furrow". Today, it still stretches, outwards, onwards and into the future.

Ecological survey at Hill Farm, Gestingthorpe and Hole Farm, Bulmer, as on 20.10.82.

1. Birds observed at Hole Farm, Bulmer. (approx. 150 acres)

Starling, House Sparrow, House Martin*, Collared Dove, Song Thrush, Mistle Thrush "Mavis", Blackbird, Robin, Hedge Sparrow, Wren, Great Tit, Blue Tit, Greenfinch, Chaffinch, Bullfinch, Goldfinch, Spotted Flycatcher*, Lapwing, Pheasant, Red-Legged Partridge (French), Grey Partridge (English), Wood Pigeon, Magpie, Fieldfare*, Swallow*, Skylark, Yellow Hammer, Tree Sparrow, Corn Bunting, Cuckoo, Whitethroat*, Linnet, Twite*, Green Woodpecker, Lesser Spotted Woodpecker, Great Spotted Woodpecker, Turtle Dove*, Blackcap*, Garden Warbler*, Longtailed Tit, Marsh Tit, Tree Creeper, Jay, Lesser Redpole, Coal Tit, Goldcrest, Kingfisher, Reedbunting, Pied Wagtail, Mallard, Moorhen, Redwing*, Tawny Owl, Little Owl, Kestrel, Grasshopper Warbler*, Cirl Bunting, Snipe, Stockdove, Heron, Blackheaded Gull*, Common Gull*, Rook, Crow, Jackdaw, Willow Tit, Sparrow Hawk, Chiffchaff*.

*Migratory birds.

The family have also seen the occasional Wheatear. It is believed that Serrens–extremely rare visitors to this part of England, may also have been seen in the orchards. Says Peter Minter: "it's almost impossible to be certain unless one has a lot of time and good field glasses, but I believe that these birds are Serrens and I would be interested to have the identification confirmed or disproved".

During the survey, Tony and "Tige" (David) Minter, have found the Readers Digest A.A. Book of British Birds, and the Collins Guides to be helpful. In addition to other books we have previously mentioned, they also recommend "The Englishman's Flora" by Geoffrey Grigson (published by Paladin) for its interesting details of traditional uses and names of wild flowers and "Food from the Wild" by Judy Urquhart (published by Penny Pinchers).

This year, the brothers have extended the survey to include butterflies and moths.

2. Butterflies observed at Hole Farm, Bulmer.

Orange Tip, Green Veined White, Brimstone, Peacock, Small Tortoiseshell, Red Admiral, Wall, Large White, Comma, Small White, Gatekeeper, Meadow Brown, Large Heath, Painted Lady, Small Skipper, Common Blue, Small Copper, Ringlet.

3. Moths observed at Hole Farm, Bulmer.

Blood Vein, Clouded Border, Latticed Heath, Herald Moth, Yellowtail, Lackey, Garden Carpet, Common Heath, Ghost Moth, Garden Tiger, Heart and Dart, Silver Y, Willow Beauty, Yellow Shell, Large White Plume Moth, Dun Bar, Dot Moth, Turnip Moth, Large Yellow Underwing, Swallow Tailed Moth, Hebrew Character, Snout Moth, Common Wainscot, Shark, Lesser Yellow Underwing, Vapourer, Brimstone Moth.

4. Wild flowers at Hill Farm, Gestingthorpe.

Ox Eye Daisy, Yarrow, Mallow, Meadow Vetchling, Creeping Cinquefoil, Wild Hop, Meadow Cranesbill, Tufted Vetch, Snowberry, Stinging Nettle, Black Nightshade, Groundsel, Bugle, Garlic Mustard, Forget-Me-Not, Red Campion, White Campion, Primrose, Bluebell, Plantain (Ribwort), Lesser Periwinkle*, Germanda Speedwell, Ivy Leaved Speedwell, Thyme Leaved Speedwell, Wood Avens, Vetch (s), Cow Parsley, Figwort, (Spotted Orchid?), Ladies Bedstraw, Hedge Bindweed, Field Bindweed, Great Wild Dodder, Purple Loosestrife, Grass Vetchling, Dwarf Mallow, Dandelion, Wall Lettuce, Shepherds Purse, Sneezewort, Burnet, Herb Paris, Bladder Campion, Woody Nightshade (Bittersweet), Agrimony, White Bryony, Black Bryony, Spear Plume Thistle, Herb Robert, Hemp Nettle, Travellers Joy, Honeysuckle*, Field Scabious, Devils Bit Scabious, Hop Trefoil, St. John's Wort, Self Heal, Scarlet Pimpernel, Wild Parsley, Meleliot, Tansy, Ragwort, Knapweed (?),

King Cups, Cowslip, Oxlip, Dogs Mercury, White & Purple Violets, Stitchwort, Carlock, Chickweed, Rosebay Willow Herb, Great Willow Herb, Meadow Sweet, Dogrose, Aarons Rod, Wood Anemone, Barren Strawberry, Comfrey*, Ground Ivy, Woundwort, Hoary Cinquefoil, Alkanet, Common Calamint, Cuckoo Pint, Hairy St. John's Wort, Black Medick, Corn Marigold, Teasel, American Willow Herb, Fleabane, Common Dock, Lesser Fleabane, Scentless Mayweed, Smooth Sowthistle, Lesser Celandine, Yellow Meleliot, Hemp Agrimony, Common Persicarcia, Guelder Rose, Wild Iris*, Horse Radish, Burdock, Lesser Bugloss, Basil Thyme, Yellow Rocket, Common Poppy, Heartsize, Common Cranesbill, Mugwort, Wild Mignonette, Purging Toad Flax, Toadflax, Hemlock, Shepherds Needle, Marsh Sowthistle, Harehound, Crow Garlic, Sorrel, Giant Bellflower, Rough Hawksbeard, Marestail, Wood Woundwort, Chicory*, Red Dead Nettle, Fat Hen.

*garden flowers growing in wild locations.

5. Mushrooms and fungi at Hill Farm, Gestingthorpe.
Ink Cap, Yellow Stainer, Blueit, Puff Balls, Candlesnuff, Chicken in the Wood, Shaggy Parasol, Ochre Russula, Lilac Thickfoot, Tawny Deceiver, Fairies Bonnet, Boletus (several)

In addition to the list of wild flowers at Hill Farm, Tony and David Minter, have also identified (amongst others), the following extra wild flowers at Hole Farm.
Angelica, Archangel, Arum, Borage, Brooklime, Black Knapweed, Cuckoo Flower, Common Catsear, Common Centuary, Corn Chamomile, Cnidium, Field Mouse Ear, Goats Beard, Harebell, Marjoram, Perforate St. John's Wort, Swinecress, Wall Pepper, Yellow Wort, Annual Mercury, Sulphur Cinquefoil.

*   *   *

Visiting the Minter family itself, is a bit like going on long distance safari to Africa. One arrives at the household just after lunch, and in a strange, effortless way, cups of tea and refreshments appear at periodic intervals. Suddenly you realise that you have been sitting round their dining table for about six hours and a mass of books, lists, birds eggs and wild flowers have accumulated around you. The two Bank Holiday afternoons that I spent at Hole Farm provided me with some of the most pleasant memories in the research of the "Long Furrow".

Possibly though, having included a list of what is still to be found in the area, it is appropriate to reiterate Peter Minter's closing remarks:

"What particularly worries me, is the fact that so many of our nesting bird and wild flower sightings are of only one or two pairs or sites. The whole ecological spectrum is held precariously in the balance. That is why it is so essential for *all of us* to continue making this special effort to identify what is still left and then attempt to preserve it."

A wide range of publications provided background material during the research of the "Long Furrow". The following are nationally available and are listed in sequence:

PART ONE

"Trees and Woodland in the British Landscape": Oliver Rackham. Published by J. M. Dent. 1976.

"Prehistoric England": Graham Clark. Published by Batsford. 1948.

"Farming Technique from Prehistoric to Modern Times": G. E. Fussel. Published by Pergamon. 1965.

"Ancient Agricultural Implements": Sian Rees. Published by Shire Archaeology. 1981.

"The Agrarian History of England & Wales". Vol. I & II. A.D. 43-1042, edited by Finberg: University Press.

"Anglo Saxon England": Peter Blair Hunter: Published by Cambridge University Press.

"English Society in the Early Middle Ages 1066-1307": Doris Mary Stenlon. Published by Pelican Books.

"Essex and the Peasants Revolt": Compiled by W. H. Liddell and R. G. E. Wood: Essex Record Office Publication No. 81.

"Wool; East Anglia's Golden Fleece": Nigel Heard. Published by Terence Dalton.

"The Agrarian History of England & Wales. Vol. IV. 1500-1640". Edited by Joan Thirsk. Cambridge University Press.

"Five Hundred Points of Good Husbandry": Thomas Tusser. Edited by Dorothy Hartley. Country Life.

"General View of the Agriculture of the County of Essex": Arthur Young. Published 1805. (Available on prior request, in the reference sections of most local libraries: the report for the County of Suffolk is equally fascinating.)

"Rural Discontent in Nineteenth Century Britain": Dunbabin. Published by Faber & Faber.

"Sharpen the Sickle" (History of N.U.A.A.W.): Reg Groves. Published by Merlin Press.

"Captain Swing": E.J. Hobsawm and George Rude. Published by Lawrence & Wishart 1969

PART TWO

"Farm Tools Through the Ages": Michael Partridge. Published by Osprey. 1973.

"Life & Tradition in Suffolk & North East Essex": Norman Smedley. Published by J. M. Dent. 1980.

"Discovering Horse Drawn Farm Machinery": D. J. Smith. Shire Publications. 1979.

"The Horse in the Furrow": George Ewart Evans. Published by Faber & Faber. 1960.

"The Farm and the Village": George Ewart Evans. Published by Faber & Faber. 1969.

"The Pattern under the Plough": George Ewart Evans. Published by Faber & Faber. 1966.

"Discovering Traction Engines": Harold Bonnett. Published by Shire Publications. 1969.

"Agricultural Records A.D. 220-1977": J. M. Stratton. Published by John Baker. 1978.

"Economic Survey of Agriculture in the Eastern Counties 1931". Published by Cambridge University Press.

"The Tithe War': Doreen Wallace.

"Farm Tractors in Colour": Michael Williams. Published by Blandford Press. 1974.

PART THREE

"A.A. Book of the British Countryside": Drive Publications for the A.A.

"Essex County Flora": Stanley T. Jermyn.

"Farming and Wildlife": Kenneth Mellanby. Published by Collins. 1981.

"Trees and Woodlands in the British Landscape": Oliver Rackham. Published by J. M. Dent. 1976.

"The Flowering of Britain": Richard Mabey and Tony Evans. Published by Hutchinson, 1980.

In addition to "Notes on the Parish of Gestingthorpe" by Alfred Patchett, (printed in 1905), the availability of historical information for the "target area" of our villages between Sudbury and Halstead, had been considerably enhanced in the past decade, with the publication of a number of excellent and invaluable booklets.

"Bulmer: Then and Now": Bulmer W.E.A. 1979.
"Wickham St. Pauls: Church and Village": Mrs. Huband.
"Gestingthorpe 1693-1903": Slaughter & Brown. 1975.
"An Essex and Suffolk Alphabet": Basil Slaughter. 1981.
"Sudbury and District News": Steven R. Bixley. 1981.
"The Matmaker and the Magistrate": Richard Deeks. 1980
"A History of Little Yeldham": Adrian Corder Birch. 1981.
"Sudbury's Story": Edith Freeman, 1982.
"A Pictorial History of Halstead and District": Halstead and District Local Historical Society.

A visit to the Toppesfield Horse Museum and the Abbot Hall Museum of East Anglian Life at Stowmarket, proved most beneficial in establishing a greater understanding of the horse era implements which so many of our contributors had used.

The quest for information was further assisted by the Essex Records Office at Chelmsford (manorial manuscripts, maps and county directories); The West Suffolk Records Office at Bury St. Edmunds (old newspapers and census records); The Essex Archaeological Society Library at Hollytrees House, Colchester (rare books: especially "The Kings Evil";see Chapter Seventeen); Gestingthorpe Church Records (manorial documents), Colchester Natural History Museum, Cambridge Botanical Gardens (in particular the bed of introduced species) and the ADAS regional library at Brooklands Avenue, Cambridge, which contains the agricultural statistics for England and Wales for the past hundred years.

In Valediction

At the onset of this work, I thanked all those who had assisted or contributed in any way. In conclusion, I must pay especial thanks to my father, for briefly resuming relinquished agricultural responsibilities; Basil Slaughter for his timely encourgement. Alastair Tuffill for the photographs, Ben Perkins for proof reading and Jack Cornell and Evelyn Reeve for their unreserved assistance.

In addition I would like to acknowledge the outstanding co-operation of Messrs. Colin and Don Freeman of Halcyon Print in illustrating and preparing the manuscript for publication.

In conclusion, a word of real thanks to a group of close friends, who for twelve months have endured my erratic and often unsociable lifestyle.

I am sincerely grateful for all of your support.

12th November 1982   Hill Farm, Gestingthorpe